E, IN THE COUNTY OF

Hill. Which seems to be an Ancient British Fort, both from it's

mn after the Revolution. ————   *1. 1. Snowden Hill.*

according to Act of Parliament April 9.ᵗʰ 1742.

A GWYNEDD ANTHOLOGY

IAN SKIDMORE

A GWYNEDD
ANTHOLOGY

CHRISTOPHER DAVIES

Published by
Christopher Davies (Publishers) Ltd.
P.O. Box 403, Sketty
Swansea, SA2 9BE

ISBN 0 7154 0638 8

*Printed in Wales by
Dinefwr Press
Rawlings Road, Llandybïe
Dyfed, SA18 3YD*

ENDPAPERS:
Front: *West View of Dolbadarn Castle* by Samuel & Nathaniel, Buck.
(By permission of Gwynedd Archive Service).
Back: *The South East View of Clunofvaur Abbey* by Samuel & Nathaniel, Buck.
(By permission of Gwynedd Archive Service).

For Celia,
Gwynedd's only rival

Contents

III.   THE SEA

IV.   THE PEOPLE

V. THE FABLES

VI. THE FAITH

VII.   THE POETS AND SCHOLARS

VIII.   THE LEADERS

IX. THE LED

X.   THE ROADS

XI. THE TRAVELLERS

Foreword

My world is bounded by the A5, which crosses Anglesey, and the forest at Newborough where sunsets are made.

I live, surrounded by trees, in a tiny Regency lodge on the estate of the Marquess of Anglesey, who lets me walk my lurcher in his woods. There is no danger to his pheasants because my dog, Miss Kip, is the only lurcher in Wales ever to be frightened by a rabbit. It is an idyllic life. I earn my living by reading newspapers, listening to the wireless and then writing about what I have heard and read. Occasionally, I write books. I have one day off a week, which I spend in secondhand bookshops in Gwynedd, looking for contemporary copies of the works of Dr Johnson and his friends in the literary world of eighteenth century London.

The rest of the time I read or I tend the garden and think about what I have read. This book is the result of that reading and the thinking it provoked. It lays no claim to be comprehensive, nor is it designed for the academic historian.

I want it to be read by people who, like me, venerate the heaven on earth which is Gwynedd, to the degree that we mourn any day spent away from it.

Certainly that would be true of many of the writers I have assembled for your entertainment. How could it be otherwise? Only a dead soul could travel through this county and not be caught by it. And it is astonishing how many great writers have been drawn here from Giraldus Cambrensis to John Betjeman.

Some years ago I wrote my own minor contribution to the literature of Gwynedd. Since it was published I have had kindly letters from all over the world. This book contains the ingredients that went into the making of that one. I hope you will enjoy it.

IAN SKIDMORE

I

LAND, LAKES AND MOUNTAINS

1. *Anglesey*

Anglesey is a platform from which to admire the beauties of Caernarfonshire.

Folk saying

2. *Mona*

Anglesey, anciently by Latin writers called Mona, is an island, and one of the counties of North Wales according to the present division, separated from the main land by a narrow arm of the sea. It is seated in a temperate air, enlivened by a benign sun, and enriched with a good and bountiful soil.

The Rev. Henry Rowlands,
Vicar of Llanidan, Ynys Môn

3. *Night and Morning*

One stormy night when I went out to walk on the shores of the Menai, silently pondering, the wind was high and the white waves were wild, and the sea was dashing over the walls of Caernarfon.

Anon, *Englyn*

4. *Merionethshire*

In form this Shire somewhat resembleth a Welsh Harp, though small is the Music that to her Inhabitans she makes, being the roughest, and most unpleasant to see to (as Giraldus their own Historian writeth) in all Wales. The air for great pleasure, nor the soil for great profit, I cannot greatly commend, unless it be for the many and mighty great winds, that for the most part therein do rage, and the spired hills cluttered together so near and so high, as the same author affirmeth, that Shepherds upon their tops falling at odds in the morning, and challenging the field for fight, before they can come together to try out the quarrel, the day will be spent, and the heat of their fury shut up with their sheep.

John Speed, *Atlas of Wales,* 1627

5.   *Snowdon*

The dim night is silent, and its darkness covers all Snowdon; the sun in the bed of the sea, and the moon silvering the flood.

Gwallter Mechain, *Englyn*

6.   *Caernarfonshire*

The soil cannot be much commended for the fertility, except those parts of the sea coasts, which lie on the West towards Ireland: but for the heart of this Shire, it is altogether mountainous, as if Nature had a purpose here, by rearing up these craggy hills so thick together, strongly to compact the joints of this our land, and to frame the inland part thereof for a fit place of refuge to the Britains, against those times of adversity which afterward did fall upon them; for no Army though never so strongly, or scarce any Travellers, though never so lightly appointed, can find passage among those so many rough and hard Rocks, so many Vales, and Pools here and there, crossing all the ways, as ready obstacles to repel any Inroads of foreign assailants. These Mountains may not unfitly be termed the British Alps, as being the most vast of all Britain, and for their steepness and cragginess not unlike to those of Italy, all of them towering up into the Air, and round encompassing one far higher than all the rest, peculiarly called Snowdon-Hill, though the other likewise in the same sense, are by the Welsh termed *Craig Eriry*, as much as Snowy Mountains, taking their name as doth (by Pliny's testimony) Niphates in Armenia, and Imaus in Scythia: For all the year long these lie mantelled over with Snow hard crusted together, though otherwise for their height they are open and liable both to the Sun to dissolve them, and the winds to over-sweep them.

John Speed, *Atlas of Wales,* 1627

7.   *Merioneth*

Living paradise of flowers, land of honey, land of violets and blossoms, land rich in crops, land of nut-bushes, and dear land of the hills.

Machreth, *Englyn*

8.   *Mountain Lakes*

The calm green lakes are sleeping in the mountain shadow, and on the water's canvas bright sunshine paints the picture of the day.

Gwilym Cowlyd, *Englyn*

9.   *Llyn Idwal*

Hopeless as it would be to attempt here a notice of the numerous lakes and tarns and waterfalls that lie buried amid the mountains, on either hand, I may perhaps indulge in one backward glance across the valley to the gloomy glen that comes down from one of the wildest and most sombre of Welsh tarns, Llyn Idwal. In former days the shepherds believed the latter to be the abode of demons, and were all assured that no bird dare fly across its precipice-shadowed waters. But we know already that Idwal, the youthful son of the Great Owen Gwynedd, was murdered here and flung into the dark watery depths by his foster-father Dunawt ap Nefydd hardd.

A. G. Bradley, *Highways & By-ways of North Wales,* 1892

10.   *The Mountains*

The extent of this prospect appears almost unlimited. The four kingdoms are seen at once; Wales, England, Scotland, and Ireland —

forming the finest panorama the empire can boast. The circle begins
with the mountains of Cumberland and Westmorland; those of
Ingleborough and Penygent, in the county of York, and the hills of
Lancashire follow; then are observed the counties of Chester, Flint,
and Denbigh, and a portion of Montgomeryshire. Nearly the whole
of Merioneth succeeds; and, drawing a line with the eye along the
diameter of the circle, we take in those regions stretching from the
triple-crown of Cader Idris to the sterile crags of Carnedds David and
Llewelyn. Snowdon, rising in the centre, appears as if he could touch
the south with his right hand, and the north with his left.

Samuel & Nathaniel Buck, *Beauties, Harmonies and*
Sublimities of Nature

11. THE SNOWDON SUNRISE

In one of these excursions, travelling then
Through Wales on foot, and with a youthful Friend,
I left Bethgelert's huts at couching-time,
And westward took my way to see the sun
Rise from the top of Snowdon. Having reach'd
The Cottage at the Mountain's foot, we there
Rouz'd up the Shepherd, who by ancient right
Of office is the Stranger's usual guide;
And after short refreshment sallied forth . . .

The Moon stood naked in the Heavens, at height
Immense above my head, and on the shore
I found myself on a huge sea of mist,
Which, meek and silent, rested at my feet:
A hundred hills their dusky backs upheaved
All over this still Ocean, and beyond,
Far, far beyond, the vapours shot themselves,
In headlands, tongues, and promontory shapes,
Into the Sea, the real Sea, that seem'd
To dwindle, and give up its majesty,
Usurp'd upon as far as sight could reach.
Meanwhile, the Moon look'd down upon this shew
In single glory, and we stood, the mist

Touching our very feet; and from the shore
At distance not the third part of a mile
Was a blue chasm; a fracture in the vapour,
A deep and gloomy breathing-place through which
Mounted the roar of waters, torrents, streams
Innumerable, roaring with one voice.
The universal spectacle throughout
Was shaped for admiration and delight,
Grand in itself alone, but in that breach
Through which the homeless voice of waters rose,
That dark deep thoroughfare had Nature lodg'd
The Soul, the Imagination of the whole.

William Wordsworth

12.   *A Snowdon Climb*

We began our march at a quarter past one. The clouds were gathering over the mountains and threatening us with either darkness or rain. We however escaped both, and were only amused with every variety they could give the landscape by hiding or half obscuring the moon, and by blotting out now one mountain and now another until about two o'clock, when the dawn began to appear, they covered the moon and we saw her no more . . . In ascending an almost perpendicular green slope, on a sudden I saw at my feet an immense chasm of a depth I could not guess. It answers in some respects to the idea I have formed of the crater of a volcano, but it is evidently not that as there is no mark of fire, the rock being composed, as it is in general throughout the country, of a sort of slate . . . You think that you are now at the top, but you are mistaken. I am indeed standing at the top of the abyss, but with a high rock peak rising on each side of me, and descending very nearly perpendicularly into the lake at the bottom . . . I look up and see the upper part illuminated by a beautiful rose coloured light, while the opposite part still casts a dark shade over its base, and conceals the sun from my view . . . I arrived at the highest peak at a quarter past four, and saw a view of which it is impossible to form an idea from description. For many   miles around it was composed of tops of mountains of all the various forms that can be imagined; some appeared swimming in an ocean of vapour; on others the clouds sat like a cap of snow, appearing as soft as down . . . The whole prospect was bounded by the sea except to the east and south-east, and the greatest part of the land in those points was blotted out by the clouds, while the sun rose so far towards the north-east as to be still hanging over the sea.

Elizabeth Smith, *An Account of a Snowdon Climb,* 1798

13.   *Dinorwic Power Station*

One of the most exciting and challenging engineering projects in the world is under construction at Llanberis in North Wales where the McAlpine-Brand-Zschokke Joint Venture (M.B.Z.) is carrying out the main Civil Engineering Contract in the building of Europe's largest pumped storage power scheme.

The Power Station complex is located deep below the disused Dinorwic slate quarry on the edge of the Snowdonia National Park and the external works have been carefully designed and built to blend into the natural environment of the area. In addition, the high voltage cables are all being led away underground from the Power Station to the grid sub-station near Bangor, some 10 km away.

Hydraulic tunnels some $2\frac{1}{2}$ kilometres in length, together with a vertical shaft 440 metres deep and 10 metres in diameter, will carry more than $6\frac{1}{2}$ million cubic metres (1,500 million gallons) of water from Marchlyn Mawr Reservoir, 630 metres above sea level, to the Turbines during a full generating cycle providing a constant ouput of 1680 MW to the national grid for five hours.

The water then flows out into the lower reservoir Llyn Peris at 100 metres above sea level, through the Tailrace tunnels.

The Turbines will operate in reverse as motor pumps at off-peak times to pump water from the lower to the upper reservoir, the full pumping cycle taking six hours.

During the generating and pumping cycles the water levels in the upper and lower reservoirs will fluctuate by up to a maximum of 33 and 14 metres respectively.

About 500,000 cubic metres of highly faulted and folded slate has to be excavated to form the complex network of huge tunnels and caverns that make up the Power Station proper. A further 750,000 cubic metres of rock excavation is being carried out in associated tunnels and shafts.

The main access tunnels are more than adequate to accommodate two double decker buses side by side and the chamber for the main power plant will be one of the largest excavated caverns engineered in the world — twice as long as a soccer pitch and higher than a 16 storey building.

C.E.G.B. Handout, 1979

14.   MY HEART IS IN MERIONETH

Low ye hills in ocean lie,
That hide fair Meirion from my eye;
One distant view, Oh! let me take,
Ere yet my longing heart shall break.

Anonymous, 16th-17th century folk verse

15.   ANGLESEY DAWN

For a while
The morning is lying in wait,
Enthralled
I see
The shutters of heaven withdrawn.
Mist is over the Isle
And covers the Strait,
But the white-walled
Houses of Anglesey
Flash with the dawn.

Edwin Stanley James, *The Little Land,* 1958

16.   *The Summits of Snowdon*

Generally, though incorrectly, only the mountain ranges which dominate the extreme north-west of Wales are known by the name *Snowdonia* – *Eryri* in the old Welsh. The error arises from the presence here of the prince of the Welsh mountain scene, *Yr Wyddfa (Snowdon)*, so it is assumed that only those mountains flanking the central massif bear the name. In fact, *Snowdonia* covers a far larger domain of over 2,000 square kilometres (840 square miles) and extends far south to Bala and beyond.

Walkers who venture into the hills of Snowdonia will find themselves among mountains that have an affinity with higher ranges elsewhere in the world. The terrain is often rugged and broken; evidence of the carving hand of ice is encountered everywhere; summits, in the main, are sharp and accessible only by routes that are devious, steep and rocky, and connecting ridges have at least one side which falls steeply to a valley or *cwm*. In winter it is a paradise, or a deathtrap, according to one's ability. What may not be readily grasped, for the geology of Snowdonia is not easily understood, is that the whole area was once completely under the sea: fossil sea shells found in the sedimentary rocks of Snowdon, Moel Hebog and elsewhere prove this point. (Yet it is interesting to note that when, less than two hundred years ago, George Louis Leclerc, Comte de Buffon, a French naturalist, propounded his prescient theory that sea shells found embedded in high mountain rocks were evidence that the sea had once been there, no less an eminent man of letters than Voltaire disputed the theory as 'mystical nonsense', saying simply that the shells had been take there by pilgrims.)

Terry Marsh, *The Summits of Snowdon*, 1984

17.   *Across the Straits*

The huntsman blew his horn and away they went to the river bank.

I joined the hunt for several reasons. I am by nature a countryman and a hunter; I love the cry of hounds and the craft of hunting and I loved the rivers where the otters lived. Unfortunately, I loved the otters as well.

As the hounds eagerly covered the river banks, Jack and Evan Jones, who had hunted these waters years before, meeting early in the morning and with only a few friends to make up the field, remained inconspicuously in the background, viewing the pantomime with a certain cynicism but always ready to dispense their great knowledge if called upon by the master. The field usually split into two groups; one massing the banks to view the possible chain of bubbles that showed an otter on the move, and the other laughing and gossiping in the buttercupped meadows.

Sometimes the country was at its best. The sun shone; the water, glistening and racing, sang as it ran down towards the sea. I always enjoyed it most when we met on one of the mountain streams, for the country was most beautiful and the chances of killing an otter were very slight. Here were fast-running streams, waterfalls and deep pools, and the voices of the hounds in the gorges created glorious echoing music.

One day, after meeting at Tan-y-Bwlch in the Maentwrog valley, hounds found an otter on the low-lying tidal stretch of the Dwyryd and chased him up in the deep gorge where the river Prysor crashes down from Trawsfynydd in a series of waterfalls. It was a slow, un-satisfactory hunt for the hounds, for they were unused to the precipitous slopes and dangerous water that swept over rocky ledges to deep green pools below. Eventually under a tall waterfall the hounds became silent, and word went round that the otter had indeed been killed and its body had sunk to the bottom of a deep slimy pool.

The Border Counties had their man for such a moment. Bravinton-Smith, a tall grizzled ex-England rugby player, who always wore hunt uniform with blue shorts instead of knickerbocker breeches, volun-teered to retrieve the body. He took off his coat, his shoes, then his snow white shirt, and with a faint breeze playing on his hairy chest he stood for a moment, an heroic figure on the rock above that black pool. There was a gasp of admiration from the ladies as with a superb dive he plunged downwards and out of sight beneath the chill waters of the Ceunant ddu.

We waited silently until in the middle of the pool a grey head appeared. Bravington-Smith brushed the water from his mouth with one hand. 'I've got it!' he cried, and a cheer went up as he made for the rocky bank dragging a sodden weight behind him.

Admiringly we watched as he scrambled ashore. The masculine rugby torso emerged, and he stood like some Greek water-god with the river Prysor lapping his mighty frame. 'Here he is!' he cried, and raised the object above his head with a great muscular heave.

No cheer went up now, for we saw to our horror that the object was no otter but the decomposing body of a mountain ewe.

Bravington-Smith dropped it with a roar and scrambled back on to the rocks as it slowly disappeared once more to the depths from whence it came.

Someone laughed, but a hunt official silenced this unsporting outburst with a withering glance. Someone said, 'Bad luck, old boy,' and a murmur showed that everyone agreed. The horn blew and slowly we left that horrid place and made our way down to the welcoming meadows of Maentwrog.

It was in the low-lying land of Lleyn, where the streams ran narrow like gutters, that the Border Counties Otter Hounds found it easier to kill, but even so, without the help of supporters who screamed their 'Tally Ho's', they would have been hard put to it to win a victory.

The Erch, the Soch and the Cymerau — these were the rivers that gave the hunters a chance to carve yet another notch on their poles, and it was on the Cymerau on a hot and lovely day in August that I witnessed a so-called hunt that will leave me with a feeling of shame every time I remember it or pass that way.

Near the bridge below Penmaen and the Bodegroes woods the river flows silent and narrow between reedy banks and poor meadowland. Nowhere is it very deep. In this large ditch they found an otter. Hounds' voices broke into a great chorus that brought the hunters running to line the banks and gaze down with excitement to catch a glimpse of their quarry. Brave men leaped into the water up to their waists and formed barriers of legs and hunting poles that hemmed the otter into a strip of water a hundred yards long. The banks were solid with people, the river was blocked effectively as if there were lock gates; and in this overpopulated piece of water was one otter that had no hope of escape. The huntsmen callously threw thirty hounds into the muddy gutter.

I should have gone home then, but somehow I couldn't tear myself away from the scene. This wasn't hunting, this wasn't sport; it was killing, and everyone seemed happy at the thought of it, and savoured the agonies of the animal they said they admired.

A small head came up to breathe among the reeds, but he was spotted immediately and the whole pack was hurled in as the otter slipped away into the churning mass of water. Soon the olive green was turned to the brown of milky tea as the mud was stirred up by the threshing hounds.

'There he is!' came the cry twenty yards away. 'Tally Ho', came another cry further on, as the tired animal surfaced more frequently from weariness.

The sun beat down on the festival scene. The well-lunched field was getting its money's worth and was joined by hordes of locals who had heard the noise of hounds and hunters.

An hour went by, and still the otter avoided the frustrated hounds. Sometimes its whole body could be seen as it rolled over feebly, to dive again from the snapping jaws. The human barrier or stickle moved inwards: heartless men determined to destroy. After about an hour and a half the hounds were almost snapping at themselves as they swam in this ever-decreasing pool with the half-drowned otter somewhere between their legs.

A pathetic head poked up between the reeds near a large fox-hound. Hound saw otter and lunged forward to kill. Amazingly, there was just enough strength left for the otter to slide away, but the jaws bit somewhere into the drowning body so that the muddy water was stained with red.

The slow murder continued until there was a sudden silence. It seemed as if the otter might have managed to slip through the stickle or creep into a drain in a last effort to elude his tormentors. The people on the banks waited, the stickles were motionless, the hounds were mute. Then slowly a brown body rose to the surface of the muddy water. It was the otter and it was dead. Dead not because it had been killed by thirty hounds and sixty men, but because it had drowned. In one way I suppose it had won a victory since they were unable to take it alive; but the hunters didn't think so. There was a cry of triumph and the huntsman leaped into the water to drag the corpse from the frenzied hounds.

Cheerfully they brought it ashore; jolly men and women crowded round as it was virtually dismembered. The rite had been observed, the festival was over. Happy people retired to the road to unload hampers, to drink whiskey and cups of tea and to eat cool cucumber sandwiches.

Kyffin Williams, *Across the Straits,* 1973

18. *The Coast in early times*

Evidence accumulated from the geological record has shown that during the New Stone Age, somewhere between four thousand and six thousand years ago, a considerable subsidence of the western shores of Britain took place. In the region since known as North Wales this gradual downward movement turned what must have been, in some places, a broad coastal plain into areas of shoal water extending in front of her northern and western seaboards, and flooding the heads of the main indentations of the resultant coastline.

It is possible that the earth movements of those early times were, at one period, sufficiently accelerated to bring about the catastrophic inundations that gave rise to the legends of Llys Helig and Cantref-y-Gwaelod, the villages under the sea. But however that may be, the general submergence, coming at the end of a long period of denudation and glacial action during which whole mountain ranges were planed down almost to the level of the sea, was the master-stroke which completed the picture of the coast as it is today.

Before the downward movement ceased the densely forested regions, lying at the foot of the seaward slope of the North Wales mountains, had been submerged beneath the sea; and the undulating plateau, stretching north-westward from the centre of the range, had been cut off from the mainland to form an island many centuries later to be given the name of Ynys Môn or Anglesey. Vestiges of the drowned forests may be seen today on the shore at Rhyl, Colwyn Bay, and at several points on the coast of Anglesey. Half shrouded in sand and gravel the naked seaworn stumps and roots of the trees still cling to the sodden soil, a matted humus formed of the leaves of unnumbered autumns, wherein lie embedded the prostrate boles and branches of the forest giants and the bones of the wild beasts that once roamed this ancient woodland.

The shoreline, roughly following the five fathom line of present day charts, lay some ten miles to the northward of Rhyl, and extended westwards to Point Lynas in Anglesey, embracing Great Ormes Head and Puffin Island. The whole of Beaumaris Bay was occupied by a low-lying plain, through which flowed the River Conway, and a stream, possibly the River Ogwen, flowed northeastward along the bed of what is now the navigable channel of that part of the Menai Strait, and entered the sea through Puffin Island Sound.

On the west of Anglesey the coastline extended from Carmel Head to North Stack, the coastal plain filling what are now Holyhead and Beddmanarch Bays; while the outlying shoals of modern charts, such as Careg Hen off Rhoscolyn, formed dwindling islands fringing a slowly foundering coast. In the south of Anglesey a river, flowing down the south-western part of the Menai Strait, debouched into

Caernarvon Bay on a shore that swept in a broad curve from Rhoscolyn to Porth Dinllaen.

On the south side of the Lleyn Peninsular the head of Cardigan Bay was occupied by the low-lying Cantref-y-Gwaelod, which extended from Bardsey Island to Aberystwyth.

In addition to the submerged forests these drowned lands exhibit the remains of what may once have been villages, courts, or strongholds, and even roads, as at Rhos-on-Sea, Llys Helig in Beaumaris Bay, and Caer Arianrhod in Caernarvon Bay; while the sarns of Cardigan Bay suggest causeways or seawalls above a land prone to frequent inundation by the sea. Although the tragic stories associated with these ancient plains provide an imaginative picture of their final flooding, it is, perhaps, more probable that the submerging movement was imperceptibly slow, and had all but ceased by the time of the Roman invasion of Anglesey in the first century A.D., when the coast and the Menai Strait must have been very much as they are today.

F. H. Glazebrook, *Anglesey and the North Wales Coast*

19. *Môn and Manaw*

The two Fortunate Islands, so much talked of and celebrated by the ancient poets, have been for many ages last past utterly lost and not to be discovered. Among many supposals let us add some. They were two, and so are these: they went both by one general name, and so did these; being called *Monae*, that is, the one *Môn*, the other *Manaw*; the one the bigger, the other the lesser; the one the nearer, the other the more remote.

The ancient philosophers and poets were great celebrators of virtue, and thereupon for encouragement of men did affirm there was a place of pleasure or rest, whereto after this life they were carried who had lived regularly: and that place was sometimes called the Elysian Fields, as at other times the Fortunate Islands.

They did farther fancy, that though there were other delights, yet above all, the pleasure of converse with the just, and a relaxation from care, was most valuable; they might therefore conceit the better of these islands above other places, because of the strict life of the Druids, a religious people here dwelling, sequestered from the cares of the world, and doubtless of a great name and virtue, at their first sitting down.

Their name *Monae* imports also a solitary place, as monastical among the religious has the like signification from the Greek language. The two Fortunate Islands were, in the judgement of the best writers, generally, by the report of Natalis Comes, a noted mythologist, seated upon the western coast of Britain; they were in the Atlantic Ocean by common consent; and these are there also; for in ancient time that tract of sea lying beyond the coast of Africa and Europe to the West, was called from the mountain Atlas (probable enough) the Atlantic seas; the straights thereby being the outlet of them to the Grecian and Roman countries, who successively lorded it over this part of the world.

The Elysian Fields or Fortunate Islands were said to be full of shades; the Druids here nourished many woods to perform their superstitious rites in; Anglesey was called *Ynys Dowyll**, a dark and shadowy island, from the wood there growing; the Greek and Latin poets anciently reckoned the North their right hand, and the South their left, from their way of looking to the West, towards the Elysian Fields. More might be said (says the author) to this purpose, which I omit. I will add in the close the opinion of some few of note: Homer thought they were on the coasts of Britain; Isacius Tzetzes, a Greek author of account in Camden's opinion, reports they were with the Britons: and the story of Plutarch, in the life of Sertorius, I will repeat, which methinks is not distant from what we are now speaking of.

Anonymous letter to 18th century antiquarian

20. THE SEVEN WONDERS OF NORTH WALES

> Pistyll Rhaeadr and Wrexham steeple,
> Snowdon's mountain without its people,
> Overton yew-trees, Gresford bells,
> Llangollen bridge and St Winifred's well.

Anon, 18th century

---

* Ynys Dowell.

21. CADER IDRIS AT SUNSET

Last autumn, as we sat, ere fall of night,
Over against old Cader's rugged face,
We mark'd the sunset from its secret place
Salute him with a fair and sudden light.
Flame-hued he rose, and vast, without a speck
Of life upon his flush'd and lonely side;
A double rainbow o'er him bent, to deck
What was so bright before, thrice glorified!
How oft, when pacing o'er those inland plains,
I see that rosy rock of Northern Wales
Come up before me! then its lustre wanes,
And all the frith and intermediate vales
Are darken'd, while our little group remains
Half-glad, half-tearful, as the vision pales.

Charles Tennyson Turner

22. AT A WELSH WATERFALL

It was a hard thing to undo this knot.
The rainbow shines, but only in the thought
Of him that looks. Yet not in that alone,
For who makes rainbows by invention?
And many standing round a waterfall
See one bow each, yet not the same to all,
But each a hand's breadth further than the next.
The sun on falling waters writes the text
Which yet is in the eye or in the thought.
It was a hard thing to undo this knot.

Gerard Manley Hopkins, Maentwrog

II

LIVING THINGS

1. *Prehistoric Anglesey*

At the time when man may have returned to Wales, Anglesey would still have been cold and dry, with birch and pine as the only trees. In South Wales and in Derbyshire there are inhabited caves dating from this period (c. 10,000 — 8,000 B.C.) which contain flint implements showing strong links with the old Palaeolithic traditions, but alongside them are a number of smaller points, the forerunners of the true Mesolithic industries of this country. None of these have yet been found in North Wales or Anglesey, but as the climate gradually improved the human population may be expected to have increased and spread.

By the time the Mesolithic hunters are likely to have reached Anglesey (c. 6,000 B.C.) the summers had become warmer, with hazel, pine and alder replacing birch as the dominant trees, and mixed oak woodland making its first appearance. The animals living in these woodlands may have included deer, bison, bears, forest horse, pig, elk, hyaena, lion, wolf and certainly ox for the bones of one have been found in the peat of the submerged forest at Trearddur Bay.

France Lynch, *Prehistoric Anglesey*, 1970

2. *A Snowdon Lake*

The other lake is noted for a wonderful and singular miracle. It contains three sorts of fish — eels, trout and perch, all of which have only one eye, the left being wanting; but if the curious reader should demand of me the explanation of so extraordinary a circumstance, I cannot presume to satisfy him. It is remarkable also, that in two places in Scotland, one near the eastern, the other near the western sea, the fish called mullets possess the same defect, having no left eye. According to vulgar tradition, these mountains are frequented by an eagle who, perching on a fatal stone every fifth holiday, in order to satiate her hunger with the carcases of the slain, is said to expect war on that same day, and to have almost perforated the stone by cleaning and sharpening her beak.

Giraldus Cambrensis, *The Itinerary Through Wales,* 1191

3. *Dulyn*

There is a lake in the mountains of Snowdon, called Dulyn, in a rugged valley, encircled by high steep rocks. This lake is extremely black, and its fish are deformed and unsightly, having large heads and small bodies. No wild swans are ever seen alighting upon it (such as are on all the other lakes in Snowdon), nor ducks, nor any bird whatever. And there is a causeway of stones leading into this lake; and if any one goes along this causeway, even when it is hot sunshine, and throws water so as to wet the furthest stone, which is called the Red Altar (yr Allawr Goch), it is a chance if it do not rain before night. Witness, T. Prys, of Plas Iolyn, and Sion Davydd, of Rhiwlas, in Llan Silin.

Greal, 1805

4. *Beavers of Nant Ffrancon*

Nant Ffrancon signifies 'the valley of the beavers', the presence of that valuable and marvellous little beast in ancient Wales being well assured by the high place accorded to its skin in the list of prices fixed by the great law-making king, Howel Dda, in the tenth century. Any one familiar with the meadows created by the beavers in the backwoods of Canada, could well bring himself to fancy that the green flats below, through which the naturally impetuous Ogwen steals in so subdued a current, had been the scene of their industry in former days.

A. G. Bradley, *Highways & By-ways of North Wales,* 1898

5. *Heather Flowers*

Gaily they grow, the quiet throng, fair gems, the folk of sun and wind, the swinging bells of the high crags, flowers of the rocks, like cups of honey.

Eifion Wyn, *Englyn*

6. *Of the Wild Fowl & First of Ye Land Wild Fowl & Birds of Passage*

The Wood Cock (called here Kyffylog) visits us about . . . October, finding the Northern Countries it seems too Cold. I have been credibly Informed by a Master of a Ship that in his voyage homeward bound from Muscovy, a great flight of woodcocks flew by his ship in their way to Britain, and some few tired ones Lighted upon his deck. He had seen them ashore in ye Northern countries in Flight. As this Island abounds with Furze, it is a good Shelter for them, and they afford good diversion & profit. The *wind-thrush** or Caseg Eira is here generally in Frost or Snowy weather. And in ye spring the Cuckoo commonly called the Welsh ambassador with his Servant pays us a visit.

As I have not seen in any authors any tolerable account of this Bird and its manner of Breeding, Sleeping, &c. It will not be disagreeable to ye curious to read ye following acount which I Deliver here for Truth & real matter of Fact; I took the account myself from the mouths of ye Persons concerned and this can be proved by a Hundred Living Witnesses.

In ye year 1739, about Christmas — daughter of Margaret Ellis of Aberffraw, Being in a field near Aberffraw where there were a few Gorse Bushes, and with other Children playing found the Bed of a Cuckoo &c. and in another Just within a few yards of the Bed of her Servant, Called in Anglesey Gwas y Gog, The Cuckoo's Servant, a small bird which always follows her. Both these birds were in their Beds most curiously made like a Coffin to Close about them, and they were both fast asleep, and no sign of life to be perceived. The nests or beds & Birds in Harry Morris's house for several months to be seen &c.

This Little bird makes his own nest & lays his Eggs, but the Cuckoo drinks his Eggs and lays her self an Egg there, which the foolish bird Hatches, and feeds till they fly. I have taken them in ye nests and have seen this small bird feed them.

From hence no doubt the original of ye word Cuckold came, and this small Bird may properly be called a Cuckold for breeding the young of another. This small bird must lay a second time, and the Cuckoo's season being over, he hath Quiet rest to breed his own kind.

Lewis Morris, *Note Books,* 1748

* "Field fare" written above *wind-thrush.*

7.   *The Birds of Llanddwyn Island*

Spring comes to the Isle of Saint Dwynwen (Llanddwyn Island) long before the Calendar proclaims the advent of that joyous period of Nature's re-awakening.

Even as early as mid-February one may see the advance guard of the feathered host of prospectors commence their survey of the coast.

The first to stake their claims are the ravens; but not without due consideration, and with a practical eye for essentials in the matter of choosing just the right spot. As often as not, this is high up on some bold headland with 'inaccessibility' as its main feature. But occasionally the site is approved more on account of its 'usefulness' and because of the likelihood of its remaining undisturbed due to its remoteness, not so much from human habitation as from the clamour of other nesting species.

A week or two sees the nest completed; a structure of twigs and odd scraps of driftwood, coarsely interlaced but surprisingly strong and able to withstand the severest weather.

February passes into March and the equinoctial gales are still sweeping up from the South-West, though not always with the grim ferocity of the winter storms, when the four or five beautiful eggs make their appearance, and the Raven's hidden treasure becomes the subject of enthusiastic speculation on the part of the delighted parents.

During February a general movement is noticeable among the shore birds. The flock formation is breaking up. Shelduck, which have been consorting together in great numbers, now range in lesser detachments which gradually dwindle into amorous couples. Oyster Catchers are breaking 'form' and spreading out in smaller parties and pairing off. The Ringed Plover are returning to their summer haunts and the Curlew wistfully to his mate. Only the Turnstones and the Purple Sandpipers remain in little flocks among the rock pools. The Redshank, on the other hand, seem to follow a different plan, for during the winter these birds are to be met with singly, but in the spring they gather in the marshes of the Cefni and the Braint.

The first week in April finds the Guillemots and Razorbills home from their ocean wandering, though occasionally solitary birds may be seen near the shore in mid-winter. They come in small parties to feed near the shores of the Island, but their nesting colonies are elsewhere.

About this time the migratory birds begin to pass up the coast. Two or three pairs of Gannets may be seen wheeling out over the bay and it is a thrilling sight to watch their dramatic hundred-foot plunge into the sea, in pursuit of their finny prey. Among the land birds, on the move from more northern fields, may be mentioned the White Wagtails, which visit the Island in small companies and whisk playfully before the Pilots' cottages in search of tit-bits. Nothing could be prettier than the flitting to and fro of these dainty wayfarers, whose sweet song is, alas, as short as their sojourning. They may, however, be looked for in their return passage in September.

And now, with the advance of April, the nesting species commence their labour. Wheatears in their smart spring dress start warily from the entrance hall of rabbit burrows marked 'to let'. Rock Pipits and Stonechats fly hurriedly from crannied pinnacle or time-worn dyke, whilst the Wrens are busy amid the tangle of the ivied cliffs. A pair of Rock Pipits make their home yearly in the neighbourhood of Porth Tŵr Mawr and, by the third week in April, there is usually a fine clutch of seven brown-speckled eggs in the cosily sheltered nest. There is scarcely a cove which does not contain at least one nest of the Ringed Plover, and other sites may be found at intervals along the shore towards Aber Menai, and even in the sandhills themselves, cunningly hidden and most difficult to detect among the litter of shells, pebbles and dried seaweed cast up by the winter storms.

Instinct would seem to be rather at fault in the behaviour of these birds at the approach of a human being, for they advertise both their own presence and that of their nest by sounding their alarm notes when, by keeping quite still, they would be less likely to attract the attention of the passer-by. Instead, they begin to leave the nest at the first appearance of a stranger and almost immediately begin to call. They invariably make down the beach for the water's edge and keep up their piping so long as there is a remote possibility of their secret hoard being discovered. This gives away the locality if not the position of the nest. The Ringed Plover usually remains on the shore, unless closely approached and then it will take wing for a short excursion out of harm's way, being as often as not joined by its mate who has been watching anxiously in the vicinity. Instinct, perhaps wisely, urges the bird to look after itself and leave the eggs to take care of themselves, trusting in natural camouflage to keep them hid from prying eyes.

Another common species, Oyster Catchers, act very much in the same manner, becoming alarmed and running away or taking to flight sooner than the Ringed Plover. Both birds would be well nigh invisible if they remained on the nest, the former looking just like part of the dried seaweed thrown up at the top of the beach, and the latter 'disappearing' into the surrounding pebbles and sand. The Ringed Plover is a very careful and attentive sitter, however, and will sit through the fiercest gale though the air be thick with driving sand when, if she were to desert her nest for a few minutes only, it would be obliterated by the storm. But master Sea Pie seems rather careless. A pair nesting near Twr Bach thought nothing of leaving their eggs uncovered for a whole day. They were nevertheless very much on the *qui vive* for predatory gulls or crows and attacked them vigorously if they came near. The hen bird will leave her nest at the slightest provocation, and sometimes through sheer boredom, while the male does all the scouting and defending.

It is extraordinary how these shore birds return to the business of nesting within a day or two of the same date, year after year. How careless of consequences they sometimes are, in the choosing of a suitable location for the nest, may be instanced by the experience of a pair of Ringed Plovers which made their nest and laid their eggs in the middle of the path leading down to Porth Dafydd Owen. A choice which resulted in catastrophe, when the three precious eggs were destroyed by the trampling of a flock of sheep.

Among the birds which more rarely visit the Island must be mentioned the Manx Shearwater. He is more often heard than seen. His curious, hoarse cry (which has been aptly said to resemble a husky 'it-is-yor-folt' oft repeated) may be heard late at night, as the mysterious bird flies swiftly homeward from the feeding grounds.

To human ears the effect of this mournful voice calling through the dark and mist o'nights is weird indeed; so that one is more than pleased when at last a glimpse of this sea-ghost is obtained for the first time. He will be seen, perhaps, flying very swiftly in wide circles about the bay, his wings now beating in rapid yet purposeful strokes, now outstretched to their fullest extent. Then he will heel over on a sharp swerve until one wing-tip skims the surface of the water. At such times a good view is obtained of his dark back and wings or, alternatively, of his silvery white under parts. At a distance he appears a swiftly moving black speck. His homeward track will sometimes take him in a bee line across country but, except at the breeding colony, he is most often to be met with out at sea and it is there his perfect air mastery may best be admired.

April is well advanced when at last the eagerly looked-for Terns, or Sea Swallows, make their first appearance over the Island. The advent of these beautiful migrants is always an occasion for rejoicing, for with their return from the south is ever associated the coming of our northern summer. It is a sheer joy to awake one spring morning, with the sun streaming through the little window, to hear their unmistakeable call sounding over the sea for the first time. Here at last is the advance patrol of an army of white-winged seafarers and one conjectures on the number and variety of them that will make the 'Isle of True Lovers' their abode for the summer.

Terns arrive in Menai Straits some time before they settle on the Island. April 15th is not too early to look for them on the Foryd, and they have been known to reach the Straits as early as April 5th, but it is seldom earlier than the twentieth of the month that they come to spy out the Island. It is usually during the first week in May that the main body arrives at Llanddwyn and it is very noticeable how punctual they are in this respect. For the years 1924-1928 the dates of the settling down of the Terns on the island were May 9th, 5th, 4th, 4th and 5th respectively. The most interesting variety of Tern to be seen here is the Roseate. Besides being rarer than the other varieties, he is the most wayward and the most handsome of all the Terns.

The Commons and Arctics are by far the most numerous among the varieties which come here annually, but in addition to these one may sometimes observe a pair or so of Sandwich Terns and the Lesser Tern, the latter coming over from the long shore to fish in the island coves when the whitebait are in.

By the middle of August the business of rearing the young is complete and the Terns disappear as mysteriously as they came. A few still linger in Menai Straits and sometimes, after a stormy summer, a spell of fair weather will set in in September and a number of Terns will come to the Island to fish for whitebait, which have been driven into coves in immense shoals by the mackerel. It is probable that these are not the Terns that nested here, but are a party of migrants turning aside from their southward course beguiled by halcyon days. The fine spell is soon over, alas, and the rearguard of the Terns at once departs. A curious sense of loneliness settles down on the isle, for with their going comes the thought that many a long month must pass before the white-winged hosts bring summer back with them once more.

F. H. Glazebrook, *The Bird-Life of the Coast of Anglesey.*
Saint Dwynwen's Isle (Spring)

8.   *Of Sea Fowl*

The Puffin is a remarkable bird that breeds upon the Coasts of Anglesey. In Priestholme Island (Ynys Seiriol), in Skerry Island (Ynys y Moelrhoniaid, literally the Isle of Seals) and in the Ynys Lawd or ye South Stack by Holyhead.

This is ye Bird called by Clusin Anas Arctica, the Pica marina of Gemer (?Gerner) in North Wales Pwffing, in South Wales Goulden head, in Cornwall a Pope. It is about ye bigness of a Jackdaw or less and hath a Bill resembling that of a Parrot but Thinner & broader with ye Edge forward. Black & White Feathers. Red feet & bill, dives & flies but little, and with great difficulty take the wing on plain ground, unless in Sight of ye Sea.

They lay their Eggs in Rabbit holes, which they'll beat out of their Strongholds. *Their* eggs of ye bigness of those of a young hen is what they say. The Egg is not so white as a Hen's Egg, But Eats as well. If you can reach them with your hand in their burrows you may take them out, but they'll bite severely if they can catch hold. The bird is generally let loose and the Eggs taken. This in ye month of June. I have not taken notice whether this retards their departure. They feed their young with the Fry of Fish which they take under water and carry them by 3 or 4 at a time in their bills.

As to the place these Birds Lodge in winter. There can be no pretence of their being able to go to any distant country nor to ye moon according to ye vulgar opinion about Birds of Passage, For as they are such Heavy flyers, and never seen off far at sea, Their Lodging for their winter's rest must no doubt be near at hand, and where can it be but in a cave in the Rocks which goes a great distance under ground.

The Young Puffins before they are Quite Feathered, are Fledged and opened and straw'd with pepper & salt & Broiled and Eat pleasant enough. But the nice way of managing them is to Pickle them, and these are sent as rarities for ye Tables of the Great. They are of an exceeding high Gust.

Lewis Morris, *Notebooks,* 1748

9. *Shorelands Diary*

On the evening of March the 27th, my wife and I crossed over Telford's great bridge which spans the Menai Straits, and entered the island county of Anglesey. We were no strangers to this fair country, but our journey today was different from all previous ones for, at the end of it, in a little grey village at the head of an estuary, there was an empty house which we hoped to call home as soon as we could get our belongings into it. Our other visits had been short holidays, spent chiefly in watching and drawing birds and landscape of which there was great variety. Several sketch-books had been filled with studies of Anglesey and its birds, and we had been specially delighted to find that the island in spring and autumn was a calling place for many migratory birds, while summer and winter had their own particular and different species. Occasionally, to add to the excitement, a rarity would appear. Whatever the season there were always birds and this fact had greatly influenced us in our choice of a new home.

Our intention to establish ourselves in this Celtic land was not to be accomplished without opposition however, for Anglesey, the Mother of Wales, had built a little church on one side of our lane, and the stone wall of a cottage garden on the other. The furniture vans were monstrous and stuck fast between church and garden wall and could proceed no farther. After we had scratched our heads in perplexity, and listened to suggestions from interested observers, Môn Mam Cymru relented and sent a coal lorry to our aid. The sun shone, the furniture went into the house via the coal lorry, and the Shelducks on the sands laughed and cackled all day.

There followed days of arranging and re-arranging and gradually order emerged from chaos, the proceedings often suspended while we gazed from the windows. Field-glasses and telescope were always kept in readiness for a sudden grab, but it was astonishing how often they became buried under other material not yet put in its proper place. Such was the case when we heard the call of wild geese one evening. Books and paper went flying, field-glasses were unearthed, raised and focussed on a fine skein of Grey Lags as they flew past the house and down the estuary. What a grand clamour they made! We watched them until, with impetuous tumbles, they came to rest on the sands two miles away. Wild geese viewed from our own front door! It was a warming thought, and as we watched there were other small but significant happenings. Stonechats haunted the gorsey patch beyond the lounge window, often perching on the boundary wall and gazing in at us. Yellow-hammers, which were surely more vivid in colour than the Cheshire Yellow-hammers, flitted about this same wild patch, and about the old stone walls Wrens hunted confidingly. We felt that we had made a good choice.

The house is well named "Shorelands" for only a stout wall and a row of rough upright timbers protect it from the tides of a mile-wide estuary. Years ago the estuary extended almost into the very heart of the island, but in the year 1812 a sea wall was built, and the inland area over which the tides used to flood was reclaimed and is now good farmland, dotted about with grey stone farmsteads, and intersected by numerous dykes and raised earth banks. The sea wall is called locally "The Cob," and it has its beginning very close to the village at a spot where a bridge spans the river and its two flood-water canals. River and canals are disciplined by high man-made banks for some miles inland, indeed as far as the river is tidal. The bridge marks the end of the village street and the beginning of the road over the marsh. After crossing the bridge the road swings slightly inland, then deviates shorewards again and touches the Cob at its far end. Thus, between Cob and road, there is an area of brackish pool and swamp which is beloved of the birds, and both road and Cob make ideal vantage points for their study. Many are the happy hours I have spent there. The pool in this diary is called "Cob Lake." On the other side of the road are fields which are often flooded and, even in summer, are rarely without water. Here too the birds love to congregate, and there have been occasions when I have not known which way to turn, Cob Lake or field pools, because of the richness of bird-life on them.

But to return home: the windows in the front of the house command views from east to south-west. Looking south-east, with the Cob extending across its whole width, is the mile-wide estuary. Beyond, filling the middle distance, is a long ridge of high ground criss-crossed by hedges and dotted about with farms, which at its seaward end deteriorates into rock and sand-dune, and above this ridge loom the great mountains of Caernarvonshire, the kingdom of Eryri, with Snowdon lording it over all — a stupendous panorama. The view looking south, if not so high and mighty, is just as good, for now the river, after running parallel with the house, makes a lovely S-bend across the sands before turning again to meander to the sea. Still looking south the ridge of the middle distance is now sand-dune, and just over the curve of a wind-scalloped hollow a little white speck can be discerned — the top of the lighthouse on Llandwyn Island three miles away. Beyond rise the shapely blue hills of Lleyn with the tree peaks which the English call "The Rivals," and whose proper name is Yr Eifl, which means "The Forks," looking much higher than they are in reality, for their steep sides fall sheer to the sea. To the southwest Lleyn continues in a series of lesser hills, losing itself eventually below the sea horizon beyond the bar, and then appearing on the horizon again like an island which is, I suspect, Mynydd Anelog at the very end of Lleyn.

From the house to the bar, the distance is nearly three miles, three miles of sand through which the river winds its serpentine way, sands which hold thousands, nay, tens of thousands, of birds. It may have been these sands which gave our village its name of Malltraeth — which in English means the "Bad Strand," for I have no doubt that to the sailors of old it was a wild and dangerous place in stormy weather.

On March the 29th I took a walk along the Cob and, to my delight and surprise (for I had not previously seen this species in Anglesey), I found two Great-crested Grebes swimming on Cob Lake. It was good to know that in leaving my native Cheshire I had not necessarily cut myself off from these strange and interesting birds, and I wondered if they nested in Anglesey or whether they were just birds of passage. They were slim and alert as they watched my progress along the Cob. With them swam a solitary Pochard drake with a fine copper-red head and neck. Neither he nor his Grebe companions bothered to dive, safe as they were in the middle of the lake. Out on the sands Shelduck fed in groups and often the ducks sent out their weird witch-like calls. How immaculate they were in their spring plumage! The drakes were growing the knob at the base of their bills, that special decoration for the breeding season, indeed in some drakes it appeared well-grown.

On the fair saltings the Curlew were calling and, as I watched, some of them came up the estuary and, flying almost overhead, continued up the marsh, suddenly soaring up and sideways as a shot rang out from a rabbiting farmer. Away in the distance of the marsh they sped, calling, calling all the way, an exquisite choir. I returned along the Cob, past the Welsh Black cattle grazing there, and, for a time, watched the homing gulls as they flew in formation down the marsh, over the Cob to their roosting place on the sands. Then I, too, went homeward, full of hope and anticipation of riches to come.

C. F. Tunnicliffe, *Shorelands Diary,* 1952

III
THE SEA

1. *Hilaire Belloc's book,* The Cruise of the Nona, *tells of a passage southward from Holyhead, finally docking at Folkestone. It was not an easy voyage, but Belloc never was afraid of the elements:*

I looked at the Carnarvonshire coast there close at hand, the sinking lines of the mountains as they fell into the sea, and I discovered myself to be for the first time in my life entirely indifferent to my fate . . .

Anyhow, here I was in Bardsey Sound, with many deaths moving over the howling fury of the sea, and not one of them affecting me so much as a shadow passing over a field.

The end of that adventure was odd and unreasonable — as things will be at sea. It was perhaps because we had been buffeted and pushed into some edge of the conflict between wind and water where the tide runs slacker; or it was perhaps because the wind had risen still higher. But, at any rate, after three separate raids forward (in the second of which we were very nearly out of our peril and into smooth water), and as many set-backs (one of which got us into the worst violence we had yet suffered) the *Nona,* in a fourth attempt (it was her own, not ours — we could do nothing but keep her, as best we might, to her course), slipped out and reached an eddy beyond the tide. For a moment it was very difficult to keep her to it, she slewed round; but then again she got her head southerly, and we found ourselves running past the great Black Rock which stands there — the Carrig Dhu — and marks the smooth water beyond the edge of the tide.

We breathed again; and as I took her on through an easy sea, close under the land with not too much strain upon the helm (for the high shore now broke the gale), I was free to look over my right shoulder and watch, passing away behind us, further and further, the hell of white water and noise, through which we had barely come to safety.

Danger keeps men awake and makes them forget necessity, but with this relief, our fatigue came upon us. My friend and I had now been awake for some twenty-five or twenty-six hours, and it was time for sleep.

We got the poor *Nona* which had behaved so well, up into a lonely little bay where was an old abandoned mine working, but no other sign of man. The Welshman with us told it was good holding ground; we let go the anchor and stowed sail. I remember how I fell half asleep as I stretched the cover over the mainsail boom and yard and tied it down at the after end. The gale still blew, yet, as it seemed, more steadily and less fiercely. There was no danger of dragging. We were well under the lee of the land. I gave one look, under the violent but clear morning sky, to seaward before I went below; and there I saw how, at a certain distance from the land, in a long line, the white water began. It was like being in a lagoon, like being protected by a bank from the sea outside; but really it was only the effect of the lee of the land making a belt of smooth water along shore. Then we all lay down to sleep and slept till evening.

Hilaire Belloc, *The Cruise of the Nona*

2.   *Hundred of Nant Conwy*

There are found here in a large fresh water mussel called *creggin y diluw*, or deluge shells, pearls, which I am told are of a large size and occasionally of a fine lustre. Some have been sold for above two guineas, and there is a vague report that the great pearl in the crown of England was brought from the Conway and presented by Sir John Wynne to Queen Elizabeth.

E. Hyde Hall, *A Description of Caernarvonshire*

3.   *Lavan Sands*

A Scotsman being drowned on Lavan Sands last winter, by the ferrymen's refusing or neglecting to go for him, two of the said ferrymen on the morrow went in quest of the Corpse, tore out his pockets, stole his money, and afterwards finding his Box and Pack, carried them also away and hid them in the Point under gravel and tang, which some of the Town's people observing, four of them 2 sailors and 2 shipwrights went there in the night, took them up and shared them amongst them and two or 3 more of the confederacy.

The Town Magistrates and the neighbouring Country Justices having either neglected or refused to take proper examinations, and to secure the Criminals, the Judges of the Circuit (Viz) Mr Taylor Whyte and the booby Rogers Holland sent for Mr Lewis and myself and press'd it upon us that we should take the Examinations of such people as should be brought to us by the Solicitor of the prosecutor, all the Criminals were of the Borough of Beaumaris; and the Constables of the Borough took them and brought them before us, which took up all our time for the most part of 3 days.

William Bulkeley, Squire of Brynddu, Anglesey,
Diary, 1735

4. *Passage from Holyhead*

March 26th, 1735. Set out for the Head (Holyhead) about 7 and being obliged to go about we did not arrive there till 12 in the forenoon; paid the Customs House fees for searching my portmanteau, 2s.; paid 6d. for carrying it ashore; paid in the house 10s. Set sail at 9 in the evening. Very calm all night.

March 27th. About 11 in the forenoon we came in sight of the Hill of Hoath; came to the bay at 4 in the evening, and was near 8 before we landed at Ring's End; (23 hrs); paid Quilho the Master of the Packet Boat £1 1s. od. for our passage; gave the cabin boy 6d.; paid the boatman that carried us from the Ship to Ring's End 1s.; spent at Ring's End in staying for a coach 11d.; paid for a coach to Dublin 2s. 10d. Twas near 11 at night when we came to Dublin, my poor daughter being mightily tired, and almost starved with cold.

April 2nd. One o'clock in the evening had notice of the *Prince Frederick* Packet being to go over that evening; took a coach half an hour past two in the evening; came to George's Quay, paid 1s. for a small bowl of Punch, took water at 4, and came on board the Packet Boat, taking leave of my good friend and Cousin William Parry on the Quay (Having left his daughter in Dublin).

April 3rd. The wind E.S.E.; weighed anchor at 4 in the morning; sailed all that day against the wind; made very little way, being not above 7 leagues from the Irish shore by night, the wind continuing E., sometimes N.E., all the night; I was at this time heartily tired of my voyage, but not sick.

April 4th. The wind due E.; the old crazy ship stretching the 6 hours ebb to the north and the 6 hours flood to the south (*sic*) to gain 2 leagues in a tide. Before night we were got within 4 or 5 leagues of the Head, but about sunset a great storm arose and blew easterly all night and by the morning we were driven back again in sight of the Irish shore. Could not rest for the noise aboard all night. The Master at last resolved to give over any further attempts for the Welsh shore, and to turn back to Dublin, where we arrived at eight in the evening (64 hrs.).

April 5th. Being Easter Eve; gave the Master 5s. for what I ate and drunk aboard; gave the men 1s.; came ashore and took lodgings on George's Quay; entertained the Master of the packet Boat at supper, together with Mr Hugh Hughes of Rhoscolyn, who is an Excise officer at Wicklow, for whom I paid 4s.

April 10th. (After a cold and stormy four days.) The wind S.E., raining very hard all the morning as it did most part of the night. About 5 this morning I was alarmed with a knocking at my chamber door, that the Packet Boat was just going off, which was something surprising, because I had been assured the night before she would not go till Friday. No delay being made in the matter I was forced to get up, pack up my things in a hurry and go aboard where I arrived about 9; paid my lodgings to clear the house 4s. 6d.; paid for Mr Lewis Morris, Surveyor of Customs of Holyhead, to Mr Wm. Parry to buy him Ink and other materials for Printing, 10s.; paid the porter for carrying the things to the wherry to go aboard the ship, 4d.; gave the boatman 4d.; paid wherry for bringing me to the ship, 2s. 6d.; weighed anchor about 10; made no great way, the wind being contary and calm.

April 11th. The wind N.E., pretty still and cold, came within sight of the head by day and landed in Holyhead Bay at 12 in the forenoon (about 26 hrs.). Gave Thomas Hughes the master 10s. 6d., for my passage; came to Mr Vickers the Postmaster's house where I had lodged before; met with great company of Custom House, Salt and Excise Officers, where we drank all the evening; it cost me nothing.

April 12th. The wind S.E., a fair calm day but cloudy. Gave the ship's crew 1s.; set out from the Head about 9 in the morning and arrived at home upon Mr Vicker's horses at 2 in the evening; gave his man that came along with me 2s.

William Bulkeley, Squire of Brynddu, Anglesey,
Diary, 1735

5.   *The Sailors*

I have seen, on a surreptitious peep into the kitchen (i.e., a part of her father's house where servant girls could receive their sweethearts) four young sailor boys sitting round as solemn as deacons, holding their caps between their knees, all clad in navy blue and good strong woollen jerseys. I was in that kitchen the other day for the first time since that scene of sixty years ago, and, upon my word, it all came back to me in a flash. I can name some grand children of those young men and women, too! Those lads were strong and healthy, hard work at sea and good food ashore any way. They used to walk the quarter deck back and fore in front of the Britannia on the Llawr Gam each spitting for the farthest. Old John Felix who kept the Britannia was a most amusing old man.

Miss Buddug Pugh, *Recollections of a 19th century childhood in Aberdyfi*

6.   *The Royal Navy visit Llandudno*

Farce attended a naval visit to Llandudno, on 13 September 1919, when HMS *Queen Elizabeth*, HMS *Lion* and HMS *Venomous* anchored in the bay as part of a grand victory cruise. The battleships made an impresssive sight off the Great Orme and North Wales was present in force to see the humiliation of Admiral Sir Charles Madden, commander-in-chief of the Atlantic Fleet, and Rear-Admiral Sir Roger Keyes, commander at the Zeebrugge and Ostend raids. The two admirals had come ashore to pay their respects at the Town Hall and to invite a party of civic dignitaries to join them for lunch on board the *Queen Elizabeth*. With careful timing the returning top brass, walking along the pier, and the admiral's steam pinnace crossing the bay, should have met at the pier head. As it was the pinnace, running a few seconds late, came in too fast and rammed the pier steps. The hapless lieutenant in command turned about, presumably in an attempt to return to his parent ship, but the damaged pinnace sank between the pier head and Pen Trwyn, its crew being rescued by the paddle-steamer *St Trillo*. After an exchange of semaphore signals another pinnace was sent out, only to repeat the performance of the first, although in this instance the coxswain had the wisdom to run his boat ashore. Before the day was finished a total of four naval steam pinnaces had been sunk at Llandudno and Admiral Madden let it be known that he had banned all future visits by the Royal Navy until the pier head had been rendered safe.

I. Wynne Jones, *Shipwrecks of North Wales,* 1973

7. *The Caves of the Great Orme*

There are several caves in the cliffs near the sea, and they are reached by boats, a pleasant excursion on a fine day. One of them (Ogo' Colomenod, or the Pigeon's Cave) we have mentioned.

The most curious of the caves (a little way south-west of the Lighthouse) is that called Llech (a word meaning a stone, especially a flat stone or slab), and sometimes Monk's Cave, a square room about six feet and a half in extent, and ten feet in height. The shape of this cavern, to use the words of Dr Ingleby, 'is semi-octagonal, terminated in front by two square columns of freestone. A font and seats are in perfect preservation; but of the stone table, which many years ago occupied the centre, the pedestal only remains. The font, or rather stone basin, is supplied by a spring of most delicious water, which, at certain seasons, flows in copious quantities into an artificial bath, excavated in the rock below. It is said the cave was fitted up as a grotto, or pleasure house, by some ancestors of the Mostyn family'. Near this, and further to the south-west is Ogo' Hornby, or Hornby's Cave, so called from the fact that a vessel of that name was dashed on the shore at this place on the night of New Year's Day, 1824, when only one person was saved. Westward of the Pigeon's Cave is a flat stony ledge, which is covered about two feet in depth at high water, called Mainc-y-stiwardiaid, or the Stewards' Bench, where, according to tradition, the steward of the Mostyn family, if convicted of wronging any of the tenants, was compelled to sit naked during the washing of two tides. (This may be compared with the story of Ysgolan, preserved in a twelfth-century Welsh MS., and in a divergent form also in Brittany. He had 'burnt a church, slain the cow of a school, and put a book to drown,' and to do penance for this, 'was placed a full year at Bangor, on the pole of a wire; dire were his sufferings from the sea-worms'). Besides the caves we have mentioned there are Ogo' Dutchman, a little to the east of Ogo' Colomenod, and Ogo' Hyfnant, east of the Lighthouse.

George Lerry (ed.), *Gossiping Guide to Wales*, 1954

8. *The First Printing Press in Wales*

Wales's first printing press was in a mountain cave in Llandudno. Operating in the 1580's, a good 130 years before the first official press at Newcastle Emlyn, the Llandudno example has received little attention from historians. For the press, in part of the cave system known as Rhiwledyn on the Little Orme, was a clandestine one, printing religious tracts and propaganda for the Roman Catholic cause, at a time when such activities were punishable in only one way — death, usually by being hanged, drawn and quartered.

According to printing historian Stan Wicklen, the press had a short life, operating for about four years from 1583 to 1587. It seems that its output during those years — all of it in the Welsh language — was quite high, high enough, indeed, to attract the displeasure of the Crown, but only a few examples of its work are extant, the main one being the *Drych Cristianogawl* or *Book of Piety* (literally 'Christian Mirror'), now in the National Library of Wales, Aberystwyth.

Certainly materials for the press were supplied from France. Cases of leaden type, cross-timbers and uprights for the body of the machine, the large wooden screw that exerted pressure on the platten to create an impression, even the paper and printing ink — all had to be smuggled into the cave by boat, an extremely hazardous task at the best of times. Oarsmen were guided to the cave by lanterns, visible only from the seaward approach.

In spite of all this cloak and dagger scenario, it is likely that the whereabouts of the press and the identities of the printers were known to the authorities long before it was forced to close. Its chief supporters were members of a well known local landed family, the

Pughs of Penrhyn Creuddyn. Indeed Squire Robert Pugh counted himself as one of the 'craftsmen', along with his son Phylip and his daughter Mary, possibly one of the first women to break into the male-dominated printing industry.

Though two centuries later Wales was to be swept by Methodism, in the 1580s there was still much sympathy for the Catholic cause. Several blind eyes were obviously turned towards the clandestine press in the cave, and even when its end came in 1587 it was hardly a rout. It had catered for a Welsh-speaking population in an area of tight family loyalties.

When the order finally came from London to Sir Thomas Mostyn of Gloddaeth 'to seek out those engaged in unlawful actions on the Creuddyn Peninsula' the sequence of events is typical of an area, remote from central government, where local ties are more important than national politics.

According to a letter written by Dr William Griffith, a magistrate in the Caernarfon area, on April 16, 1587, and contained in the State Papers of Elizabeth I, a local informer reported 12 priests working at a printing press in a cave at Rhiwledyn.

Sir Thomas Mostyn, commanded to deal with the matter, led a party of 40 men to the mouth of the cave but, according to Dr Griffith, did not enter, fearing an ambush. Instead he mounted a guard at the entrance but, curiously, in the morning when this enthusiastic band of 16th-century storm-troopers went in not only had all the 'priests' vanished but all their equipment had disappeared with them.

The only evidence that a printing press had existed anywhere near the site was some pieces of metal type found on the shore. Sir Thomas had done his duty to the Crown and honour was satisfied, but Squire Pugh, his neighbour, had escaped along with the other 'priests'.

That same year, Mary, Queen of Scots, was executed. The following summer the country rallied behind Queen Elizabeth to defeat the Spanish Armada. The secret press never returned to its cave.

Celia Lucas, Arcade, 1982

9. *Letter to Richard Morris*

December 12, 1757

My Dear Compatriot,

Here we are, through the Providence of the Most High, having come thus far in fine health, without death or illness or sea-sickness or any other mishap overtaking us, despite having a great deal of cold, stormy weather whilst we were in the Downs and from the Downs here. How splendidly resolute my wife and the three little Welshmen have held out without sea-sickness or nausea (apart from a little dizziness the day we came from the Nore to the Downs), whilst the English she-thieves, yes and the thieves, and a few of the ship's crew were spewing their guts out. Woe to the lot of them! The seamen are a frightfully vile bunch of men. God be my keeper, every one of them has taken to himself a strumpet from amongst the she-thieves and do no work except whoring wantonly in every corner of the ship. Five or six of them have already contracted the pox (dare I mention it) from the women, and there is no doctor here save myself and my copy of Dr Shaw's book, and it is with its help that I tend them a little with what medicines are to be had in the chest which is here. I fear sometimes lest I should get it myself from being amongst them. I baptised one child (his name was Francis Trial) and buried him later, and a she-thief and thief besides. It was today that I buried the woman. Do you remember how this tadpole of a captain promised that my wife could have one of the she-thieves to serve her whilst at sea? One of them is here in the cabin, but it was to serve this husband's penis, and not to wait upon my wife, that she was brought here. There never was seen a worse beast of a man than the master. For the past fortnight he has compelled us to drink stinking water or else choke (for there is no drop of small ale aboard) and to watch him drinking his wines and beer with his strumpet, smacking his devilish lips to whet our appetite and saying, 'It is very good'. What, say you, will become of us before journey's end? But I do have an unopened barrel of porter and a little rum. I half-fear that he will one day so anger me (by hitting one of my chidlren or some other trick, for he has a hundred mean tricks) that I shall run my sword under his short ribs, and thank him for lending me such a fine, sharp-pointed weapon. May God preserve me from such an evil.

Convey my regards to Mr John Owen and show him this, and to the Llew, Mr Parry, and Mr Humphreys. If I have time I shall send a letter to Dr Nicholls. We sail as soon as the wind is favourable with the rest of the fleet, which consists of some 300 vessels. This day the captain and I went on board the *Seaford*, man of war, for instructions which we accordingly had. May God grant you and us health and a fair voyage. I am,

Your obedient servant,

Gronwy Ddu

Goronwy Owen, *Letter to Richard Morris Esq.,*
at the Navy Office, London.

10. *U-Boat Rendezvous at Llandudno*

The extravagant assignment of two U-boats to rendezvous at Llandudno with three escaped prisoners-of-war, in August 1915, is evidence enough of the importance of the mission in the eyes of the Imperial German Navy. The venture was all the more remarkable for having been planned in the rural remoteness of Dyffryn Aled, a house taking its name from its setting on the banks of the River Aled, 6 miles west of Denbigh — and planned long before any enemy submarine had penetrated the Irish Sea, let alone the busy waters of Liverpool Bay . . .

Korvettenkapitan Hermann Tholens was among the first to be interned at the Dyffryn Aled prisoner-of-war camp. Born on 19 May 1882, he had been in the Navy since 1900 and was second-in-command of the 4,550-ton cruiser *Mainz* when she was sunk . . .

During the last week of September 1914, Tholens was joined by a more colourful officer, Kapitänleutnant Heinrich von Hennig, a year younger and one rank junior, but of far greater value to the Reichsmarine . . .

. . . The two men discussed the feasibility of escaping and returning to Germany by submarine, and they chose the westernmost point of the Great Orme for the rendezvous. They entrusted their plan to a civilian who had been interned as an enemy alien resident in Britain on the outbreak of war but who was being sent home in a Christmas exchange scheme. The dates for the rendezvous were to be sent to Tholens and von Hennig by a prearranged code, in letters from relatives acting under instructions from the Reichsmarine.

It was a daring scheme, and on 23 January 1915 the *U-21*, commanded by Lieutnant Hersing, left Germany to test the route and become the first enemy warship to sail on the Irish Sea since 1797. A drifter spotted her off Bardsey Island on 28 January, but she carried on, rounded Anglesey into Liverpool Bay, and sailed up the Lancashire coast to shell an airship shed at Barrow. The shore battery at Walney returned the fire and the *U-21* submerged to sail south as far as the Mersey Bar where, on 30 January, she sank three steamers, the *Ben Cruachan, Linda Blanche* and *Kilcoan.* Hersing, who had already made history as the first submarine commander to sink a British warship, was given a hero's welcome when he returned to Wilhelmshaven on 4 February.

That same day Germany declared all British waters to be in the war zone and said every merchant ship encountered in those waters after 18 February would be sunk. The declaration was given emphasis on 20 February when the *U-30* sank the 3,112-ton *SS Cambank* five miles off Point Lynas. On 25 February the *U-20*, commanded by the notorious Korvettenkapitän Schweiger, and the *U-27* under Korvettenkapitän Bernd Wegener, left the Ems for the Irish Sea, the latter pioneering a new route for submarines via the North Channel, which separates Northern Ireland and Scotland, and sinking the armed merchant cruiser *HMS Bayano* on his way through on 11 March.

By their return to Germany these pioneering U-boat comanders demonstrated that the plan drafted at Dyffryn Aled was well within their capabilities.

Korvettenkapitän Wegener was an acknowledged Irish Sea specialist by the time he sailed the *U-27* from Germany on 4 August. Korvettenkapitän Max Valentiner left Wilhelmshaven the next day, in command of the *U-38*. The two were to rendezvous off Llandudno on 13 August so that one or the other, or the survivor in the event of a mishap, could move in under the Great Orme on the following night to embark the escaping prisoners.

By this time, Tholens and von Hennig had been joined by a third conspirator, probably because he had stumbled on their plan . . . Contemporary newspapers described him as Hans Werner von Heldorf.

The method of escape from Dyffryn Aled has been described by Tholens. The night guard at the camp comprised two sentries at the front of the house, two at the rear, and one at either end, compared with a total of two when the escape was planned. Security arrangements had also been augmented by the addition of powerful lamps at each of the four corners of the compound, which were switched on at 9 p.m. It was agreed that the best time to escape would be in the twilight just before the night guard took over.

'Our plan was this. We intended to get through the iron-barred window of the room which was inhabited by my two fellow-escapers — for we had by now added a third to our number. Our next obstacle was the first of the two entrance gates, which led through the barbed wire fence which surrounded our prison. If the gate could not be opened, we should have to cut the barbed wire fence next to the room from which we started, and endeavour to crawl through it. Thus our preparations had to consist in cutting one of the iron window bars and in removing the hanging lock from the aforesaid entrance gate as soon as possible before the time fixed our our escape. Further, we had to procure a pair of clippers for cutting wire, a map of the coast, a compass, and an electrical pocket lamp. Plain clothes were still in our possession, as we had been allowed to wear them during the first two months. When this had been forbidden, and our clothes had to be delivered, of course we kept some back and concealed them beneath the floors of our rooms.'

Everything went according to plan, and at 8.45 p.m. on 13 August the three men broke out of camp and set off at a brisk pace on their 20-mile walk to the Great Orme headland. By 8 a.m. they were in Llandudno which was bristling with the Saturday morning activity of a garrison town. Relying on the likelihood of their not being missed before 9 a.m. roll call at Dyffryn Aled, they ate a good breakfast at one of the town's cafes before making their way on to the headland.

Having decided where they would descend the cliffs at nightfall, the men hid beneath some bushes — and then their plans started to go wrong. Leaving their hideout at 10 p.m., they were unable to find their route. 'If any of you know the Great Orme's Head you will remember that it is a very difficult place to climb down on a dark night,' wrote Tholens.

Meanwhile, the *U-27* and *U-38* had met north of Llandudno, where Valentiner, a personal friend of von Hennig, opted to complete the mission, releasing Wegener to sail south — where Valentiner had sunk twenty-two steamers, five trawlers and three sailing ships on his way to the rendezvous. While the escaped prisoners were rueing their predicament at the top of the cliffs, the *U-38* moved in close to the lighthouse, neither party detecting the presence of the other.

As dawn approached, both parties retreated, knowing that three successive nights had been allocated for the mission. On the night of 15 August the prisoners succeeded in reaching the shore, while the U-boat used the previous night's observations to sail partly submerged to within a few yards of the cliffs. Again no contact was made, and more than three years were to elapse before the participants learnt the ironic fact that they had been so close to success, being hidden from each other by only 500 yards of rock.

When a northerly wind developed on the afternoon of the third day, the prisoners — by then thirsty, hungry and demoralised — decided there was no hope of rescue, although there is some evidence that Valentiner kept up the vigil. As they walked back into town the men split up, to give Tholens an opportunity of using his English to board a train for London. Alas, Tholens was the first to be caught, and not in the dramatic way he has described by a tap on the shoulder as he was buying his railway ticket — he had £23 8s 3d (£23.41) in his pockets when recaptured.

Shortly before 9 a.m. on 16 August, Tholens entered the shop of W. S. Herbert, tobacconist and hairdresser, at 26 Mostyn Street, and asked for a packet of Abdulla cigarettes. By this time there was a full-scale alert throughout North Wales and the German's accent was immediately suspect. Speaking Welsh to another customer, a milk roundsman named Griffith John Hughes, Mr Herbert asked him to follow Tholens until he met up with a soldier or a policeman.

Strolling up the road, Tholens called at the Cocoa House, 66 Mostyn Street, and ordered a cup of coffee and a cake. Constable Morris Williams was told of Mr Herbert's suspicions and a watch was kept from the opposite side of the street. Re-emerging briefly, Tholens then went next door but one, into the Tudno Hotel, where he remained for about five minutes. When he came out he was challenged, and arrested, to spend the night in a cell at the old Llandudno Police Station.

His two companions were more fortunate. Tholens's arrest resulted in the rapid deployment of the 15th, 16th and 17th Battalions of the Royal Welch Fusiliers to seal off and search the Llandudno peninsula. Despite this activity, von Hennig and von Heldorf remained at liberty until 11 p.m. when they were spotted near the Pier gates by a cab-driver, Alfred Davies.

'Cab, sir?' he asked, and as the men took their seats he knew they were the fugitives everyone was looking for. He drove them the short distance to Bryn Elli, 17 Gloddaeth Street, then forming part of the headquarters of the 15th (1st London Welsh) Battalion, and alerted the sentry. Mr Davies's cab was used to convey the prisoners first to the Imperial Hotel, where they appeared before the Brigade Major, 113 Brigade, and from thence to the Royal Hotel, still in civilian use, in Church Walks. There von Hennig and von Heldorf, coming under military jurisdiction, were well fed before spending the night in the luxury thought appropriate for officers; while Tholens languished in his ancient police cell, only a very short distance away in Court Street.

The three prisoners were re-united next day when a military escort arrived by rail from Denbigh. They were taken back to camp in a motor ambulance provided by the London-Welsh community for the use of the 15th Battalion, and were sentenced to three months imprisonment, which they served at Chelmsford Gaol, later returning to Dyffryn Aled.

I. Wynne Jones, *Maritime Wales*

11. *To William from his brother-in-law, John Jones,*
     Lightkeeper at South Stack, Holyhead

August 26th, 1852

Dear Brother,

In obey your Mothers wishes I write these few lines to you to inform you that your brother John is for going to Liverpool for a place on the sea, your dear mother is very much vexed about him. She has tried every manner in her power to prevent him but without prosper. He is only waiting his clothes to be ready. His father cant get him to work as he would wish so they cant agree, indeed his mother is in great sorrow between them. You dear mother most humbly desire if possible for you to prevent him from go to sea. She would be glad if you can make him go to school for a Quarter if you have no objection for him to stay with you. She would pay for his lodging & school. For a word in reply she would be truly thankful.

I hope this will find you in good state of health as we are here and at Tŷ Mawr.

From your brother,

J. Jones

12. *Mary Hughes, Ty Mawr Mynydd,*
to her brother William in Liverpool

24th January, 1854

My dear Brother,

I feel much oblige to you for the newspapers you so kindly send us. They give us a great deal of Pleasure to read them these cold nights as we cant do much more than moving our chairs toward the fire and kicking the cats away to have a little more room. I often speak of your warm parlour and the good fire in it, if it is the same as when I was there and I often think of all your kindness to me which I can never return.

I am sorry to tell you of a Shipwreck that happened to a large Vessel on the sixteenth of this month.

Hapily no lives were lost as some go to the boats, they jumped on the rock in the Ryda by Porth Ruffydd in Penrhos y Feilw. There were twenty one in number. The boat landed in Porth y Nammerch and Penrhos feilw boats went out to get them that was on the rock and after a greate deal of difficulty they got them all, there was one black man amogst them and the Welshmen from the South, also the Captens wife was in it but no Capten he was dead since three weeks they said. It was coming from China loaded with tea — it went to pieces — no one knoes how it came as it was not very dark but very raining all night and very rough weather, on tuesday the tea was spreading about in all directions — grat many chests of it was landed at the pistyll ar henborth and people were going to there shoulders in the sea for it and one poor man lost his life. He fell down the cliff at yr hen borth. He was taken up alive, brought to Richard Roberts house were he died.

Father is gone to Llanerchymedd in such stormy weather. It is very wet here all last week and this week he cant sow the wheate for some time — we had a letter from John last Saturday — he was quite well, his time will be up in three weeks — our cousin Ann was very glad of the newspaper you send her. She is gone back to London for another six months and if she cant pass the Examination she must be longer. We are expecting a letter from Hugh very soon. Mr Owen Hughes Pen y Mynydd had a letter from America from his daughter-in-law with the bad news that his son Owen was dead. Father got the bascet on Saturday and Mother is Very thankfull for it, we are all in good health Margret and the girls was here to tea yesterday and John Jones was with us on Sunday, they are all well there — Thomas was here last night, he was sorry that he had so little of the tea, our cousin Louisa Jones Ty'n y Pwll was here for a night last week, they were all well there then. We have heard that William Jones is going to be master at Trearddur, pepel said once that he was married with Elizabeth Lloyd but that was untrue. Evan Hughes Twr is busy nursing, his wife has a baby — I conclude, as I am afraid of troubling you to much with my news, I had nothing better. I hope this will meet you well and that you will feavour us with a letter soon.

I am your affectionate sister,

Mary Hughes
Letter to William Hughes, 1854

13. *Castell March*

Between Abersoch and Llanbedrog stands the ancient house of Castell March, which tradition associates with a king of that name. The following yarn is told about a one-time owner of this house.

'Towards the end of the 17th century there lived here a certain knight, Sir William Jones, and like many jovial squires of that day he was on most admirable terms with the smugglers that plied their trade right merrily upon this sequestered, indented coast. Now in his day there was a particularly daring gang who were accustomed to run their cargoes ashore under the headland of Llanbedrog, and were even suspected, at times of being something more than smugglers. With these other matters, however, the good Sir William, J.P. and D.L., had nothing to do, but his dealings in the matter of brandy and French wines were continuous and confidential. Now it happened that the squire, who was an easy-going man, chafed much under the dominion of an over-zealous and strong-minded domestic. He had dismissed him from his service again and again, but his faithful butler treated the matter as a joke, and at last the poor Sir William arrived at such a state of submission that he could no longer call his soul his own; the burden had grown too intolerable to bear. At last, while turning and twisting in his mind various plans for regaining his freedom, a brilliant idea struck the knight, and upon the first opportunity he sought an interview with his friend, the captain of the smugglers' vessel, and asked him in confidence what his price would be for ridding him for good and all of his officious dependent. The smuggler named the figure, and it was agreed that he and his men should come to Castell March at night, seize, bind, and gag the butler, and carry him off to the South of France, or anywhere.

This proved as may be imagined a very simple affair, and went off quite smoothly, leaving Sir William once more master in his own house and prepared to enjoy life once again. But the cruise of the smuggler was a long one, and the force of character which had asserted itself in the pantry, began gradually to show itself upon the ocean. In fact, before the end of the long voyage was reached, the abducted domestic was such a popular and useful man on board, that all thoughts of landing him were abandoned, and he was sworn in as a member of the gang. Other business, perhaps of a more profitable and questionable kind than smuggling, kept the vessel away from the Bay of Abersoch for a year or two, and in the meantime the outraged butler had become a leader among his companions, and now felt prepared to execute a dark design that had been his consolation, no doubt, through many a long night watch. This was no less than to carry off Sir William in the same fashion that he himself had been spirited away. The job was executed as neatly as the other had been; the squire was seized, gagged and bound and carried off in the middle of the night to the vessel, and when morning broke he found himself looking sadly upon the vanishing coast of Lleyn from the deck of the smuggler, and once more under the sway of his old butler, only upon infinitely worse terms. History does not say how long Sir William was compelled to exchange the joys of hunting hares on the Llanbedrog hills, and getting drunk at Pwllheli market, for a life on the ocean wave in a smuggler sloop. But it is understood that he saw a good deal of the world, the watery part of it at any rate, before his evil genius considered that he had expiated his crime, and restored him to his friends and fireside and his bullocks. Even though a considerable sum of money was exacted as ransom, and so thoroughly frightened was the doughty knight by the whole adventure that he removed to Caernarvon where he spent the remainder of his days safe beneath the shadow of King Edward's Castle from his buccaneering butler.'

F. H. Glazebrook, *Anglesey and the North Wales Coast*

14. *The Pole Star*

A lamp are you, above all stars of night, to guide sailors in the dusk; lovely is your colour, sweet maid, standing in the doorway of the Pole.

Carnelian, *Englyn*

15. *The Wreck of the* Mary, 1675

In March 1675 the Right Honourable Joseph Williamson, Principal Secretary of State to Charles II, received this despatch from John Anderton from the Crown Office in Chester Castle.

'That the *Mary* yacht is certainly ship-wrecked I have it from the mouths of two gentlemen that escaped from aboard her who relate thus:

'On Thursday the 25th instant about two o'clock in the morning in foggy weather the ship launched upon a rock to the N.W. of the Skerrys that lie to the Eastward of the Bay of Holyhead. The seamen and the passengers were for the most part snug under decks. The first touch raised the seamen who cried all was well but immediately the ship struck upon another rock and there sank. The Skerrys is a small isle — an appendage to Anglesey about a league from the shore. The rock on which the ship struck was so near land that when the sea made the ship roll the mast touched land by which only means of escape lives were preserved.

'The Earl of Meath and about 34 more perished in the ship whereof the master Captain Burslow, the Boatswain and two more sailors were of this number. The master and 23 mariners with 15 passengers got safe upon the island. Amongst the 15 passengers were the Earl of Ardgloss and Lord Ardee, son of the Earl of Meath and now his father's successor in the family estate.'

The captain who bravely went back to lead the Earl of Meath across the mast lost his own life in the attempt. The despatch continued:

'It was 12 noon on Thursday at Noon on the 25th instant before the mast gave way — the captain to save the Earl of Meath and the rest lost himself.

'The preserved were on the island from Thursday morning until Saturday afternoon and had relief by a flask of gunpowder by which they struck fire with a steel and of the wreck boards of the ship made a fire. Now they roasted some mutton but had no bread nor any liquid but salt water till providence cast ashore a small cask of whisky which they divided proportionate among themselves.

'A Wicklow vessel from Beaumaris went as near the Isle as she durst and took in the 15 passengers and 24 seamen and landed them on Sunday last at Beaumaris which is the most particular account I can give you of this sad accident . . .'

King Charles II, *State Papers of 1675*

Editor's Note:
The *Mary* occupies a unique place in British maritime history. She was the first Royal Yacht and in her Charles II originated the sport of yacht racing, against his brother the Duke of York.

'Jachts' (the word means Hunter) had recently made their appearance in the Dutch Navy of the day. Light and fast they were used in wartime as patrol boats and in peacetime, luxuriously appointed, they carried the nobility round the country along the network of canals.

When Charles II, exiled in Holland, was restored to the English throne he made the journey from Breda to Rotterdam in a 'jacht' owned by the Prince of Orange.

It was love at first sight, and the burgomaster of Amsterdam was left in no doubt when he was presented to that merriest of monarchs that a 'jacht' would be the perfect present for a king who had come into his own.

The hint was taken. The *Mary* was purchased from the Dutch Admiralty, fitted out by the country's finest craftsmen and with a smaller yacht, the *Bezan*, sailed to England under a Dutch seaman, Captain John de Groes, 'a symbol of the esteem in which the citizens of Amsterdam hold the king'.

Captain de Groes was immediately commissioned into the Royal Navy and the *Mary* became the ancestor from which the thousands of sailing dinghies and racing yachts which sail round Britain today are descended. She was, in fact, the first yacht to be owned or sailed outside Holland.

16.   A RELIC OF THE ROYAL CHARTER

And so he bringeth them to the haven where they would be.

Yes, billow after billow; see, they come
Faster and rougher, as her little boat
Nears evermore the haven. Oftentimes
It seems to sink and fall adown the wave,
As if borne backward by the struggling tide;
Yet mounting billow after billow, wave

On wave o'er riding, tempest-tossed, and shattered,
Still, still it nears the haven evermore.
"Poor mariner! art not thou sadly weary?"
Dear brother, rest is sweeter after toil.
"Grows not thine eye confused and dim with sight
Of nothing but the wintry waters?" True;
Him, whose dying love and pow'r
Sailed its tossing, hushed its roar;
Safe in the expanded wave,
Gentle as a summer's eve;
Not one object of His care
Ever suffered shipwreck there!
See the haven full in view,
Love divine shall bear thee through;
Trust to that propitious gale,
Weigh thine anchor, spread thy sail!
Saints, in glory perfect made,
Wait thy passage through the shade:
Ardent for thy coming o'er,
See! they throng the blissful shore!

W. F. Peacock, *A Ramble to the Wreck of the Royal Charter,* 1860

17.   The *S.S. Hindlea*

On 26 October, 1959, while Dick Evans and his crew were attending
the memorial service which is held every year for the dead of the *Royal
Charter* at Llangallo church (where many of them are buried) the
S.S. Hindlea was fighting for her life in similar conditions in the same
patch of sea in which the *Charter* was lost.

Early next day, in a relief lifeboat, the *Edmund and Mary Robinson*,
a craft of which he had only taken delivery the previous day and
which he had been warned was a difficult boat to handle, Dick and a
crew of four —one of them a novice making his first sea trip — braved
some of the worst recorded seas to go to her aid.

There are no better words to relate this epic of the sea than Dick's
own — as he sits on his boat on the beach at Moelfre, pipe glowing
and looking twenty years younger than his 74 years.

'You see, every lifeboat I have been coxswain of belonged to me. The RNLI had nothing at all to do with it. It was my lifeboat, I thought the world of it. Even a scratch on the paint was like a scratch on my own body. It was my whole life.

'But I knew very little about the *Edmund and Mary Robinson*, the relief boat. She was totally different from my lifeboat, the *Watkin Williams*. She was a modern lifeboat with modern means of navigation. There was nothing like that in the *Edmund and Mary Robinson*. She was an old boat, in fact 26 years of age, and I dreaded thinking of going out in her until I had what we seamen call the 'feel' of her. How would she take a beam sea? How would she run before a gale? Every boat takes the sea different. Some lifeboats can run before any sea. Others can't.

'Little did I think of the experience I was to have with this boat.'

Dick was helping his wife to prepare lunch on October 27, 1959, when the testing time came.

'I received a telephone call from the coastguard, Captain Owen Roberts, that a ship was dragging her anchor in Lligwy Bay. The wind was rapidly veering to the north and she was being driven towards the rocks. All the other ships had managed to get out to sea but the *Hindlea* was riding hard.

'I immediately went down to the boathouse. By this time the wind was blowing a full hurricane from the north, ninety miles an hour and still increasing. Slates were being blown from houses and I had to dodge from being hit. Hay from the small-holdings had been torn from the stacks and was hanging from the telegraph wires. I could hardly stand.

'The mechanic, Evan Owen, was already at the boathouse and the lifeboat engines were running. Also my second cox, Murley Francis, had gone to the boathouse thinking that we were bound to be needed. Another member of the crew, Hugh Owen, arrived. Now we were four. I could not telephone the remainder of the crew, all the phone wires were blown down.

'The coastguard, Captain Roberts, came to the boathouse. He was frantic. He asked me to launch the lifeboat immediately. I very well remember his words. He said, "I hate having to send you boys out in this terrible storm. But that ship is being driven onto the rocks and once she gets into the breakers you won't get near her."

'There was one man in the boathouse, Hugh Jones, who helped on the slipway. I asked him would be volunteer and he immediately responded — although he had never been in a lifeboat before.

'If these four men would have refused nobody could have blamed them. It was almost suicide to go out in a lifeboat in such terrible seas. But as soon as I said "We'll go boys" they immediately climbed the ladder into the lifeboat. I instructed them to make sure their life-jackets were tied down and we fastened each other's to be sure — although I'm afraid they would have been of little use in that terrible sea. By now the wind was gusting up to 104 m.p.h. A northerly wind is the worst possible wind in Moelfre Bay. It was *Royal Charter* weather.

'I'd never been out in the *Edmund and Mary Robinson* in bad weather but we cleared the slipway and the crew hauled the radio masts up. I told them to pack themselves under the forrard canopy. I had to tie myself to the wheel. It isn't an easy thing to do. The sea was a boiling mass of fury. My grandfather taught me all the seamanship he knew but he never taught me how to deal with this kind of sea. It was coming up from all angles.

'The *Hindlea* was only about half a mile from the slipway but it took us an hour and a half to get to her. The sea in the bay was terrible. What it would be like on the other side of the Moelfre Island I had no idea. I did what I always did in the lifeboat. I prayed. I prayed desperately. There were only four words in the prayer and I must have said them continuously, "Please God Guide Me", and I'm sure I would not be talking to you today unless some superhuman power had guided me that day.

'This is something not clearly understood by any of us but I am absolutely certain that every time I prayed I felt a renewed strength running through my body.

'The *Hindlea* was about one and a half miles north of Moelfre Island. Her anchor was still dragging. She only had one anchor down. She should have had two but the captain could not send his men to the fo'c's'le head to put the other anchor down. They would have been washed overboard. She had this one anchor out with 100 fathom of chain and she was striking rapidly. She had got into real trouble. She was veering to 90 degrees with the engines racing. I decided to go up on the lee side but by the time I approached her she was yawing so much I was coming up on her weather side.

'When she was about 200 yards from the rocks the master gave orders to abandon ship and the crew of eight lined up on the port side of the deck. Huge seas washed clean over her. I looked at my gallant crew and, believe me, they were gallant men. I knew them well, I knew their families. I'd nursed their children. I thought to myself "What right have I to take these men to their deaths?" A coxswain has to make terrible, cruel decisions and this was surely one of them. I knew they trusted me and their lives were in my hands. But I could hear a faint cry "Save us, lifeboat!" and I knew we had to try.

'Now the ship was in the breakers which I had been afraid of all the time. I decided to come about, and just before I turned the boat round I thought of my own wife and three sons, probably sitting by the fire, huddled together, listening to the wind howling and the rain lashing against the window: waiting for the telephone to ring and afraid of answering it. But there was no time for sentiment. Eight men were going to die soon unless I did something. I came about and edged the lifeboat round the stern of the *Hindlea*. When you run against a breaking sea you usually put a drogue out to keep the stern of the boat dead on the breakers but I couldn't use a drogue. We were so near the rocks it could easily have tangled with the propeller and that would have been the end of us all. I had to run in through the breakers without it. It was a tremendous strain on my arms — turning the wheel to keep her head on to the sea.

'I intended to come in on the post quarter. As we passed her stern the *Hindlea*'s propellers were whining above our heads and we were just round when we were hit by a solid wall of water. It was the biggest wave I have ever seen in my life. It was like a mountain. It could have swamped us and the *Hindlea*. The little lifeboat rolled right over on her beam ends, her mast going under water. Desperately I fought to bring the lifeboat under control. I thought it was the end: she was capsizing. I used maximum engine revs to stem the sea, then, slowly at first, at an angle of 25 degrees to the coaster, she came up like a fighting cock.

'Now the two boats were thrown violently against each other. I could see the propeller. It was three yards from tip to tip and whirling round like a windmill. It was only 15 feet away and it would have cut us into chips if we'd drifted under it. I knew now that the lifeboat was going to be seriously damaged — but she still responded to the helm, and one man jumped from the *Hindlea* into the lifeboat.

'Hugh Owen, an old friend, dashed out from the canopy, ignoring the seas that could have washed him away for ever. He dragged him to shelter. Instantly we were washed 30 yards away from the ship. We had to go back. In fact we went back ten times in all. As the lifeboat was lifted on a wave, level with the *Hindlea*'s deck, one after the other

her crew jumped into my boat until there was only one man left.

'By this time the *Hindlea* was terribly close to the rocks. Now I had another terrible decision to make. Would it be wiser to leave that one man and save the men who were already in the lifeboat? Yet: I knew I could not leave him behind. I took a desperate gamble and drove the lifeboat back again to the *Hindlea* where the man was hanging from the side.

'Suddenly I felt the lifeboat being lifted up the side of the ship and before I knew where we were she was sitting high and dry on the deck of the *Hindlea*. We just had time to grab the last man before a second wave lifted us clear.

'Now we were in real trouble, trying to get out of these terrible breaking seas. The *Hindlea* was very, very close to the rocks; the wind was screaming as we came clear. I had to put the boat beam on to the sea to get round Moelfre Island. I knew that my crew were not in good fettle and the survivors were in a very bad way. Time was the essence. I nursed the *Edmund and Mary* like a child, bringing her head on to the breaking seas and then, when I saw a lull, edging her round. I could not see the island for the seas breaking over it. I had to turn the boat now and run before this terrible sea without the help of a drogue. There were 13 of us in the boat, the crew and survivors jammed together under the canopy, me at the wheel.

'My waist was sore from the chafing of the ropes I had used to lash myself to the wheel and my hands were too numb to unfasten the knots. If we had capsized I'd have had to go down. Every so often I had to hammer my fists against the wheel to get the circulation going. My eyes were sore and gummed up with salt. In the end a single wave at least 30 feet high swept us on its crest the whole length of the island and we found ourselves alongside the slipway.

'As they had done down the centuries the women of Moelfre were waiting to take the survivors to the chapel vestry where there was a roaring fire, dry clothes and hot food. I sat on the slip utterly exhausted. My eyes were caked up with salt, my cheeks were bleeding and I was desperately tired. Suddenly I realised tears were streaming down my face.'

When Dick Evans reported the rescue to his Head Office he was ordered not to take the lifeboat out again until she had been completely overhauled. But within 25 minutes he was at sea again, going to the aid of a coaster with a flooded engine room.

'We got a rope onto the ship and waited for a call to take the crew

off. We were desperately tired. We had been out since mid-morning
and now it was evening. But we knew the Beaumaris lifeboat had been
ordered to launch and relieve us. They had a terrible passage coming
from Beaumaris Sound into a northerly hurricane. They took over at
6.30 p.m. and we returned to Moelfre. We got the boat onto the
slipway. By now the crew were exhausted and I sent them home. I
went with Evan Owen, the mechanic, to his house where his wife
made us a meal. Then we went back to the boathouse and spent the
whole night trying to patch up the damage to the lifeboat.'

Ian Skidmore, *Anglesey and Lleyn Shipwrecks*

18.   MADOC

Let Evan of generous growth hunt
Upon his fair land, his true patrimony;
In an auspicious hour, I also on water,
With the consent of the generous one,
    will be a hunter.
Madoc am I, who throughout my life will seek,
Upon the water, that which I have been used to.
Madoc the bold, of expanding form,
True whelp of Owain Gwynedd,
Would not have land (my kindred soul),
Nor great wealth, but the seas.
I am a Madoc to my age, and to his passion
For the seas have I been accustomed.
I will walk by sea and river,
Along the strand with my circled net.

Maredudd ap Rhys, 1430-1460

19.   *'Of the voyage and return of this Madoc'*

Of the voyage and return of this Madoc there be many fables famed,
as the common people do use in distance of place and length of time,
rather to augment than diminish; but sure it is that there he was. And
after he had returned home, and declared the pleasant and fruitful

countries that he had seen without inhabitants, and upon the contrary part, for what barren and wild ground his brethren and nephews did murder one another, he prepared a number of ships, and got with him such men and women as were desirous to live in quietness, and taking leave of his friends took his journey thitherward again. Therefore it was to be presupposed that he and his people inhabited part of those countries; for it appeareth by Francis Lopez de Gomara, that in Acuzamil, and other places, the people honoreth the cross: Whereby it may be gathered, that Christians had been there before the coming of the Spaniards. But because this people were not many, they followed the manners of the land and used the language found there. This Madoc arriving in the country, into the which he came in the year 1170, left most of his people there, and returning back for more of his own nation, acquaintance, and friends to inhabit that fair and large country, went thither again.

David Powell, *Historie of Cambria, now called Wales,* 1584

20.   MADOC

Two princes of base passions quarrelled fiercely;
Their sire was loved by all and people mourned to
    see his sons at war;
Their ambition was to wrestle for the land of their father;
They brought disaster on a noble name.
How much nobler was Madoc, not yet a prince, yet noble as a prince,
A dreamer, he loved the seas more than the land which sired him,
Determined to risk all for a dream,
The dream of finding a fair land far across the oceans, unknown
    and unproved.

Ieuan Brechfa

21.   PORTHMADOG

Thirteen little ships sailed
On a bright morning.
Hail, Madoc, brave his soul,
Captain of the fleet,
In search of lands unknown.

A good army
And a strong fleet
That was his desire.

Horn Gwennan, brought to the Gele
To be given a square mast,
Was turned back to Afon Ganol's quay
For Madoc's famous voyage.

Traditional poem — *Porthmadog*

22. *The Gwennan Gorn*

The Gele is a very small stream flowing into the sea at Abergele in Denbighshire. Probably it was larger in Madoc's day, as was the Clwyd, not far away. If Madoc's ship had been repaired, or partially fitted out there, Sir Thomas Herbert could have believed it to be built in that place. He was not closely associated with Wales and he may easily have confused Abergele with Abergwili, or, alternatively, his printer may have done so. The latter seems to be the likeliest explanation.

Certainly if *Gwennan Gorn* was the ship Madoc used on the voyage it would have been from North Wales he sailed. All legends of *Gwennan Gorn* centre around Anglesey, Bardsey, Caernarvonshire and Denbighshire.

Richard Deacon, *Madoc and the Discovery of America,* 1966

23. *Madoc's Journey to America*

During which turmoils and unnatural strife the said Madoc, loath to be an Agent of Discord to either party, and feeling propositions of peace ineffectual, studies by all good means to avoid the knowledge of it, and aims at some foreign place of ease and profit, neither discouraged by improbabilities nor likely disasters ... Madoc ingeniously perusing the older illustrations and seeing in some things the prophecy of this authentic Bard accomplished . . . employing his patrimonial estate upon men, ships and provisions . . .

Madoc was overjoyed and had reason to account his happy estate superior to that his brothers strive for, so eagerly emulating with ambitious hate and blood each other for a little Territory, incomparable to that good destiny allotted him, being a vast and weal Kingdom, obtained in some part without opposition, and able to satiate the most covetous. There he planted, fortified some advantagious places, left a hundred and twenty men to finish what he had begun and returned home after some bad winds, guided by supreme providence and the benefit the Pole-Star gave him in the night.

'When he had landed and had accounted his happy and miraculous voyage, told the hopes of succeeding Conquests, and other motives of persuasion and admiration, these and the words of Madoc himself drew so many willing minds and purses to a return, that he attempted it with ten good Barques, loaded with all necessary provisions, a matter that confidence required.

At his arrival he found many of his Britains dead, caused by the Natives' Villany, or alternation of the clime, which notwithstanding he digested patiently, and with Edwoll and Encon, his brothers, bettered the first intention, living with content, and dying in no less distance from Heaven, than when at home, unhappiest in this that their own Nation forgot them quite, either judging them lost, because their own Beings were turned topsy turvy by the fatal end of the last unhappy Prince Lluellyn ap Griffith . . .

Sir Thomas Herbert, *An Account of Madoc's journey to America*

24.   NIGHT AND MORNING

One night of tempest I arose and went
Along the Menai shore on dreaming bent;
The wind was strong, and savage swung the tide,
And the waves blustered on Caernarfon side.

But on the morrow, when I passed that way,
On Menai shore the hush of heaven lay;
The wind was gentle and the sea a flower,
And the sun slumbered on Caernarfon tower.

Anonymous, *Folk Verse,* 16th-17th century

25. A BAY IN ANGLESEY

The sleepy sound of a tea-time tide
Slaps at the rocks the sun has dried,

Too lazy, almost, to sink and lift
Round low peninsulas pink with thrift.

The water, enlarging shells and sand,
Grows greener emerald out from land

And brown over shadowy shelves below
The waving forests of seaweed show.

Here at my feet in the short cliff grass
Are shells, dried bladderwrack, broken glass,

Pale blue squills and yellow rock roses.
The next low ridge that we climb discloses

One more field for the sheep to graze
While, scarcely seen on this hottest of days,

Far to the eastward, over there,
Snowdon rises in pearl-grey air.

Multiple lark-song, whispering bents,
The thymy, turfy and salty scents

And filling in, brimming in, sparkling and free
The sweet susurration of incoming sea.

John Betjeman, *High and Low,* 1966

26. *The Card*

Ruth chose Llandudno, Llandudno being more stylish than either
Rhyl or Blackpool, and not dearer. Ruth and Nellie had a double
room in a boarding-house, No. 26 St Asaph's Road (off the Marine

Parade), and Denry had a small single room in another boarding-house, No. 28 St Asaph's Road. The ideal could scarcely have been approached more nearly.

Denry had never seen the sea before. As, in his gayest clothes, he strolled along the esplanade or on the pier between those two girls in their gayest clothes, and mingled with the immense crowd of pleasure-seekers and money-spenders, he was undoubtedly much impressed by the beauty and grandeur of the sea. But what impressed him far more than the beauty and grandeur of the sea was the field for profitable commercial enterprise which a place like Llandudno presented. He had not only his first vision of the sea, but his first genuine vision of the possibilities of amassing wealth by honest ingenuity. On the morning after his arrival he went out for a walk and lost himself near the Great Orme, and had to return hurriedly along the whole length of the Parade about nine o'clock. And through every ground-floor window of every house he saw a long table full of people eating and drinking the same kinds of food. In Llandudno fifty thousand souls desired always to perform the same act at the same time; they wanted to be distracted and they would do anything for the sake of distraction, and would pay for the privilege. And they would all pay at once.

This great thought was more majestic to him than the sea, or the Great Orme, or the Little Orme . . .

. . . He simply could not stir out of the house without spending money, and often in ways quite unforeseen. Pier, minstrels, Punch and Judy, bathing, buns, ices, canes, fruit, chairs, row-boats, concerts, toffee, photographs, char-à-bancs: any of these expenditures was likely to happen whenever they went forth for a simple stroll. One might think that strolls were gratis, that the air was free! Error! If he had had the courage he would have left his purse in the house as Ruth invariably did. But men are moral cowards.

He had calculated thus: Return fare, four shillings a week. Agreed terms at boarding-house, twenty-five shillings a week. Total expenses per week, twenty-nine shillings — say thirty!

On the first day he spent fourteen shillings on nothing whatever — which was at the rate of five pounds a week of supplementary estimates! On the second day he spent nineteen shillings on nothing whatever.

On the Monday morning he was up early and off to Bursley to collect rents and manage estates. He had spent nearly five pounds beyond his expectations. Indeed, if by chance he had not gone to Llandudno with a portion of the previous week's rents in his pockets, he would have been in what the Five Towns call a fix.

On the Tuesday evening he returned to Llandudno, and, despite the general trend of his thoughts, it once more occurred that his pockets were loaded with a portion of the week's rents. He did not know precisely what was going to happen, but he knew that something was going to happen; for the sufficient reason that his career could not continue unless something did happen.

What immediately happened was a storm at sea. He heard it mentioned at Rhyl, and he saw, in the deep night, the foam of breakers at Prestatyn. And when the train reached Llandudno, those two girls in ulsters and caps greeted him with wondrous tales of the storm at sea, and of wrecks, and of lifeboats. And they were so jolly, and so welcoming, so plainly glad to see their cavalier again, that Denry instantly discovered himself to be in the highest spirits. He put away the dark and brooding thoughts which had disfigured his journey, and became the gay Denry of his own dreams. The very wind intoxicated him. There was no rain.

It was half-past nine, and half Llandudno was afoot on the Parade and discussing the storm — a storm unparalleled, it seemed, in the month of August. At any rate, people who had visited Llandudno yearly for twenty-five years declared that never had they witnessed such a storm. The new lifeboat had gone forth, amid cheers, about six o'clock to a schooner in distress near Rhos, and at eight o'clock a second lifeboat (an old one which the new one had replaced and which had been bought for a floating warehouse by an aged fisherman) had departed to the rescue of a Norwegian barque, the *Hjalmar,* round the bend of the Little Orme.

'Let's go on the pier,' said Denry. 'It will be splendid.'

He was not an hour in the town, and yet was already hanging expense!

'They've closed the pier,' the girls told him.

But when in the course of their meanderings among the excited crowd under the gas-lamps they arrived at the pier-gates, Denry perceived figures on the pier.

'They're sailors and things, and the Mayor,' the girls explained.

'Pooh!' said Denry, fired.

He approached the turnstile and handed a card to the official. It was the card of an advertisement agent of the *Staffordshire Signal,* who had called at Brougham Street in Denry's absence about the renewal of Denry's advertisement.

'Press,' said Denry to the guardian at the turnstile, and went through with the ease of a bird on the wing.

'Come along,' he cried to the girls.

The guardian seemed to hesitate.

'These ladies are with me,' he said.

The guardian yielded.

It was a triumph for Denry. He could read his triumph in the eyes of his companions. When she looked at him like that, Ruth was assuredly marvellous among women, and any ideas derogatory to her marvellousness which he might have had at Bursley and in the train were false ideas.

At the head of the pier beyond the pavilion, there were gathered together some fifty people, and the tale ran that the second lifeboat had successfully accomplished its mission and was approaching the pier.

'I shall write an account of this for the *Signal*,' said Denry, whose thoughts were excusably on the Press.

'Oh, do!' exclaimed Nellie.

'They have the *Signal* at all the newspaper shops here,' said Ruth.

Then they seemed to be merged in the storm. The pier shook and trembled under the shock of the waves, and occasionally, though the tide was very low, a sprinkle of water flew up and caught their faces. The eyes could see nothing save the passing glitter of the foam on the crest of a breaker. It was the most thrilling situation that any of them had ever been in.

And at last came word from the mouths of men who could apparently see as well in the dark as in daylight, that the second lifeboat was close to the pier. And then everybody momentarily saw it — a ghostly thing that heaved up pale out of the murk for an instant, and was lost again. And the little crowd cheered.

The next moment a Bengal light illuminated the pier, and the lifeboat was silhouetted with strange effectiveness against the storm. And someone flung a rope, and then another rope arrived out of the sea, and fell on Denry's shoulder.

'Haul on there!' yelled a hoarse voice. The Bengal light expired.

Denry hauled with a will. The occasion was unique. And those few seconds were worth to him the whole of Denry's precious life — yes, not excluding the seconds in which he had kissed Ruth and the minutes in which he had danced with the Countess of Chell. Then two men with beards took the rope from his hands. The air was now alive with shoutings. Finally there was a rush of men down the iron stairway to the lower part of the pier, ten feet nearer the water.

'You stay here, you two!' Denry ordered.

'But, Denry—'

'Stay here, I tell you!' All the male in him was aroused. He was off, after the rush of men. 'Half a jiffy,' he said, coming back. 'Just take charge of this, will you?' And he poured into their hands about twelve shillings' worth of copper, small change of rents, from his hip-pocket. 'If anything happened, that might sink me,' he said, and vanished.

It was very characteristic of him, that effusion of calm sagacity in a supreme emergency . . .

The next morning at 5.20 the youthful sun was shining on the choppy water of the Irish Sea, just off the Little Orme, to the west of Llandudno Bay. Oscillating on the uneasy waves was Denry's lifeboat, manned by the nodding bearded head, three ordinary British longshoremen, a Norwegian who could speak English of two syllables, and two other Norwegians who by a strange neglect of education could speak nothing but Norwegian.

Close under the headland, near a morsel of beach lay the remains of the *Hjalmar* in an attitude of repose. It was as if the *Hjalmar,* after a long struggle, had lain down like a cab-horse and said to the tempest: 'Do what you like now!'

'Yes,' the venerable head was piping. 'Us can come out comfortable in twenty minutes, unless the tide be setting east strong. And, as for getting back, it'll be the same, other way round, if ye understand me.'

There could be no question that Simeon had come out comfortable. But he was the coxswain. The rowers seemed to be perspiringly aware that the boat was vast and beamy.

'Shall we row up to it?' Simeon inquired, pointing to the wreck.

Then a pale face appeared above the gunwale, and an expiring, imploring voice said: 'No. We'll go back.' Whereupon the pale face vanished again.

Denry had never before been outside the bay. In the navigation of pantechnicons on the squall-swept basins of canals he might have been a great master, but he was unfitted for the open sea. At that moment he would have been almost ready to give the lifeboat and all that he owned for the privilege of returning to land by train. The inward journey was so long that Denry lost hope of ever touching his native island again. And then there was a bump. And he disembarked, with hope burning up again cheerfully in his bosom. And it was a quarter to six . . .

. . . At ten o'clock two Norwegian sailors, who could only smile in answer to the questions which assailed them, were distributing the following handbill on the Parade:

WRECK OF THE *HJALMAR*

HEROISM AT LLANDUDNO

Every hour, at 11, 12, 1, 2, 3, 4, 5, and 6 o'clock. THE IDENTICAL (guaranteed) LIFEBOAT which rescued the

crew of the

HJALMAR

will leave the beach for the scene of the wreck. Manned by Simeon Edwards, the oldest boatman in LLANDUDNO, and by members of the

rescued crew, genuine Norwegians (guaranteed)

SIMEON EDWARDS, *Coxswain*

Return Fare, with use of Cork Belt and Lifelines

if desired, 2s. 6d.

A UNIQUE OPPORTUNITY

A UNIQUE EXPERIENCE

P.S. — The bravery of the lifeboatmen has been the theme of the Press throughout the Principality and neighbouring counties.

E. D. MACHIN

At eleven o'clock there was an eager crowd down on the beach where, with some planks and a piece of rock, Simeon had arranged an embarkation pier for the lifeboat. One man, in over-alls, stood up to his knees in the water and escorted passengers up the planks, while Simeon's confidence-generating beard received them into the broad waist of the boat. The rowers wore sou'-westers and were secured to the craft by life-lines, and these conveniences were also offered, with lifebelts, to the intrepid excursionists. A paper was pinned in the stern: 'Licensed to carry Fourteen.' (Denry had just paid the fee.) But quite forty people were anxious to make the first voyage.

'No more,' shrilled Simeon, solemnly. And the wader scrambled in and the boat slid away.

'Fares, please!' shrilled Simeon.

He collected one pound fifteen, and slowly buttoned it up in the right-hand pocket of his blue trousers.

Arnold Bennet, 1867-1931

IV

THE PEOPLE

1. *The Early Inhabitants*

Little is known of the earliest inhabitants of the coast of North Wales beyond what has been deduced from a careful study of 'finds', including skeletal remains, household utensils, and weapons excavated fromt he caves which they inhabited.

After the gradual retreat of the Ice Age there followed a long period, known as the Old Stone Age, during which the region was occupied by the pioneers of the human race. The only trace remaining of these people is a few uncertain flint chippings such as have been found at Braich Llwyd, Penmaenmawr, the manufacture of which was doubtless continued into the succeeding New Stone Age.

Of this later period of the Stone Age considerably more is known from the fact that it had become the custom of the inhabitants to bury their dead in tombs constructed from unhewn slabs of rock. The slabs were set upright in the form of an oblong chamber surmounted by a single huge capstone, and covered with a mound of stones and earth, and sometimes surrounded by a ring of upright stones. Many of these tombs are to be seen today, more particularly in Anglesey, but from most of them the mound has been removed. They are known locally as cromlech(s), and because of their appearance have sometimes been erroneously called altars. Large numbers of human remains have been found interred together in one tomb. Objects found in the tombs include flint arrowheads, stone axe-hammers, and other weapons and implements carefully chipped or ground to shape and sometimes polished, together with coarse but occasionally ornamented pottery.

It would seem to be the accepted theory that these earliest inhabitants of North Wales originated in countries bordering the Mediterranean Sea and the Iberian Peninsular, and that they were a race small in stature, narrow of skull, and dark as to eyes and hair, features which are typical of many Welshmen of the present day.

As the Stone Age passed gradually into the Bronze Age, during the second millennium B.C., the population was overcome by a fresh wave of immigration, probably a coastwise invasion from the south-east. This consisted of the Goidels, a fair haired, grey eyed, round headed, and more powerfully built people who introduced the Goidelic tongue, Gaelic, Irish, Manx, who manufactured weapons and implements of bronze, and who began to desert the primitive cave dwellings of their forefathers for crude huts. Their settlements, the remains of which are to be found in various localities at the present day, were either grouped into small villages on the hill slopes or set in lonely isolation upon some lofty sea cliff as an outpost against raiding parties from adjacent districts or from across the Irish Sea. The method of burial also underwent a change. The dead, instead of being placed in great stone tombs, were buried in stone cists or coffins often covered with a barrow or mound of earth. In mid-Bronze Age cremation came into practice, and the ashes of the dead were placed in an ornamented earthenware vase or urn, sometimes placed in an inverted position, and usually protected by a stone cist covered with a small tumulus or mound of earth, and sometimes placed near the base of a monolith or maen-hir. Finds now include bronze axes and other comparatively highly finished weapons and tools, and ornaments of bronze and gold, together with more advanced pottery.

Towards the close of the first millennium B.C., the Bronze Age was giving place to the Iron Age, and the descendants of those pioneer tribes who had passed on over the sea were making frequent raids on the coast of North Wales. This was the period of hill fortresses and native settlements or hut villages, well known examples of which are to be found in Anglesey and Caernarvonshire. These hut villages, or Cytiau-'r-Gwyddelod (Huts of the Goidels), consisted of irregular groups of dwellings often surrounded by a wall and guarded by earth-works. The huts were usually circular but sometimes elliptical or rectangular in plan with, in some cases, a short entrance passage. Their walls were comprised of a double row of upright slabs of stone, standing two or more feet high, packed with pebbles and earth, thus forming a foundation upon which was raised a sloping or dome-shaped roof of poles thatched with rushes, heather or turf according to the local supply of material. The interior of the dwelling was some-times paved, contained a hearth or fireplace, and even stone slabs indicating beds or seats. Some of the more elaborate huts were divided into chambers. Besides utensils, implements and weapons of stone, pottery, bronze and iron, finds include ornaments of glass, jet, silver and Roman coins. The sites of primitive forges show that the inhabitants were industrious metal workers as well as doughty fighters, while the unearthing of lumps or cakes of crude copper provides evidence that the rich ore of Parys Mountain on Anglesey had been tapped even at this early date.

The Goidels, with a certain admixture of the Iberic aborigines, were the predominant race in North Wales at the time of the Roman occupation, which, though lasting for a comparatively short period, about three hundred years, had a profound effect on the domestic and political life of the inhabitants and on the future history of the region. The Romans found the inhabitants largely occupying the higher ground, for the lowlands and valleys were either marshy or thickly forested, and such tracks as existed between the villages followed the ridges of the hills. The original system of tracks was in all probability utilised by the invaders in forming their lines of communication, while at certain strategic points forts, such as Kanovium (near Llanrwst) and Segontium (Caernarfon), were built and garrisoned. From various causes these garrisons were either reduced or entirely evacuated on no less than three occasions, until, in A.D. 390, owing to trouble nearer home, the Romans were forced to retire from North Wales.

During the later Iron Age and the Roman conquest of Britain a new people, the Brythons, had followed the Goidels into North Wales. Under the leadership of Cunedda Wledig they were to be found spreading westwards into Caernarvonshire and Anglesey. Cunedda's grandson, Caswallon-Law-Hir (Caswallon of the Long Hand), completed the conquest of the region, but on occasions found it necessary to defend his newly won territory against Irish invaders. In A.D. 450 he defeated Serigi, an Irish chieftain, in a great battle at Holyhead. The descendants of Caswallon, through his son Maelgwyn Gwynedd, were destined to rule over North Wales in an almost unbroken line for over a thousand years. During this long period the Brythons were constantly having to defend themselves from marauding bands of Scandinavian rovers and sporadic invasions from Saxon and Norman England until, in the thirteenth century, they in their turn came under the sovereignty of the English Kings. This occured, in fact, in 1282, when Llywelyn-ap-Gruffydd (Llywelyn the Last) was slain fighting against the English army of King Edward I. The overall history of the region can, perhaps, best be summed up in the form of a list of the most important periods from prehistoric times to the present day. Such a list is as follows:

To about 4000 B.C.   *Old Stone Age.* Uncertain chipped flints.

To about 1800 B.C.   *New Stone Age.* Cromlechs, stone axes, pottery. General subsidence of the coast leading to the preservation of forests under the sands of certain beaches, and to the separation of Anglesey from the mainland.

To about 300 B.C.   *Bronze Age.* Burial cists and cinerary urns. Stone and bronze weapons and implements. Goidelic settlements, hut circles. Ornaments of jet, amber, and Irish gold.

To and during the Roman era.   *Iron Age.* Bronze and iron weapons and implements, domestic pottery including Samian Ware. Hut villages, hill and cliff forts. Mining activities. Irish raiders, Brythonic invasion. Early Celtic legends. Roman coins, roads and forts.

A.D. 50-390.   *Roman Occupation.*

A.D. 400-1000.   *Early Mediaeval.* Early Celtic church and art. Crosses, holy wells, hermits' cells and inscribed memorial stones. Age of Saints. Early Welsh Princes. Celtic legends. Scandinavian rovers, Saxon and early English invaders.

A.D. 1000-1485   *Later Mediaeval.* Later churches and art. Later Welsh Princes. Celtic legends. Norman and English invasions. Castles. Llywelyn the Last slain. Rebellion of Owain Glyndŵr.

1485 onwards.   *Modern Era.* House of Tudor, Civil War. In the 18th century, mining and shipbuilding activities, smuggling, lighthouses, early tourists. In the 19th century, threat of invasion by Napoleon, growth of communications with Ireland, wrecks, lifeboats, yacht clubs, tourists, seaside health resorts.

F. H. Glazebrook, *Anglesey and North Wales Coast*

2. *Vortigern*

Ascend from *Nefyn* for a considerable way up the side of the high hill; and after a short ride on level ground quit our horses, in order to visit *Nant y Gwrtheyrn*, or *Vortigern's valley*, the immense hollow, to which Vortigern is said to have fled from the rage of his subjects, and where it was said that he and his castle were consumed with lightning. *Nennius* places the scene near the *Teivi*, in *Caermarthenshire*; but I believe that the historian not only mistakes the spot, but even the manner of his death. His life had been profligate; the monks therefore were determined that he should not die the common death of all men, and accordingly made him perish with signal marks of the vengeance of Heaven. Fancy cannot frame a place more fit for a retreat from the knowledge of mankind, or more apt to inspire one with full hopes of security from any pursuit. Embosomed in a lofty mountain, on two sides bounded by stony steeps, on which no vegetables appear but the blasted heath and stunted gorse; the third side exhibits a most tremendous front of black precipice, with the loftiest peak of the mountain *Eifl* soaring above; and the only opening to this secluded spot is towards the sea, a northern aspect, where that chilling wind exerts all its fury, and half freezes, during winter, the few inhabitants. The glen is tenanted by three families, who raise oats, and keep a few cattle, sheep, and goats; but seem to have great difficulty in getting their little produce to market.

Just above the sea is a high and verdant mount, natural; but the top and sides worked on by art. The first slatted: the sides marked with eight prominent ribs from top to bottom. On this might have been the residence of the unfortunate prince; of which, time has destroyed every other vestige. Till the beginning of the last century, a tumulus, of stone within, and externally covered with turf, was to be seen here; it was known by the name of *Bedd Gwrtheyrn*: tradition having regularly delivered down the report of this having been the place of his interment. The inhabitants of the parish, perhaps instigated by their then minister, Mr *Hugh Roberts*, a person of curiosity, dug into the cairn, and found in it a stone coffin, containing the bones of a tall man. This gives a degree of credibility to the tradition, especially as no other bones were found with it; no other *tumuli* on the spot: a proof at least of respect to the rank of the person; and that the place was deserted after the death of the royal fugitive, about the year 465.

Thomas Pennant, *Tours in Wales*

3.   *Dinas Emrys*

Dinas Emris. At the bottom rises a vast rock, insulated, and clothed with wood; the famous *Dinas Emris*, from early times celebrated in *British* story; for here

> Pophetic *Merlin* sate, when to the *British* king
> The changes long to come, auspiciously he told.

Its Legend. When *Vortigern* found himself unable to contest with the treacherous *Saxons*, who he had, in the year 449, invited into *Britain*, he determined, by the advice of his magician, on building an impregnable fortress in *Snowdon*. He collected the materials, which all disappeared in one night. The prince, astonished at this, convened again his wise men. They assured him his building would never stand unless it was sprinkled with the blood of a child born without the help of a father. The realm was ransacked: at length one of his emissaries overheard some boys at play reproach another, and call him an unbegotten knave. The child and his mother were brought before the king. She confessed he was the offspring of an *Incubus*; a species of being, now unhappily out of all credit. The boy, whose name was *Merlin*, was ordered to be sacrificed; but on confounding all the magicians with his questions, and explaining the cause of the miscarriage, got his liberty, and

> to that mighty king, which rashly undertook
> A strong walled tower to rear, those earthly
>   spirits that shook
> The great foundation still, in dragon's horrid shape,
> That dreaming wizard told, making the mountain gape
> With his most powerful charms, to view those
>   caverns deep;
> And from the top of *Brith*, so high and wondrous steep,
> Where *Dinas Emris* stood, shew'd where the serpents
>   fought,
> The WHITE that tore the RED: from whence the
>   prophet wrought
> The *Britons* sad decay, then shortly to ensue.

This is the poetical translation of the legend. *Merlin*, or *Merddin Emris*, of *Ambrosius*, was in fact the son of a noble *Roman*, of the same name. His mother, a *Vestal*, to save her life and honour, invented the fable of his father.

Ibid.

4. *Merlin. Vortigern. Owen Gwynedd.*

Not far from the source of the river Conwy, at the head of the Eryri
mountain, which on this side extends itself towards the north, stands
Dinas Emrys, that is, the promontory of Ambrosius, where Merlin*
uttered his prophecies, whilst Vortigern was seated upon the bank.
There were two Merlins; the one called Ambrosius, who prophesied
in the time of king Vortigern, was begotten by a demon incubus, and
found at Caermardin, or the city of Merlin; the other Merlin, born in
Scotland, was named Celidonius, from the Celidonian wood in which
he prophesied; and Sylvester, because when engaged in martial
conflict, he discovered in the air a terrible monster, and from that
time grew mad, and taking shelter in a wood, passed the remainder of
his days in a savage state. This Merlin lived in the time of king Arthur,
and is said to have prophesied more fully and explicitly than the
other. I shall pass over in silence what was done by the sons of Owen
in our days, after his death, or while he was dying, who, from the
wicked desire of reigning, totally disregarded the ties of fraternity;
but I shall not omit mentioning another event which occurred likewise in our days. Owen,** son of Gruffyth, prince of North Wales, had
many sons, but only one legitimate, namely, Iorwerth Drwyndwn,
which in Welsh means flat-nosed, who had a son named Llewelyn.
This young man, being only twelve years of age, began, during the
period of our journey, to molest his uncles David and Roderic, the
sons of Owen by Christiana, his cousin-german; and although they
had divided amongst themselves all North Wales, except the land of
Conan, and although David, having married the sister of king Henry
II, by whom he had one son, was powerfully supported by the
English, yet within a few years the legitimate son, destitute of lands or
money (by the aid of divined vengeance), bravely expelled from
North Wales those who were born in public incest, though supported
by their own wealth and by that of others, leaving them nothing but
what the liberality of his own mind and the counsel of good men from
pity suggested: a proof that adulterous and incestuous persons are
displeasing to God.

Giraldus Cambrensis, *The Itinerary Through Wales,* 1191

** Owen Gwynedd, the son of Gruffydd ap Conan, died in 1169, and was buried at
Bangor. When Baldwin, during his progress, visited Bangor and saw his tomb, he
charged the bishop (Guy Ruffus) to remove the body out of the cathedral, when he had

a fit opportunity so to do, in regard that archbishop Becket has excommunicated him heretofore, because he had married his first cousin, the daughter of Grono ap Edwyn, and that notwithstanding he had continued to live with her till she died. The bishop, in obedience to the charge, made a passage from the vault through the south wall fo the church underground, and thus secretly shoved the body into the churchyard. *Hengwrt. MSS.*
Cadwadlader, brother of Owen Gwynedd, died in 1172.

* The Merlin here mentioned was called Ambrosius, and according to the Cambrian Biography flourished about the middle of the fifth century. Other authors say, that this reputed prophet and magician was the son of a Welsh nun, daughter of a king of Demetia, and born at Caermarthen, and that he was made king of West Wales by Vortigern, who then reigned in Britain.

5. *Cromlech of Llanedwen*

. . . We have one great altar of stone, of considerable bigness, upon the bank of the river *Menai*, now in the parish of *Llan Edwen*, which may seem to have been, as the biggest, so the first and chiefest one of the whole island; whereon the first-fruits of the place might be offered to God by those very first men who came into it. Though afterwards other such altars were erected for the religious worship and the performances of oblations and sacrifices in the several colonies of it, of which not a few remain standing here and there to this day.

These altars of stone (where stone served to raise them up) were huge broad flattish stones mounted up and laid upon other erect ones, and leaning, with a little declivity in some places, on those pitched supporters; which posture, for some now-unaccountable reasons, they seem to have affected. These altars were and are to this day vulgarly called by the name of *Crom-lech*; either from their bending position, which is generally believed; or rather (that bending posture being not always to be found in every one of those monuments, nor indeed applicable to the idea and notion of *Crom* in our language) that these first men — I shall adventure to guess — carried the name with them from Babel, as they did several other words, and called it *Caeraem-lech*, from the Hebrew . . . *Caerem-luach*, a devoted stone or altar.

It is not improbable neither, but that they did sometimes prefix the word *Caerem* or *Crem* to other things belonging to their sacrifices besides stone-altars, though now such names be quite disused and utterly lost and forgotten; save in one or two places, which are called *Crem-lwyn*, or *Cremlyn*, as generally pronounced; in one of which places there are some stone-monuments and a standing *Cromlech* near it (as if it had been one of their *Cremlwynau* or sacrificing groves) shewing tokens of some extraordinary celebration of that place.

Henry Rowlands, *Mona Antiqua Restaurata*

6. *Prehistoric Anglesey*

Sixteen megalithic tombs survive on the island at present. Their distribution is mainly coastal and it is noteworthy that most of them lie on, or close to, areas of light, easily drained soil. The main concentrations lie on the limestone areas around Brynsiencyn and close to Benllech and Moelfre. The surviving monuments must represent only a proportion of those that existed originally; even in the eighteenth century the Rev. Henry Rowlands was able to record a number of sites in the Llanidan area which have subsequently vanished without trace. There are, in fact, a number of eighteenth and nineteenth century accounts of destroyed sites, but unfortunately all are so vague that no archaeological conclusions can now be drawn from them, except that the distribution of tombs must have been remarkably dense in the areas around Brynsiencyn and Moelfre, the parts of the island where surviving tombs are still most common. The pattern of distribution, therefore, is not materially altered.

Since there is such a mixture of traditions in Anglesey it is difficult to reconstruct the historical sequence, that is, to decide which tombs were built by the first farmers and which represent traditions brought in by later groups. Types of tomb which are similar to those built elsewhere will be dealt with first, and a date may be hazarded for some on the basis of this foreign evidence.

Such a goup, which may belong to an early phase in the history of Neolithic settlers in Anglesey, are the simple passage graves. They have a widespread distribution in the Irish Sea area but are never found in large numbers. In Anglesey there are three. The tombs in question are Bodowyr, Tŷ-mawr and Tŷ Newydd, all situated towards the south-western corner of the island.

Frances Lynch, *Prehistoric Anglesey*

7. *Druid's Circle*

In the days of Charles I, in a survey of Penmaenmawr, the Druids' Circle is described as consisting of twelve stones, some of them 'two yards and three quarters' above the ground. Mr Longueville Jones ('Archaeologia Cambrensis', 1846) says the circle 'is a double one; the inner consisting of eleven large stones, some eight feet high and three feet square, much weathered, with smaller stones placed between them. The outer circle is much broken in, but the inner one is nearly complete, and within this again there is a trace of a still smaller circle — not concentric, but touching the inner circumference, as if it had been the foundation of a circular dwelling-house.'

The circle is popularly called the 'Druids' Circle' from the groundless and long-exploded notion that 'rude stone monuments' were the work of the Druids. The remains have been looked upon as sepulchral, but some believe that they had an astronomical object, and Sir Norman Lockyear holds that to a great extent the circles were used as calendars, by which time could be told. Sir John Wynn of Gwydir, writing early in the seventeenth century, says there was a wall round the cricle, and he thus describes the use of 'the circle within these long stones, which we call Meini Hirion': 'It would seem that this was a place whereunto the ancient Britons came from the Dinas aforesaid (Penmaenmawr) to encamp themselves and train their soldiers; it stands in a place fit for jousts and tournaments, and this circle thus rounded with these long stones might be the place where the king's tent was pitched and near to this circle there are three pretty big stones upon their ends standing triangle-wise like a tribbett (the Welsh trybedd; a noted Pembrokeshire cromlech is called Llech-y-drybedd), whereupon as they say was set a great cauldron to boil meat in, and surely the three stones do look as if they had been long in a great fire.' The three stones mentioned here do not retain their position in the present age, but in the circle there are still two or three of remarkable size. Some sharp eyes profess to discover that one of the upright stones resembles in shape a human figure; therefore it had been dubbed the Deity Stone and the British public has freely cut its initials on it! Another, which has a vacity at the top, is popularly called the Stone of Sacrifice, a name which embodies another 'Druidical' myth.

George Lerry (ed.), *Gossiping Guide to Wales*

8. *Tre'r Ceri*

For Tre'r Ceri, on one of the peaks of Yr Eifl, from the gate
mentioned in the last paragraph but one we keep almost straight on
(by the middle of three tracks) for a little while, and then bend to the
right, making for the left of a rocky point, where, when we reach it, we
see Tre'r Ceiri. The path then runs to a fence, which is crossed, and we
make straight for the hill, and ascend by a path, which runs rather to
the left and then winds to the right, to one of the gateways in the walls.
The summit is reached in an hour from Llithfaen.

If the ascent is made from Llanaelhaiarn, which can be reached by
the motor 'bus Pwllheli-Caernarvon service, we walk for ten minutes
or a quarter of an hour along the road towards Llithfaen, and where
the wall turns to the right and runs far up the hill, we go by this wall,
pass through a sheepfold, and follow a path which leads to the left,
keeps round the hill, and finally ascends as already described.

Tre'r Ceiri, or Tre Ceiri (the Giants' Town), is perhaps the most
important of all the remains of prehistoric fortified towns in North
Wales, and said to be the best preserved old stone fortress in Great
Britain. Parts of the wall which enclosed the town are fifteen feet high
and ten feet broad, and more than a hundred cytiau, or circular
houses, have been found within the inner walls, an area of about five
acres; but the stones which cover the ground prevent us from seeing
the real proportions of the works. The Rev. S. Baring-Gould and Mr
Burnard explored some of the cytiau in the summer of 1903, and discovered a little pottery and a small number of other articles, including
two porcelain beads of Egyptian manufacture, one of which was the
finest ever found in the United Kingdom. The explorers came to the
conclusion that the buildings were Celtic, probably British, that the
works were constructed in the first or second century, and only
temporarily occupied, and for a short time, in the summer season.
The place was again explored in 1906 under the direction of Profesor
Boyd Dawkins by Mr Harold Hughes and others, and a large number
of articles of domestic use and bones of animals were found. Reports
of the explorations, with valuable illustrations, will be found in
'Archaeologia Cambrensis' for January, 1904, and January, 1907,
where Professor Boyd Dawkins expresses the opinion that Tre'r Ceiri
belongs to the prehistoric iron age, and was probably used in later
times by the Goidels. Unfortunately, the huts were ravaged about
half a century ago when an old woman of Llithfaen dreamt that a

copper cauldron full of gold was buried in Tre'r Ceiri, and the people of the district made a search and greatly injured the cytiau.

Ibid.

9.   Penrhyn Castle

Penrhyn Castle is of no antiquity, but its great towers stand proudly up above the surrounding woodlands. Besides the thousands of human beings who live and work upon its rich possessions here, there are vast estates in the Peninsula of Lleyn, which we shall hear of later. Though not an ancient building, it is an ancient and famous seat. Indeed, a palace of Roderic, grandson of Cadwallader, stood here in the 8th century.

> 'Abode of native chiefs, of bards the theme,
>   Here princely Penrhyn soars above the stream,
>   And phoenix-like in rising splendour drest,
>   Towers o'er its wide domain with regal crest.'

Archbishop Williams, or 'Keeper Williams' of Conway memory, came to own it before he died, and he lies buried in the little church yonder of Llandegai. From the marriage, too, of Henry VII's Breton son, De Velville, into this house, it will be remembered, came the famous Catherine of Berain, the 'Mother of Wales'. For the Griffiths lived here in the time of Elizabeth, whose last male representative should be held in high and lasting honour as the only North Welshman who cut a brilliant figure among the sea captains of that stirring age. Sir Piers Griffith, at the first whisper of the Armada, manned and victualled a ship at Beaumaris in hot haste, and sailed round Cardigan Bay and the Land's End to join the Channel squadron, and afterwards served with much distinction with Drake and others in the Spanish main. Indeed, this Lord of Penrhyn had such a taste for sea roving, that, like his great leader, his restless soul took little reck of truces or treaties, and he so continued to harry the Spaniards in time of peace as to bring much embarrassment to James

I and such fines and punishments upon himself that he had to part with his estates. Archbishop Williams, however, half a century later, who was of the Griffith blood, brought both Penrhyn and Cochwillan back into the family. Here, too, at Penrhyn, is still treasured the famous Hirlas Horn, to which Owen Cyfeiliog, Prince of Powis, wrote a well-known and stirring ode int he 12th century, that a modern bard has paraphrased:

> 'Fill high, fill high, the Hirlas horn,
> Brimmed with Sunlight like the morn,
> Deep and vast and fit to drown
> All the troubles of a crown;
> Deep and vast and crowned with mead,
> 'Tis a cup for kings indeed;
> Full of courage, full of worth,
> Making man a god on earth.
> Warriors, heroes, Cambrian-born,
> Drink — from the Hirlas horn!'

E. Hyde Hall, *A Description of Caernarvonshire*

10. *Life of Segontium*

In the life of Segontium there were three periods of military occupation, roughly 75-140 A.D., 210-290 or a little later, and a third less precisely defined, beginning 350 or 365 and ending about 380 or 390: and two intervals of disuse, 140-210 and 290-350. Naturally these dates are only approximate; the evidence is fully discussed in Dr Wheeler's paper. If I anticipate his conclusions here it is in order to indicate their bearing upon the future study of the site. The fort proper had told its story, but it behoves the people of Carnarvon and the zealous antiquaries of North Wales generally to keep a watchful eye on its unexplored surroundings, which may at any time furnish evidence such as could not be preserved within its walls.

This will become clear if we consider the probable aspect of such a military station in its prime. A high rampart, crowned with towers and pierced on the four sides by gateways, shut in the professional life of the cohort. That life had its centre in the headquarters building of which the plan in its successive stages has been so convincingly recovered. One of the altars which stood there came to light in the strong room, confirming what had been gleaned by discoveries elsewhere about the administrative personnel of such outposts. Inscribed tablets over the arched entrance of the Praetorium and possibly in the walls of granaries and barracks showed when and by whom each had been erected or restored. Larger tablets, perhaps monumental sculptures were to be seen over the gateway of the fort. But the fullest record of the troops who served here would have been found outside the walls. The religion which found its expression in the altars of the Praetorium was a matter of official routine; it was in the sanctuaries on the adjoining slopes that we should have seen the monuments dedicated by successive commandants, officers and private soldiers to gods and goddesses in bewildering variety: to 'Jupiter most good and great', to Mars and Victory, to German deiries with uncouth names that meant much to recruits from overseas, and to local Celtic powers of mountain and stream, the real gods of the land. In the cemeteries lining the main roads were inscribed tombstones and rudely-sculptured groups, pathetic memorials of officers from Mediterranean shores, soldiers from the Rhineland, traders, it may be, from Greece or Syria, wives from the British hills, and the children of their intermarriages who were proud to call themselves Roman . . .

. . . It is obvious that Carnarvon, the furthest outpost of Rome in north-west Wales, must have been a port of call for ships bringing supplies to Chester and the military region to the north, and for any squadron employed in policing the coast. The evacuation of 140 A.D. implies that no danger was then anticipated either from Welsh hillmen or Irish seafarers. There is reason to suspect an evacuation also at Llanio in Cardiganshire, but before drawing any general inference we must learn by excavation for what periods not only Llanio but Tomen-y-mur and Pennal were held. Does the re-occupation of Segontium in 210 mean that raids or migrations from Ireland had begun? . . .

. . . When the fort was restored any inscriptions relating to former building operations would naturally disappear. Elsewhere the third century has left a rich harvest of inscriptions, but at Segontium only one of those set up during the second occupation has survived, the slab commemorating the restoration of the aqueduct by the new garrison, the First Cohort of Suniei. The period ended about 290

A.D. in violence and disorder. The arched entrance to the sanctuary of the standards was wrecked, as we may infer from the arch-stones found in the strong-room beneath it, in or soon after the reign of Carausius. But for deliberate destruction such an arch might have stood far into the Middle Ages, like those of Amboglanna and Corstopitum, which were taken down and re-erected as the chancel-arches of neighbouring churches. It is plain that barbarian enemies had possession of Segontium for a time, and vented their hate — as in many other places — on monuments and buildings. It is not surprising that within the camp only one inscribed slab has survived. In the external region there may not have been time for concealment of altars, but the interval from 290 to 350 A.D. would allow nature to perform the work of burial. Such old material as lay to hand was assuredly used in the last restoration, and those buildings in their turn fell a prey to mediaeval stone-masons; but it is always the conspicuous central mass of ruins — in this case the fort — that bears the brunt of such ravages.

R. E. Mortimer Wheeler, *Segontium and the Roman Occupation*

11. *The Princes of North Wales*

Excepting the walls of a barn and Gardd y Llys, at the west end of Aberffraw, not a vestige remains to mark the spot where once stood the princely residence of the Sovereigns of North Wales.*

The chiefest of the three royal domains, established by Roderick the Great (as related in the acts of the princes), and his eldest son Anarawd, one of the three coronetted kings of the Isle of Britain kept his court here, in 877, the acknowledged Sovereign of all Wales, 'Brenin Cymru oll'; the other two princes paying him 'maelged', in token of homage, and the ancient Teyrnged to the King of London, was to be paid by the Princes of Aberffraw.

Thomas Pennant, *Tours in Wales*

* About the year 1818, some amateur artists on a visit at Bodorgan, painted a full-length portrait of Prince Llewelyn, in full armour, for a sign for the small inn in the village, kept by a widow of great celebrity, with the following lines under it:

> 'Where dwelt of old brave Prince Llewelyn,
> Betty Williams now is selling
> Bread and cheese, and good strong beer;
> Pri'thee traveller enter here!'

Thus translated into Welsh:

> 'Lle bu trigfa gynt Llewelyn,
> Prif reolwr, barnwr, brenhin,
> Cewch yn awr gan fwynlan Betty,
> Goreu bwyd a glanaf letty.'

12. *Inscriptions*

At Friars' School are imbedded in the wall three stone coffin lids, with inscriptions obscure to all, and to me illegible. The effigies of one personage is from his rosary plainly an ecclesiastic, and the pastoral staff of a second implies a bishop, and the sword of the third would seem to mark out a warrior. Near the road from Bangor to the Bishop's Mill is a witch's grave, or Bedd y Witch, of throwing stones upon which by the passengers the memory is yet preserved. In 1806 was found on the Tŷ Coch property to the south of Bangor a stone having upon it the following inscription:

N.V.M.C.

IMP. CAESAR. M

A V R H A I . I = T O N O N V S

PIUS IXX A V C I A R A B

Of architectural remains the specimens are very scanty. In a house in Bangor some wrought stones may be observed placed in the walls, and two doorways give an appearance of monastic origin. A fortress at Penrhallt of earth and stone is still clearly discernible, and the whole bank of the Menai seems studded with these sorts of posts. With one of them the name of King Edgar, I am informed, is supposed to be connected near Garth. To others the conjecture has appeared over-refined.

E. Hyde Hall, *A Description of Caernarvonshire*

13. TWO-FACED TOO

A North Wales girl was once my passion.
She'd got two costumes, both in fashion,
Two matching hats as well, the peach,
And two false faces under each.

Anonymous, 16th-17th Century Folk Verse

14. THE HILL FARMER SPEAKS

I am the farmer, stripped of love
And thought and grace by the land's hardness;
But what I am saying over the fields'
Desolate acres, rough with dew,
Is, Listen, listen, I am a man like you.

The wind goes over the hill pastures
Year after year, and the ewes starve,
Milkless, for want of the new grass.
And I starve, too, for something the spring
Can never foster in veins run dry.

The pig is a friend, the cattle's breath
Mingles with mine in the still lanes;
I wear it willingly like a cloak
To shelter me from your curious gaze.

The hens go in and out at the door
From sun to shadow, as stray thoughts pass
Over the floor of my wide skull.
The dirt is under my cracked nails;

The tale of my life is smirched with dung;
The phlegm rattles. But what I am saying
Over the grasses rough with dew
Is, Listen, listen, I am a man like you.

R. S. Thomas

15. THE ARTIST ON PENMAENMAWR

That first September day was blue and warm,
Flushing the shaly flanks of Penmaenmawr;
While youths and maidens, in the lucid calm
Exulting, bathed or bask'd from hour to hour;
What colour-passion did the artist feel!
While evermore the jarring trains went by,
Now, as for evermore, in fancy's eye,
Smutch'd with the cruel fires of Abergele;
Then fell the dark o'er the great crags and downs,
And all the night-struck mountain seem'd to say,
And these fair seas — and fairer still than they,
The white-arm'd girls in dark blue bathing-gowns,
Among the snowy gulls and summer spray.

Charles Tennyson Turner

16. *Feet in Chains*

If the place allotted to them to work was a good one and the rock easy to handle they could expect a low price, but since it was otherwise they could expect a much better price at the beginning of the month. But they were forced to accept this low price, and on top of it they all knew that the man who inspected the slates at the end of the month could discard more faulty ones when the market was weak.

Ifan often came home with three pounds for a month's work, sometimes four, and he considered taking home five pounds to be a very good wage. Once he took home just eighteen shillings after having worked hard for a whole month.

Until now Wiliam had had to depend on others for getting stones to work with, and he had no hope of anything better unless he could persuade some crew to take him on as a day labourer. But the day-wage man was paid so little that he would not be much better off after all. The only advantage would be that he would have a much better idea of what he was going to earn.

They were unable to repay any of the money they owed on the house. In fact, they were sometimes forced to borrow more money when it was necessary to buy a new cow after having had to sell the old one at a loss. They managed to raise enough pigs to pay the interest and the rates, but although Jane arranged to send six pigs a year to market instead of four by buying two porklings before the fatted ones had been sent away, she was not much better off. She had to pay more for pig meal, and she herself was far more tired at the end of the day.

It was true that Owen and Twm had won their schooling, but because the village, Moel Arian, was so isolated, it was an added expense to have to pay for the boys' lodgings during their last years at school. It would have been cruel to make them walk all the way home and then expect them to start on their ever-increasing amount of homework. They also needed better clothes and their books were expensive, although they received some grant towards these.

Wiliam and Elin were able to keep themselves — Wiliam failing sometimes — but Sioned never managed to do so. Her wages were not enough to keep her in food and clothes. But Jane Gruffydd managed to make enough clothes for Bet out of Sioned's old ones. When the mother wanted new clothes for herself — such as for the prizegiving — it meant getting deeper into debt.

She never saved on food. Unlike some others, she did not make a great effort to have butter to sell by putting less on the bread at home, or by mixing butter and margarine. She had one or two customers only, and these had their buttermilk free.

She worked morning, noon and night, doing the housework and most of the work with the animals. She made the children's underclothes and some of their outer garments. Before they went to the County School she would cut down Ifan and Wil's old trousers for Owen and Twm. She had little leisure for going anywhere or for reading. If she put on her spectacles to read in the evening, without fail she would fall asleep.

Her husband, too, was the same, toiling and moiling in the quarry; sweating and getting wet; coming home in the winter, wet to the skin, too tired to read a newspaper. In the Spring and Summer there would be work to do on the fields every evening and Saturday afternoon.

The only respite they had would be to get up later on a Sunday morning or to go to town occasionally on a Saturday afternoon. But they never grumbled about not having holidays; they would not know what to do with them if they had frequent ones. Their lot was to be eternally troubled and anxious about paying their way in the world, to keep out of debt, and acquire those things which they needed but wondered if they could afford.

But after earthing-up the potatoes or thatching the haystack, it was a great pleasure for Ifan to lean against the wall having a leisurely smoke while admiring the work of his hands, sometimes on his own, sometimes with a friend; to see the straight rows with the newly-turned earth around the dark shoots of the potatoes; to see the side of the haystack smooth and solid, and enjoy the sweet smell of the hay. So it was in the quarry when he had good stones which split cleanly and easily; he would sing as the work skimmed through his hands, and then the discussion in the shed after the mid-day meal. Yes, there was still some pleasure in life.

And at nightfall, placing his foot on the low wall at the front of the house and letting his eyes rest on the sea which was red in the setting sun, a feeling of quiet satisfaction would come over him.

Wiliam was different. He had never known worse times; but he had known better ones. That was one evil that stemmed from the practice of allowing fathers to work for their sons when they first went to the quarry. It gave the youngsters an inflated idea of the quarryman's wages, and as Wiliam saw his wages going down instead of up, he blamed what was to him the obvious cause — the managers and owners. His father, on the other hand, had known better and worse times. Ifan Gruffydd knew what it was to start work at nine years old and carry loads of heavy slates on his back before his bones had begun to harden. He knew what it was to get up at four o'clock on a Saturday morning and go to the quarry by the light of a lantern and work until one o'clock in order to turn a half-day into a whole one. He knew what it was like to go into a hole and hang by a rope when he should have been in school at his lessons; the rock-face was to him what a tree is to a squirrel.

Yet, when he had been the same age as Wiliam was now, he knew what it was to earn a living wage and dream of marrying. That was before his father had been killed in the quarry. But Wiliam never had that pleasure. He developed a taste for getting about; there was a brake service to the town, and a train would take him anywhere from there. When he was young, his father walked everywhere. That did not prevent him getting about, but it certainly helped him to save money.

A night school was started in the district at which English and Arithmetic were taught. A knowledge of Arithmetic was useful, and English allowed you to make your way in the world. It was necessary to raise the worker from his present down-trodden position. He should have a living wage. After learning a little more English than they learned in the Elementary School, the young people began to read about new ideas that were gaining ground in England and South Wales. Where their fathers (the more interested ones) had absorbed the ideas of Thomas Gee and S.R., their children grasped the ideas of Robert Blatchford and Keir Hardie.

Some of the young men began to meet in the barber's hut and they set about forming a branch of the Independent Labour Party. Wiliam was the moving spirit behind it all. Their chief task was to persuade their fellow-workers to join the Quarrymen's Union. They would not have a standard wage without that. Full of enthusiasm for the justice of their cause, they felt that every quarryman would rush to join, and then there would be no difficulty in resisting any attempt to lower their wages. Their first disappointment was seeing the lack of zeal of their fellow-workers. Some were afraid of attracting the owners' animosity; others questioned what possible good could come of it; others were just not interested. Only a few were keen. Some, like Ifan Gruffydd, paid up out of a sense of loyalty. They felt that it might prove to be a good thing in the long run, in the distant future, but not in their own lifetime.

Thus it was that the present generation came to take an interest in the plight of the worker. They gathered their ideas from English books, or from the Welsh papers that echoed the English ones. The worker in Wales came to be recognised along with his counterpart in England. It was the same problem in every country, with the same enemy — Capitalism. Wiliam read everything about the matter that he could lay his hands on. And while he was wrestling with these problems nobody bothered to tell him that the very quarry in which he was working had, in the beginning, been worked by the quarrymen themselves, sharing the profits.

Their religious outlook also changed. Their grandfathers and grandmothers — the pioneers of the Nonconformist causes scattered on the hillsides — had a profound knowledge of theology. There was devotion and self-sacrifice in their religion. But the grandchildren had lost the spirit of devotion and there was little call for sacrifice. They continued to study theology, but only coldly, as something remote from their lives. They too were interested in such topics as the person of Christ, the Incarnation, Predestination and the Atonement, but only on an intellectual level rather than as concepts having a real bearing on their lives. As the conditions of their everyday lives changed, as their world seemed to be collapsing, so their attitudes towards religion changed. The change was most evident in the young. To those intent on improving the condition of the workers, a man's duty to his fellow-men was the important thing, and the Sermon on the Mount became far more important than Paul's Epistles. Their attitude towards preachers changed. The best preachers were those who preached about social justice and man's duty towards his fellow-men. The young were placated by calling Christ a Socialist. Yet this too was a matter for the intellect, not one of belief. Their interest moved from Christ the Redeemer to Christ the Example. This did not impinge upon their lives. They enjoyed a good sermon from the pulpit and a good debate in the Sunday School. But they did not have a minister with whom to agree or disagree.

Their interest in politics was partisan. The old and the middle-aged were Radicals because they believed that was best for the workers. They regarded the Tory party as the party of the Ruling Class whose sole object was to keep the worker down. Liberalism had gained ground steadily since 1868 and the quarrymen still talked about workers' freedom and his living standards. Now here was a generation of young people learning to read English and getting to know about people who were beginning to tire of Liberalism, maintaining that the great battle of the future would be between Capitalism and Labour, and that Liberalism was only another name for Capitalism. The older people were a bit suspicious of them, and the deacons and more prominent members of the chapel openly showed their disapproval because they linked the new politics with aetheism. This, however, did not bring dissention into the Ffridd Felen family for they did not have deep religious or political views.

The Moel Arian branch of the Independent Labour Party did not attract a large membership, and the growth of its influence was very slow. But the few who belonged to it were very zealous. They constantly sought new members and encouraged the quarrymen to join the Union. During these years there were frequent minor strikes in the district, but these were not organised by the Union of Quarrymen. The men came out on their own initiative, very few of them receiving financial help from the Union. The men's wages continued to fall and things did not improve after a strike. It was useless trying to convince the workers that they would be able to negotiate a minimum wage agreement without a strong Union. One of the most disappointed was Wiliam. Whenever he had the opportunity he spoke and argued on behalf of the new party. Usually he managed to get people to agree with him, but they still refused to become active members. They admired his eloquence and showed their admiration in that peculiar remark, "A bit of a case, he is, that Wiliam of Ffridd Felen." Their admiration for Lloyd George sprang from the same source.

Kate Roberts, *Feet in Chains,* 1977
(Translated from Welsh by John Idris Jones & Idwal Walters)

V

THE FABLES

1. *Y Fuwch Frech. The Freckled Cow*

Old people have transmitted from generation to generation the following strange tale of the Freckled Cow. Whenever any one was in want of milk they went to this cow, taking with them a vessel into which they milked the cow, and, however big this vessel was, they always departed with the pail filled with rich milk, and it made no difference, however often she was milked, she could never be milked dry. This continued for a long time, and glad indeed the people were to avail themselves of the inexhaustible supply of new milk, freely given to them all. At last a wicked hag, filled with envy at the people's prosperity, determined to milk the cow dry, and for this purpose she took a riddle with her, and milked and milked the cow, until at last she could get no more milk from her. But, sad to say, the cow immediately, upon this treatment, left the country, and was never more seen. Such is the local history of the Freckled Cow.

Tradition further states that she went straight to a lake four miles off, bellowing as she went, and that she was followed by her two children the *Dau Eidion Banawg*, the two long-horned oxen, to *Llyn dau ychain*, the Lake of the Two Oxen, in the parish of Cerrig-y-drudion, and that she entered the lake and the two long-horned oxen, bellowing horribly, went, one on either side the lake, and with their mother disappeared within its waters, and none were ever afterwards seen.

Rev. Elias Owen

2. *The Legend of Llyn y Ddau Ychain*

The speckled cow had two calves, which, when they grew up, became strong oxen. In those days there was a wicked spirit that troubled Cerrig-y-drudion Church, and the people greatly feared this spirit, and everybody was afraid, even in the day-time, to pass the church, for there, day after day, they saw the evil one looking out of the church windows and grinning at them. They did not know what to do to get rid of this spirit, but at last they consulted a famous conjuror, who told them that no one could dislodge their enemy but the *Dau ychain Banawg*. They knew of the two long-horned cattle which fed on Waen Banawg. There, therefore, they went, and brought the powerful yoke to the church. After considerable difficulty they succeeded in dislodging the spirit, and in securing it to a sledge to which these oxen were yoked, and now struggling to get free, he was dragged along by the powerful oxen towards a lake on Hiraethog Mountain, but so ponderous was their load and so fearful was the spirit's contentions that the sledge ploughed the land between the church and the lake as they went along, leaving in the course that they took deep furrows, and when they came to the hill so terrible ere the struggles of the oxen to get along that the marks of their hoofs were left in the rocks where they may still be seen. When at last they reached the lake the spirit would not yield, and thus was the country rid of the evil one, and hence the name of the lake — the Lake of the Two Oxen — for the oxen likewise perished in the lake.

Ibid.

3. *Llanddona Witches*

There is a tradition in the parish of Llanddona, Anglesey, that these witches, with their husbands, had been expelled from their native country, wherever that was, for practising witchcraft. They were sent adrift, it is said, in a boat, without rudder or oars, and left in this state to the mercy of the wind and the wave. When they were first dis-covered approaching the Anglesey shore, the Welsh tried to drive them back into the sea, and even after they had landed they were confined to the beach. The strangers, dead almost from thirst and hunger, commanded a spring of pure water to burst forth on the sands. This well remains to our days. This miracle decided their fate. The strangers were allowed, consequently, to land but as they still practised their evil arts the parish became associated with their name, and hence the *Witches of Llanddona* was a term generally applied to the female portion of that parish, though in reality it belonged to one family only within its boundaries.

The men lived by smuggling and the women by begging and cursing. It was impossible to overcome these daring smugglers, for in their neckerchief was a fly, which, the moment the knot of their cravats was undone, flew right at the eye of their opponents and blinded them, but before this last remedy was resorted to the men fought like lions, and only when their strength failed tham did they release their familiar spirit, the fly, to strike with blindness the defenders of the law.

The above-mentioned tradition of the coming of these withces to Anglesey is still current in the parish of Llanddona, which is situated on the north coast of Anglesey.

It was thought that the witching power belonged to families, and descended from mothers to daughters. This was supposed to be the case with the witches of Llanddona. This family obtained a bad report throughout the island. The women, with dishevelled hair and bared breasts, visited farm houses and requested charity, more as a right than a favour, and no one dared refuse them. *Llanddona Witches* is a name that is not likely soon to die. Taking advantage of the credulity of the people they cursed those whom they disliked, and many were the endeavours to counteract their maledictions. The following is one of their curses, uttered at *Y Ffynon Oer*, a well in the parish of Llanddona, upon a man who had offended one of these witches:

'Crwydro y byddo am oesoedd awer,
Ac yn mhob cam, camfa;
Yn mhob camfa, codwm;
Yn mhob codwm, tori asgwrn;
Nid yr asgwrn mwyaf na'r lleiaf,
Ond asgwrn chwil corn ei wddw bob tro.'

The English is as follows, but the alliteration and rhythm of the Welsh do not appear in the translation:

'May he wander for ages many;
And at every step, a stile;
At every stile, a fall;
At every fall, a broken bone;
Not the largest, nor the least bone,
But the chief neck bone, every time.'

This curse seemed to be a common imprecation, possibly belonging to that family. Such was the terror of the *Llanddona Witches* that if any of them made a bid for a pig or anything else, in fair or market, no one else dared bid against them, for it was believed they would witch the animal thus bought. There was also celebrated witches at Denbigh. *Bella Fawr* (Big Bella) was one of the last and most famous of her tribe in that town, and many other places were credited with possessing persons endowed with witching powers, as well as those who could break spells.

Ibid.

4. *Witches transforming themselves into cats*

On the side of the old road, between Cerrigydrudion and Bettws-y-Coed — long before this latter place had become the resort of artists — stood an inn, which was much resorted to, as it was a convenient lodging house for travellers on their way to Ireland. This inn stood near the present village of Bettws-y-Coed. Many robberies occurred there. Travellers who put up there for the night were continually deprived of their money, and no one could tell how this occurred, for the lodgers were certain that no one had entered their rooms, as they were found locked in the morning just as they were the night before. The mystery was, therefore, great. By and by, one of those who had lost his money consulted *Huw Llwyd*, who lived at Cynvael, in the parish of Festiniog, and he promised to unravel the mystery. Now, Huw Llwyd had been an officer in the army, and, equipped in his regimentals, with sword dangling by his side, he presented himself one evening at the suspected inn, and asked whether he could obtain a room and bed for the night; he represented himself as on his way to Ireland, and he found no difficulty in obtaining a night's lodging. The inn was kept by two sisters of prepossessing appearance, and the traveller made himself most agreeable to these ladies, and entertained them with tales of his travels in foreign parts. On retiring for the night he stated that it was a habit with him to burn lights in his room all night, and he was supplied with a sufficient quantity of candles to last through the night. The request, as Hugh Llwyd was a military man, did not arouse suspicion. Huw retired, and made his arrangements for a night of watching. He placed his clothes on the floor within easy reach of his bed, and his sword unsheathed lay on the bed close to his right hand. He had secured the door, and now as the night drew on he was all attention; ere long, two cats stealthily came down the partition between his room and the next to it. Huw feigned sleep, the cats frisked here and there in the room, but the sleeper awoke not; they chased each other about the room, and played and romped, and at last they approached Huw's clothes and played with them, and here they seemed to get the greatest amusement; they turned the clothes about and over, placing their paws now on that string, and now on that button, and ere long their paws were inserted into the pockets of his clothes, and, just as one of the cats had her paw in the pocket that contained Huw Llwyd's purse, he like lightning struck the cat's paw with his sword. With terrible screams they both disappeared, and nothing further was seen of them during the night.

Next morning, only one of the sisters appeared at the breakfast table. To the traveller's enquiry after the absent lady of the house, her sister said that she was slightly indisposed, and could not appear.

Huw Llwyd expressed regret at this, but, said he — 'I must say good-bye to her, for I greatly enjoyed her company last night.' He would not be refused, so ultimately he was admitted to her presence. After expressing his sympathy and regret at her illness, the soldier held out his hand to bid good-bye to the lady. She put out her left hand; this Huw refused to take, averring that he had never taken a left hand in his life, and that he would not do so now. Very reluctantly, and with evident pain, she put out her right hand, which was bandaged, and this fact cleared up the mystery connected with the robberies. Those two ladies were two witches, who in the form of cats had robbed travellers who lodged under their roof. Huw, when he made this discovery said — 'I am Huw Llwyd of Cynvael, and I warn you of the risk you have incurred by your thefts, and I promise you I will not let you off so easily the next time I have need to visit you.'

Ibid.

5. *The Witches' revenge on Huw Llwyd*

Several months after the occurrence recorded above of Huw Llwyd, when he had just started from his home one Sunday morning to go to his Church to officiate there, for he was the parson of Llan Festiniog, he observed that the Bettws-y-Coed ladies were approaching his house, and he perceived that their object was to witch him. He knew full well that as long as his back was turned towards them he was in their power, but that when he faced them they could do him no harm, so, to avoid their evil influence, and to frustrate their designs, he faced them, and walked backwards every step from Cynvael to the Llan, and in this way he escaped being injured by his female enemies. But this was not all. Huw Llwyd knew that when he reached the Church porch he was beyond witchcraft's reach. Having arrived there he shouted out — 'I defy you now, and before I leave the Church I will make you that you can never again witch anyone.' He was as good as his word, for by his skill in the black art, he deprived these two ladies, ere he left the Church, of their power to witch people, and during the rest of their lives they were like other women.

Huw Llwyd, who was born in 1533, and died 1620, was a clergyman, and it was generally believed that priests could counteract the evils of the enemy of mankind.

Rev. Elias Owen, *Welsh Folklore*
Prize essay, National Eisteddfod, 1887

6. *Hares*

It has also been a frequent complaint, from old times, as well as in the present, *that certain hags in Wales*, as well as in Ireland and Scotland, *changed themselves into the shape of hares*, that, sucking teats under this counterfeit, they might stealthily rob other people's milk.

Giraldus Cambrensis, *The Itinerary Through Wales*

7. *Welsh Gypsies*

On one of these occasions a friend who had known something of the Welsh gypsies repeated to Rossetti an anecdote which had been told him as a 'quite true fack' by a Romani girl — an anecdote touching another Romani girl *whose wraith had been spirited away in the night from the 'camping place'* by the incantations of a wicked lover, had been seen rushing towards Ogwen Lake in the moonlight, 'While all the while that 'ere same chavi wur asleep an' a-sobbin' in her daddy's livin' waggin.'

Bye-Gones, Ap. 13, 1887

8. *Bronwen*

Bronwen, who resided at Harlech Castle, anciently called from her *Tŵr Bronwen*, (Bronwen's Tower*), was sought and obtained in marriage by Matholwch, king of Ireland. Being afterwards ill-treated by him, and insulted by a blow on the face, she left the country to return to her paternal home; but on landing in Wales we are told that she looked back upon Ireland, which freshening the memory of the indignity she had suffered, broke her heart. Bran, to avenge his sister, invaded Ireland, and destroyed an immense number of the people of that country. The historical romance also states that a square grave was made for Bronwen on the banks of the river Alaw, and there she was buried. In 1813 a most interesting discovery was made, which serves to give great authenticity to our Welsh documents, as, in the present instance, the romance has evidently been founded on historical facts. A farmer living on the banks of the Alaw, in Anglesey, having occasion for some stones, supplied himself from a *carnedd*, which was close to the river, and having removed several he came to a cist of close flags covered over, on removing the lid he found within an urn of ill-baked earth, about a foot high, placed with its mouth downwards, full of ashes, and half-calcined fragments of human bones. Another circumstance may be added, that the very spot has always been called Ynis Bronwen, or the islet of Bronwen, which is a remarkable confirmation of the genuineness of the discovery. All the circumstances together seem to place the matter beyond a doubt that the remains were actually those of Bronwen. Publicity was first given to this discovery by Sir Richard Hoare, who received the account from his friend Fenton the Pembrokeshire historian. The latter in his statement says, 'the report of this discovery soon went abroad, and came to the ears of the parson of the parish and another neighbourly clergyman, both fond of, and conversant with Welsh antiquities, who were immediately reminded of a passage in one of the early Welsh romances called the Mabinogion, the same that is quoted in Dr Davies's 'Latin and Welsh Dictionary', as well as in Richards's under the word *petrual* (square). 'Bedd petrual a wnaed i Fronwen ferch Llyr ar lan Alaw ac yno y claddwyd hi.' *A square grave was made for Bronwen the daughter of Lear, on the banks of the Alaw, and there she was buried.* 'Happening to be in Anglesey soon after this discovery,' says Fenton, 'I could not resist the temptation of paying a visit to so memorable a spot, though separated from it by a distance of eighteen miles. I found it, in all local respects, exactly as described to me by the clergyman above mentioned, and as characterized by the cited passage from the romance. The tumulus raised over the venerable deposit was of considerable circuit, elegantly rounded, but low, about a dozen paces from the river Alaw. The urn (of which a sketch is given in the Cambro Briton, vol. LL., p. 72) was preserved entire, with an exception of a small bit out of its lip, was ill-baked, very rude, and simple, having no other ornament than little pricked dots; in height from about a foot to fourteen inches.' In conclusion he remarks, 'never was there a more interesting discovery, as it greatly serves to give authenticity to our ancient British documents, even though they be introduced to minister to romance, as in the present instance, and fixes the probable date of the interment in question within a few years — a *desideratum* we despaired of being ever gratified with — a circumstance beautifully alluded to in the close of Mr Bowles's *Barrow Poem.*'

We have to add to the foregone details, from our own information, that the urn of Bronwen with its contents, became by purchase the property of the late Richard Llwyd, author of *Beaumaris Bay.* On visiting that patriotic poet, in the year 1829, we were favoured by him with a sight of that antique relic of buried ages, which minutely agreed with the account given by Fenton, even to 'the little pricked dots', and the 'small bit broken out of the lip'. Mrs Llwyd, our hosts's lady, we learnt, was quite ignorant of the antiquarian treasure of which her husband was possessed, nor did he ever enlighten her on that subject; as he felt convinced, he said, that the terror of a visit from the ghost of Bronwen would keep her sleepless ever after, or induce her to insist on the re-interment or removal of her remains. Before his death Mr Llwyd presented the urn and its contents to the British Museum.

T. Llewellyn Pritchard, Heroines of Welsh History

---

* Tŵr Bronwen, it appears was the most ancient name of this fortress. In after times it was called Caer Collwyn, from Collwyn ab Tango, one of the fifteen tribes of North Wales, and lord of Evionydd, Ardudwy, and part of Llŷn. His grandchildren flourished in the time of Griffith ab Cynan. According to Pennant he resided for some time in a square tower in the ancient fortress, the remains of which are very apparent; as are those of part of the old walls, which the more modern in certain places are seen to rest on.

9. *Merlin's Prophecy*

A prophecy, said to be one of Merlin's, was published in Welsh and English by Thomas Pugh, in 1658; foretelling the troubles of the rebellion — the restoration of Charles II &c. as follows:

'Then shall a king come to England from a princely race, with his noble descent from Aberffraw in Angelesey, the ancient seat of the Princes of North Wales; then, or in such time when this cometh to pass, let the Britons sit still at home and be quiet, while the great ones of England contend; for the crown shall go at the disposal of the subjects,' &c. The last extract shall be one quoted by John Pugh, from 'Goronwy of Mon', who fancied that an angel foretold him the regal succession, till the restoration of the British line in the Tudor race, and afterwards in the Stuarts. Rowlands, in his MS. notes, is very diffuse and clear upon this point of Walter Stuart, who he says (p. 176 Mon. Ant.) was born in the palace of Aberffraw. In my account of Rhosvair, will be seen Mr Lloyd's opinion concerning this palace, which he thinks must have been at Rhosvair. But there is no such lake in that neighbourhood to justify the bard's admiration, (in his englyn) as Llyn Coron, which is two miles in circumference, and very near to Aberffraw. From the plenty, as well as variety of fish it contains, many amateur anglers are induced to visit it during the summer months.

Thomas Pennant, *Tours in Wales*

10. *The Legend of Llys Helig*

There is a very ancient legend of the inundation of the land of Helig-ab-Glanawg, or Morfa Rhianedd, between the Great Ormes Head and Priestholme, still extant, preserved also in ancient manuscript. This Helig was Lord of Abergele, Rhos, Arllechwedd, Lleyn, Cantref Gwaelod; and he was also Earl of Hereford. In his time happened the great inundation which surrounded Morfa Rhianedd, the most delicate, fruitful and pleasant vale lying from Bangor to Gogarth (Great Ormes Head), and so to Tyganwy (Deganwy) in length, and in breadth from Dwygyfylchi to the point of Flintshire which came up from Rhuddlan to Priestholme; and in the upper end whereof did extend in breadth from Aber and Llanfair-(fechan) to the River Ell

(River Ogwen) which did divide Caernarvon from Mon (Anglesey) and did likewise divide Môn from Flintshire, running between Priestholme and Penmon, and so discharging itself into the sea a great way beyond Priestholme, and did surround many to her fruitful bottoms and vales within the counties of Caernarvon, Flint, Anglesey and Merioneth, most of them being the land of Helig-ab-Glanawg, whose chiefest palace stood in this vale, much about the middle way from Penmaenmawr and Gogarth, the ruins whereof are now to be seen upon a ground ebb some two miles within the sea directly against Trwyn-yr-Wylfa, or Point of Wailing, which is a hill lying in the midst of the parish of Dwygyfylchi, unto which hill Helig-ab-Glanawg and his people did run up to save themselves, being endangered with the sudden breaking in of the sea, and there saved their lives, and being come up to the point of that hill and looking back beholding that dreadful and ruthful spectacle instead of their incomparable vale, excelling all other vales in fertility and pleasantness, Helig and all his people wringing their hands together, bewailing their misfortune, the point of which is called to this day Trwyn-yr-Wylfa, the Point of the Doleful Hill.

The tragical occurrence was prophesied, it is said, for generations; and a threat had gone forth, that vengeance should overtake the family of Helig-ab-Glanawg for the crimes of his ancestors. Night after night, on the wild rocks and shores, amid the hills and in the valleys, was heard the fearful cry of 'Dial a ddaw! Dial a ddaw!' but the wailer was invisible to all. At length it came, and suddenly, as mighty calamities, even though dreaded, generally do; there was a great feast in the house of Helig, and the guests forgot, in their jovial carousal, that fate was only pausing to overtake them. They called for more wine, and a servant was despatched into the cellar to procure some, while the old harper sat leaning on his harp, and the tears ran down upon the strings, for his spirit foresaw some coming evil. They reproached him for his silence, and he put forth his hand to awaken the chords, when a cry struck his ear, and the next moment the servant who had gone for wine rushed wildly into the hall shrieking 'The tide! The tide!', as the tempestuous torrent burst in, swallowing land, flocks and villages, and the fertile vale of Conway for miles was all one sheet of foaming water, as it remains to this day.

F. H. Glazebrook, *Anglesey and the North Wales Coast Book*

11.   *The Well of Destiny. The Oxen at Bodedon*

There was a spring of clear water, now choked up by the sand, at which an old woman from Newborough always attended and prognosticated the lovers's success from the movements of some small eels, which waved out of the sides of the well on spreading the lover's handkerchief on the surface of the water. I remember an old woman saying that when she was a girl she consulted the woman at the well about her destiny with respect to a husband. On spreading her handkerchief, out popped an eel from the north side of the well, and soon after another crawled from the south side, and they both met on the bottom of the well. Then the woman told her that her husband would be a stranger from the south part of Carnarvonshire. Soon after, it happened that three brothers came from that part and settled in the neighbourhood where this young woman was, one of whom made his addresses to her, and in a little time married her. So much of the prophecy I remember. This couple was my father and mother.

I remember hearing an instance which happened, I believe, about one hundred and fifty years ago. The ploughing oxen at Bodedon, on April 25th, took fright when at work, and ran over a steep rock and perished in the sea. This being S. Mark the Evangelist's Day, it was considered that having done work on it was a transgression of a divine ordinance, and to prevent such accident for the future the proprietor of the farm ordered that this festival of St Mark should be for the future invariably kept a holy day, and that two wax candles should annually on that day be kept burning in the church porch of Llanddwyn, which was the only part of the building that was covered in, as an offering and memorial of this transgression and accident, and as a token that S. Dwynwen's aid and protection was solicited to prevent such catastrophe any more. This was only discontinued about eighty years ago, *i.e.* 1720.

William Williams, Llandegai, 1800

12.   *Coll ab Collfrewi*

Coll ab Collfrewi was one of the three powerful swineherds of the Island of Britain . . . he kept the swine of Dallweir Dallben, in the valley of Dallwyr in Cornwall. And one of these swine, named

Henwen, was with young, and it was prophesied that this circumstance would bring evil to the island of Britain. So Arthur assembled his host and sought to destroy the swine; but she went burrowing along till she came to Penrhyn Austin, where she plunged into the sea, and she landed again at Adberdarogi, in Gwent Iscoed. And all the way she went Coll ab Collfrewi held by her bristles, both by sea and by land, and at Maes Gwenith (Wheatfield) in Gwent, she left three grains of wheat and three bees, since which time the best wheat and the best honey have been in Gwent. And thence she went into Dyved, and there, at Llonnio Llonnwen, she left a grain of barley and a little pig; and Dyved has produced the best pigs and barley from that time to this. And from Dyved she went into Arvon, and she left a grain of rye at Lleyn in Arvon, and thenceforth the best rye has been found at Lleyn, and at Eivionydd. And by the side of Rhiwgyverthwch, she left a wolf cub and a young eaglet, and the wolf was given to Brynach Wyddel, of Dinas Affaraon, and the eagle to Benwaedd, the lord of Arllechwedd, and there was much talk concerning the wolf of Brynach, and the eagle of Benwaedd. And when she came to Maen Du in Arvon she left there a kitten, and Coll an Collfrewi took it, and threw it into the Menai. But the sons of Palug in Mona (Anglesey), reared this kitten, to their cost; for it became the Palug Cat, which, we are told, was one of the three plagues of the Isle of Mona which were reared therein, the second being Daronwy, and the third, Edwin king of England.

Myvyrian Archaiology

13. Anglesey Legends

As many things within this island are worthy of remark, I shall not think it superfluous to make mention of some of them. There is a stone here resembling a human thigh, which possesses this innate virtue, that whatever distance it may be carried, it returns, of its own accord, the following night, as has often been experienced by the inhabitants. Hugh, earl of Chester, in the reign of king Henry I, having by force occupied this island and the adjacent country, heard of the miraculous power of this stone, and, for the purpose of trial, ordered it to be fastened, with strong iron chains, to one of a larger size, and to be thrown into the sea. On the following morning, however, according to custom, it was found in its original position, on which account the earl issued a public edict, that no one, from that time, should presume to move the stone from its place. A countryman, also, to try the powers of this stone, fastened it to his thigh, which immediately became putrid, and the stone returned to its original situation.

There is in the same island a stony hill, not very large or high, from one side of which, if you cry aloud, you will not be heard on the other; and it is called (by antiphrasis) the rock of hearers. In the northern part of Great Britain (Northumberland) so named by the English, from its situation beyond the river Humber, there is a hill of a similar nature, where if a loud horn or trumpet is sounded on one side, it cannot be heard on the opposite one. There is also in this island the church of St Tefredaucus, into which Hugh, earl of Shrewsbury, (who, together with the earl of Chester, had forcibly entered Anglesey), on a certain night put some dogs, which on the following morning were found mad, and he himself died within a month; for some pirates, from the Orcades, having entered the port of the island in their long vessels, the earl, apprised of their approach, boldly met them, rushing into the sea upon a spirited horse. The commander of the expedition, Magnus, standing on the prow of the foremost ship, aimed an arrow at him; and, although the earl was completely equipped in a coat of mail, and guarded in every part of his body except his eyes, the unlucky weapon struck his right eye, and, entering his brain, he fell a lifeless corpse into the sea. The victor, seeing him in this state, proudly and exultingly exclaimed, in the Danish tongue, 'Leit loup', let him leap; and from this time the power of the English ceased in Anglesey. In our times, also, when Henry II was leading an army into North Wales, where he had experienced the ill fortune of war in a narrow, woody pass near Coleshulle, he sent a fleet into Anglesey, and began to plunder the aforesaid church, and other sacred places. But the divine vengeance pursued him, for the inhabitants rushed upon the invaders, few against many, unarmed against armed; and having slain great numbers, and taken many prisoners, gained a most complete bloody victory. For, as our Topography of Ireland testifies, that the Welsh and Irish are more prone to anger and revenge than any other nations, the saints, likewise, of those countries appear to be of a more vindictive nature.

Two noble persons, and uncles of the author of this book, were sent thither by the king; namely Henry, son of king Henry I, and uncle to king Henry II, by Nest, daughter of Rhys, prince of South Wales; and

Robert Fitz-Stephen, brother to Henry, a man who in our days, shewing the way to others, first attacked Ireland, and whose fame is recorded in our Vaticinal History. Henry, actuated by too much valour, and ill supported, was pierced by a lance, and fell amongst the foremost, to the great concern of his attendants; and Robert, despairing of being able to defend himself, was badly wounded, and escaped with difficulty to the ships.

There is a small island, almost adjoining to Anglesey, which is inhabited by hermits, living by manual labour, and serving God. It is remarkable that when, by the influence of human passions, any discord arises among them, all their provisions are devoured and infected by a species of small mice, with which the island abounds; but when the discord ceases, they are no longer molested. Nor is it to be wondered at, if the servants of God sometimes disagree, since Jacob and Esau contended in the womb of Rebecca, and Paul and Barnabas differed; the disciples also of Jesus disputed which of them should be the greatest, for these are the temptations of human infirmity; yet virtue is often made perfect by infirmity, and faith is increased by tribulations. This island is called in Welsh, Ynys Lenach, or the ecclesiastical island, because many bodies of saints are deposited there, and no woman is suffered to enter it.

We saw in Anglesey a dog, who accidentally had lost his tail, and whose whole progeny bore the same defect. It is wonderful that nature should, as it were, conform itself in this particular to the accident of the father. We saw also a knight, named Earthbald, born in Devonshire, whose father, denying the child with which his mother was pregnant, and from motives of jealousy accusing her of inconstancy, nature alone decided the controversy by the birth of the child, who, by a miracle, exhibited on his upper lip a scar, similar to one his father bore in consequence of a wound he had received from a lance in one of his military expeditions. Stephen, the son of Earthbald, had a similar mark, the accident being in a manner converted into nature. A like miracle of nature occurred in earl Alberic, son of Alberic earl of Veer.

Giraldus Cambrensis, *The Itinerary Through Wales*

14. *The Astrologer Arise Evans*

. . . the noted astrologer, and ill-favoured knave, *Arise Evans*, a character and species of impostor frequent in the reigns of *Elizabeth* and *James* I. His figure is preserved in the *Antiquarian Repertory*, and answers the description given of him by his great pupil, *William Lilly*, of having a broad forehead, beetle brows, thick shoulders, flat nose, full lips, a down look, black curling stiff hair, and splay foot. He was a deep student in the *black arts*; and *Lilly* assures us, that he had most *piercing judgement naturally upon a figure of theft*, and many other questions, he ever met withal; was well versed in the *nature of spirits*; and had many times used the *circular way of invocating* . . . His friend *Evans*, by means of the angel *Salmon*, brought to him a deed, which one of his customers had been wronged of, at the same time blowing down part of the house of the person in whose custody it was: and again, how, to satisfy the curiosity of lord *Bothwell* and Sir *Kenelm Digby*, who wanted to see a spirit, he liked to have lost his life, being carried over the *Thames*, and flung down near *Battersea*, by the spirits, whom he had vexed at the time of invocation, for want of *making a due fumigation*. These ridiculous impostures were the fashionable credulity of the times; and the greatest men were the dupes of these pretenders to occult science.

Thomas Pennant, *Tours in Wales*

15. *The Monster of Llyn-yr-afanc*

The real original 'Afanc', which gave name to the pool was an aquatic monster, like the 'piast' of certain Irish lakes. The story, found in various forms over Wales, is that he was dragged out of this and other pools by two 'Ychain Bannog' or (long-) horned oxen. He is said to have been lugged from here over Bwlch Rhiw'r Ychain (the Oxen's Slope) and past a pool, Pwll Llygad Ych (Ox's Eye Pool), stated to have been formed by the eye of one of the poor beasts, which had dropped out through sheer exhaustion. Finally, after a devious 'trek', the 'laidly worm' was duly dumped into the depth of Glaslyn (under Snowdon), whence folk, dead not so long ago, professed to have seen him emerge, and to have fled in terror at the blood-curdling sight. This local tale was first recorded by Edward Llwyd 200 years ago. He also tells how a woman witched the monster out of Llyn-yr-afanc, and lulled him to sleep on her lap, in order to bind him with iron chains, and how he incontinently woke and jumped back into the pool, taking with him one of her breasts. It was after this that the oxen dragged him out. As to the comparatively modern Welsh use of 'afanc' in the sense of a beaver, it may be said that in the old Welsh laws a beaver is always called 'llost-lydan', or broad tail, and that beavers are recorded to have been extinct in Wales, except in one river, the Teifi, before 1200. It is from this use of 'afanc' that a curious and complicated etymological myth has arisen. First of all, the word 'afanc' was manufactured by the etymologists into 'afanci', plural 'afancwn' (so as to make it mean a river-dog, from 'afon', a river, and 'ci' a dog, plural 'cwn'); next, this apocryphal 'afancwm' was invoked to explain the name of Nant 'Ffrancon', which, however, unfortunately for this theory, is so called and spelt in the 'Book of Taliesin', a MS of the 13th century. There is, or was, however, a Sarn-yr-afanc, or Avanc's Causeway, in or near Nant Ffrancon, and there is a Bedd-yr-afanc (the Avanc's Grave) near Nevern, in Pembroke-shire.

George Lerry (Ed.), *Gossiping Guide to Wales*

16.   *Merlin and the Moon in a Well*

From the holy city of Glastonbury the trail of the once and future king leads north-west into Wales. Here, the tales of Arthur and his mentor, Merlin, diverge, the king last being seen (if we are to believe some reports) on the lonely lake of Llyn Llydaw, near Llanberis Pass, and Merlin first making an historical appearance at the little town of Beddgelert (on the A498 north of Portmadoc) a few miles to the south.

Llyn Llydaw is a boomerang-shaped lake, to the shores of which Sir Bedivere is said to have carried the wounded Arthur after his fatal fight with Mordred at Bwlch-y-Sasthan ('the Pass of the Arrows') in the surrounding mountains. 'Arthur himself, our renowned king,' says Geoffrey of Monmouth, 'was mortally wounded and carried off to the Isle of Avalon so that his wounds might be attended to . . . this in the year 542 after our Lord's Incarnation.'

Elizabeth Pepper & John Wilcock, *Magical and Mystical Sites,* 1982

VI

THE FAITH

1. *Capel Gwynen*

Upon the south side of the upper lake, in the valley of Nanhwynen, are the ruins of a chapel, called Capel Gwynen, within a small walled enclosure. Divine service was performed here until about a century ago, and the chapel itself was kept in repair by the proprietors of the manor of Hafodlwyfog, which occupies this part of the parish. The last time of a congregation's assembling within these walls is said to have been when the minister's attendance was prevented by a great flood. A young squire then present mounted the pulpit and pronounced from it to the great scandal of his hearers a very licentious distict, a piece of profaneness which, says the tradition, was speedily followed by a judicial death. A similar punishment is likewise stated to have overtaken a tenant who had appropriated the woodwork of the chapel to some repairs about his farm. Here was buried in 1460 David Nannor (*sic*) the bard, as was Rhys Goch Eryri, his rival in fame and in love at Beddgelert in 1420.

From the latter, a man of large possessions, and through him from Collwyn ap Tangno, was descended the late John Hughes of Trefan, Esqr. The properties of this gentleman, Hafodgarregog in this parish and Trefan in Llanystundwy, have been lately taken from his granddaughter under circumstances of such a nature as to have excited a very general sympathy. By the non-observance of the provisions of the Marriage Act by her mother, she has in fact been illegitimated, and thus is afforded another instance of the mischief's flowing from that Law, which I cannot but regard as not only a gross and unnatural violation of natural right, but as an insolent attempt to divide the aristocracy from the rest of the people. The Royal Marriage Act is another abomination of this kind, and with all due deference to the legal dictum so commonly used, I shall venture to call that bad law whence proceed bad consequences; nor will humanity refuse to travel into the doctrine of hardships however sternly it may be driven from before the benches of justice.

E. Hyde Hall, *A Description of Caernarvonshire*

2. *The Druids*

By the second half of the eighteenth century in Britain we have, as we have seen, Druids well established in more than one role. According to taste, one could see them as Patriarchal pre-Christian Christians; savages reflecting either the good or the bad qualities of Polynesians real or imagined; worshipping in stone circles (especially Stonehenge) or in groves; sacrificing on the top of megalithic tombs or at a mistletoe-decked oak; encouraging bards or being bards themselves; as fierce anti-Roman champions of liberty as in Mason's play *Caratacus* (1759) or as the colourless and rather gentlemanly priests envisaged by Pope in his projected *Brutus* (1744). But among all these Druids-as-wished-for we have not yet considered an aspect which was to be of increasing significance as the nineteenth century wore on, the Druid as the repository of mystic wisdom or as a Priest of the Ancient Mysteries. It is here that Reinach's reference to doctrines believed to be handed down by bardic schools in Wales is significant.

The Gentleman's Magazine for October 1792 recorded a singular event which had taken place on September 23. 'This being the day on which the autumnal equinox occurred, some Welsh Bards, resident in London, assembled in congress on Primrose Hill, according to ancient usage . . . The wonted ceremonies were observed. A circle of stones formed, in the middle of which was the *Maen Gorsedd*, or Altar, on which a naked sword being placed, all the Bards assisted to sheath it.' What were these bards doing, making a stone circle, and how ancient was the usage? In answering these questions we find a nice mixture of fact, fantasy and, alas! forgery.

The Welsh bards, even if somewhat fallen on evil days by 1792, were not nonsense. In the Middle Ages, as with their counterparts in Ireland, they had formed part of the traditional Celtic hierarchy with genuine roots in the ancient past of the Celts and Druids. Traditional formulaic composition and complex metrical forms were preserved, cultivated and transmitted by poets, singers and harpists in Wales, and however tenuous, the links of this tradition in the eighteenth century with that of the Middle Ages were genuine enough. From at least the twelfth century there had been in existence an organization or 'court' for regulating and licensing accredited performers in poetry and music, and maintaining standards by competitions and awards, known as an *Eisteddfod*, a session or assembly. In the sixteenth century, *eisteddfodau* at Caerwys were organized partly to limit the number of vagrant bards: the English government, already pre-occupied with the problem of 'sturdy beggars', was concerned in Wales as in Ireland with controlling the movements of dangerously mobile elements in Celtic society. The tradition of holding an Eisteddfod intermittently in one or other Welsh town continued feebly until the exceptionally well organized meeting at Corwen in 1789, which gave the institution a vitality and a stability it maintained into the nineteenth century and beyond. But in all the Welsh meetings there had been no question of a stone circle or a Maen Gorsedd.

It is here that we turn to fancy and fabrication. A Glamorganshire stone-mason, Edward Williams, born in 1747, had been working in London from the early 1770's and was an active member of a group of Welshmen there who were interesting themselves in their national culture, language, literature and antiquities. Williams had been brought up in the poetic and musical conventions current among the traditional poets of Glamorganshire, and according to custom had adopted a 'bardic' nom-de-plume, that of Iolo Morganwg, Iolo of Glamorgan, the name by which he is best known, and in his misguided enthusiasm and local patriotism declared that the Glamorganshire bards had preserved, virtually intact, a continuous tradition of lore and wisdom going back to the original prehistoric Druids. But he did not leave his assertions unsupported. With the prevailing low standards of scholarship in early Welsh linguistics and palaeography it was unfortunately not difficult for Iolo to forge documents to prove his case, and these were in fact a part only of his large corpus of fabrications of early Welsh literature which was to cause so much confusion when more exact scholarship came to be applied to the texts. The Primrose Hill ceremony was another outcome of Iolo's crazy enthusiasm; the quaint little ritual in fact aroused no interest, partly owing to the fact that Iolo's group of associates held views notoriously sympathetic to Tom Paine and the French Revolution. Incidentally, in view of subsequent events, there is no reason to think of the 'circle of stones' reported in the *Gentleman's Magazine* as being anything much more than a ring of pebbles.

We might not have heard of the Gorsedd again had not Iolo seen an opportunity for furthering his nonsense — for it can be called nothing else — by getting it attached to the genuine if moribund Eisteddfod. At the end of the three-day session held at Carmarethen in 1819 the Gorsedd Circle, made of stones taken by Iolo from his pockets, was first set up in Wales, in the garden of the Ivy Bush Hotel, and the bardic performance took place. The Gorsedd, which Iolo originally had hoped might supersede the Eisteddfod, was now assured of a future as an integral part of it, nicely calculated to appeal to nationalists and romantics, the credulous and the pompous. The Gorsedd itself, the Druids, the Ceremony, the Prayer, the Invocation to Peace, the Symbol of the Ineffable Name and the Traditional Rites are traditional only so far as they preserve the romantic imaginings of a somewhat less than honest journeyman mason 160 years ago. As Professor Gwyn Williams has written, 'the inventions of Iolo Morganwg in the eighteenth century and, as a result, the dignified nonsense of the Gorsedd ceremony associated annually with the National Eisteddfod has helped to throw a mist of unreliable antiquarianism about the subject which scholarship has not the means completely to dispel.'

Stuart Piggott, *The Druids*

3. *The 'Jumpers'*

To the state of dissent from the Church I have so continually paid attention, that in this place I shall confine myself to the notice of the sect of Methodists called the Jumpers, whose periodical rendezvous within the county was Caernarvon while they still continued to celebrate their assemblies. Once and only once I have beheld the fantastical proceedings of these religionists, whose first care seems to be the erection of a pulpit, tribune and a due provision of preachers, able-bodied and having good lungs. As fatigue or any other calls succeed, the haranguer leaves his place, which is immediately occupied by a successor, and thus the stimulus of fanaticism is kept in full action until its effects are spread throughout the congregation. Ejaculations and sighs are first heard, then succeed an accuring murmur of groans, until at length the mass assembled swells into a storm of prayers and wild expression and jumping. The passion endured, the excitement and the fatigue ultimately produce an effect debasing to our nature and most disquieting to the bystander. Some are sick, some faint, some fall; and as they are led off, the women more particularly, the imagination seizes what may be supposed to be the appearance of a knot of witches exhausted by the orgies of their Sabbath's celebration.

In narrowing these scandalous scenes ridicule has for once been beneficially employed, and the possessors of this abominable mummery are, I am informed, rapidly declining in numbers. With respect to the charge brought against these people for profligate licentiousness of conduct during the night of their assemblies, I shall upon general grounds require the very strictest proofs before I would give credence to its existence, and above all to the manner of its existence.

E. Hyde Hall, *A Description of Caernarvonshire*

4. *Preachers, Cricket and Bicycles*

An incipient cricket club in a village with which I am intimate was quashed by the preachers on the amazing plea that it 'encouraged swearing'.

. . . Bicycles . . . cause a no inconsiderable flutter in the dovecotes. Nothing can be said against their use (on a week day) even by the preachers; but, none the less, they do not love them. The very joy of their rapid movement suggests independence and even frivolity, and is out of harmony with the sombre and circumscribed traditions of the chapel . . . When a young man or woman can ride fifty or sixty miles in a day, an independence of habit and observation is formed that is much more hostile to present conditions than any cricket or football matches.

A. G. Bradley, *Highways and By-ways of North Wales*

5. *From Squire Bulkeley's Diary*

July 27th, 1735. There was a sort of confusion in Church on ye account of the Parson's forgetting his Sermon, he went to ye Pulpit, read ye usual Prayer before Sermons, and when he should have begun, there was nothing in Church but a general Silence for 3 or 4 minutes, at last he beckoned to the Sexton, and after whispering together for some time the Sexton beckoned to ye Churchwarden to come up the Stairs of the Pulpit to the Parson where they all three had a consultation for a good while then it was resolved (I suppose) that the Churchwarden should consult the Parson's Maid, which he did, . and they two went out of Church, where they were for some long time before they returned, by virtue of which consultation together with those others before mentioned, the Churchwarden and the Parson's Maid brought in an Excellent Sermon, by them, all and every, or some of them composed, which the Parson afterwards read.

N.B. The Pulpit is placed pretty high, so that all those people had 5 or 6 steps to ascend to consult the Parson.

The Churchwardens agreed with Wm. Wms. the Smith of Rhosbeirio to make a Vane to be set on the Top of the Spire of Llanfechell for 15s . . . A Lion is to point to ye wind, the figure of which I myself cut, having a Royal crown on his head, Brandishing a scimiter over his Head, and grasping a Bundle of Darts in the other Paw. I have promised to pay for the painting of them twice over, and to have the lion gilded . . .

April 13, 1739: (Pd. Churchmize) . . . with which money they intend to build up . . . the churchyard wall to make it a convenient close for the Priest to turn in his Horses, sheep, etc., a very indecent thing, I'm sure, and ye claim grounded upon neither reason nor justice, but on a custom that prevailed in the Tyrannical times of Popery when ye Priests were Lords Paramount, that the Dormitories of Dead Christians should at ye charge of the Parish be walled in on purpose to be converted into a Park for the Priests's Use.

Squire Bulkeley *Diary*

6.   *Beuno*

Beuno had been residing near Welshpool, but as he was walking on a certain day near the Severn, where there was a ford, he heard some men on the further side inciting dogs in pursuit of a hare, and he made sure they were Englishmen, for one shouted 'Kergia!' (Charge!) to the hounds. When Beuno heard the voice of the Englishman he immediately turned back, and said to his disciples, 'My sons, put on your garments and your shoes, and let us abandon this place, for the nation of the man with the strange language, whose voice I heard beyond the river inciting his dogs, will invade this place, and it will be theirs.' Beuno left and went to Meifod, where he remained but forty days and nights with Tyssilio, and then went on into the territory of Cadwallon, king of Gwynedd, who gave him land on which to settle, far away from the hated Saxon. And he and his monks began to enclose an area with a mound and a moat. Whilst thus engaged, a woman came up with a child in her arms, and asked Beuno to bless it. 'Wait a while,' said the abbot, 'till we have done a bit of banking.' Then the child began to cry, so that it distracted the monks, and Beuno bade her still it.

'How can I do that,' said she, 'when you are taking possession of the land that belonged to my husband, and should be that of this little one?' Beuno at once stopped the work to inquire into the matter, and found that what the woman had said was true. Then, in great wrath, he ordered his chariot, and drove to the palace of Cadwallon, and asked him how he had dared to give him land which belonged to the widow and orphan.

Cadwallon answered contemptuously that he must take that or none at all. So Beuno would not take it, and swarmed off with his disciples to Clynnog, and settled there on land given him by the king's cousin, and there ended his days about the year 640.

Thomas Roscoe, *Wanderings and Excursions in North Wales*

7. *The Offering of Bullocks*

Being occasioned the last year to travel into mine own native country, in North Wales, and having tarried there but a while, I have heard by divers, of great and abominable Idolatry committed in that country, as that the People went on Pilgrimage to offer unto Idols far and near, yea, and that they do offer in these days not only Money (and that liberally) but also Bullocks unto Idols. And having heard this of sundry Persons while I was there — upon Whit Sunday last, I went to the Place where it was reported that Bullocks were offered, that I might be an eye witness of the same. And upon Monday in Whitsun Week there was a young Man that was carried thither the Night before, with whom I had conference concerning the Manner of the Offerings of Bullocks unto Saints, and the young man told me after the same Sort as I had heard of many before; then did I ask him whether was there any to be offered that Day? He answered that there was One which he had brought to be offered; I demanded of him where it was? he answered, that it was in a close hard by. And he called his Host to go with him to see the Bullock, and as they went I followed them into the close, and the young Man drove the Bullock before him (being about a year old) and asked his Host what it was worth? His Host answered that it was worth about a Crown, the young Man said that it was worth more, his Host answered and said that upon Sunday was senight Mr Vicar brough here a Bullock about the Bigness of your Bullock for Sixteen Groats. Then the young Man said, How shall I do for a Rope against even to tie the Bullock with? His Host answered, We will provide a rope; the young Man said again, Shall I drive him into the Churchyard? His Host answered, You may; then they drove the Bullock before them toward the Churchyard; And as the Bullock did enter through a little Porch into the Churchyard, the young Man spake aloud, 'The Half to God and to Beuno'. Then did I ask his Host, Why he said the Half and not the Whole? His Host answered in the young man's hearing, He oweth me th'other Half. This was in the Parish of Clynnog in the Bishopric of Bangor, in the year of our Lord 1589 — There be many other things in the Country that are very gross and superstitious; As that the People are of Opinion, that Beuno his Cattle will prosper marvellous well; which maketh the people more desirous to buy them. Also, it is a common Report amongst them, that there be some Bullocks which have had Beuno his Mark upon their Ears as soon as they are calved.

Leyland, *Collectanae*

8.   *Seiriol*

This Seiriol had also a hermitage on Penmaenmawr, and he had a chapel there, where he did bestow much of his time in prayer; the place being then an uncouth desert, steep rocks, and inaccessible owing to their steepness, and the woods so thick, that if a man entered therein, he could see neither sky, nor firmament. From Priestholme to Penmaenmawr, did Seiriol cause a pavement to be made, whereupon he might walk dry from his church at Priestholme to his chapel at Penmaenmawr, which pavement may at this day be discerned, when the sea is clear, if a man list to go in a boat to see it; sythence this great and lamentable inundation of Cantrev Gwaelod; the way and passage being stopped in this strait, in regard the sea was come in and did beat upon the rocks of Penmaenmawr, this holy man Seiriol, like a good hermit, did cause a way to be broken and cut through the main rock, which is the only passage that is to pass that strait. This way leadeth from Dwygyfylchau to Llanvair Vechen, and is the king's highway from Conway to Beaumaris, Bangor, and Caernarvon, and the only passage that the king's post hath to ride to and from Ireland.

Hanes Helig ab Glanawg Caerwys MSS

9. *Cybi*

According to this account Cybi lived about the year 650; if so, he could not be made bishop by either Hilary of Poitiers, nor our Eilian Ceimiad, (or Hilary the Bright), who lived about the year 440.

What corroborates very much this account of Cybi's living in the seventh century, is a very ancient tradition retained among the vulgar here to this day, viz. that Cybi and Seiriol had a punctual meeting, either weekly, or more frequently, at a place called Clorach, now Llanerchmedd in this county (being about half way from Caergybi to Seiriol's chapel, in the island) where there are to this day two handsome wells of fine spring water about ten yards distant, which retain their names, viz., F(f)ynon Seiriol, and F(f)ynon Gybi, and where, till of late years, a great concourse of people used to resort to wash off their several diseases. Further, 'the common people are so particular in circumstances, that because Cybi's journey was from west to east, and Seiriol's from east to west, to meet at the wells, Cybi had the sun in his face in coming and going', Seiriol having it quite contrary, Cybi therefore had the appellation of Yellow Faced added to his name, whence proceeds that ancient adage amongst the vulgar — Seiriol Wyn a Chybi Velyn.

Lewis Morris, *Life and Work,* 1748

10. *Saint Ffraid*

Saint Ffraid was born in the village of Fochart, in the diocese of
Armagh in Ireland, and died in A.D. 523. She was known as
the Virgin of Kildare, and enjoyed a great reputation as a worker
of miracles. The following account of some of Saint Ffraid's feats is
of interest:

'According to the British legend she was a nun. On entering
a nunnery, her step-mother's leg was cut off, but on her request
a leg and foot grew in its place. She extracted honey out of
the stone for a poor man. A ploughman broke his plough, and
she gave her distaff, which made him a chwelydr (chip of a
plough). The butter turned to ashes; and the ashes, in her hand,
turned into butter, and ale enough in two basins. That she gave
to the village all the cheese of the mayor's house; and though
the cheese were given away, there was not one wanting. That
she understood the fifteen prayers; and in case of hard rain she
would throw her white sheet on the beams of the sun. That
she came from Ireland over the sea, and swam to Dyfi; that
she made of rushes, in Gwynedd, the fish called smelts; that she
went to Rome, from Patrick's country, to see Peter; that she
turned the Mayor of London into a horse; that she released the
baker's wife; and between her and God bound the Devil. That
when her father proposed her in marriage to an Irish lord her
eyes dropped out of her head, and then she was sure no lord
would have her; but she cunningly took them up again, washed
them, and put them in their places, where they fitted as well as
ever; and to prevent any further solicitations she and her maids
went to the seaside, and with her knife she cut a green turf for
each of them, instead of ships, to carry them over the channel to
Wales, where they landed at Porth-y-Capel (Trearddur Bay)
near Holyhead, where she built a chapel on top of a small bank
at her landing place, whose ruins are still there (18th century),
on the left hand as you go to Holyhead from the bridge (Four
Mile Bridge). From thence she went to Glan Conwy and built a
church called still after her name, Llansanffred (Llansantffraid,
near Conway). here she performed a miracle by taking a
handful of rushes, and throwing them into the River Conway.
They turned into fish, which to this day they call there
brwyniaid, rush fish, because they smell like rushes, which in

Welsh is brwyn. These are called in London smelts, in the country sparlings, and according to this legend, this is the original of that fish which is to be found in plenty in the River Conway.'

F. H. Glazebrook, *Anglesey and the North Wales Coast Book*

11.   *The Saints of Bardsey Island*

Saints poured in here thickly from Brittany and Ireland, building cells and churches all along both the northern and the southern shore. The first of these, and the first in all North Wales was the abbey founded on the small and stormy island of Bardsey or Enlli, at the far end of the promontory. The destruction in 622, of Bangor Iscoed, near Wrexham, one of the greatest houses in Britain, by the Saxons, sent refugees from that noted massacre flying in panic to this remote sanctuary, in such numbers as to add to the importance it had already acquired. The very reasons indeed that now make localities remote were sometimes in ancient days the cause of contrary conditions. Here, for instance, Wales extended a hospitable hand far out into a sea that had greater terrors than it has for us, and it was eagerly clutched by the wandering saints and missionaries from the west, who braved the waves in fragile craft, and were glad enough to beach them on the sandy coves of Aberdaron, and Porth Nigel, and Abersoch. And Ynys Enlli, with its monastery became, above them all, a harbour of refuge, a sanctuary, and a mother of churches, dotting the coast of West Carnarvon, both north and south, with small shrines of stone and wood or even wickerwork, to be replaced in later days by walls more durable. Still more, however, was it as a place of pilgrimage that the island abbey became celebrated. Cures of body, and mind, and soul were to be had upon this lonely storm-washed rock. Above all it was a good thing to die here, and for generations, probably for centuries, men from all parts of the west limped and crawled and dragged themselves along the rude roads of Lleyn. Every church, upon both sores, became a shelter and a refuge to the pilgrims. Their endowments were charged with the task of providing food for those who came or went.

A. G. Bradley, *Highways and By-ways of North Wales*

12. *The Isle of Saints*

The island, whose spiritual concerns are at present under the care of a single rustic, once afforded, during life, an asylum to 20,000 saints; and after death, graves to as many of their bodies: well therefore might it be called *Insula Sanctorum, The Isle of Saints.* But, with Dr *Fuller*, I must observe, that 'it would be more facile to find graves in *Bardseye* for so many saints, than saints for so many graves.' But to approach the truth; let it be said, that *Drubitius*, archbishop of *Caer-leon*, almost worn out with age, resigning his see to St *David*, retired here, and, according to the best account, died in 612; was interred on the spot; but in after times his body was removed to *Llandaff.* The slaughter ot the monks of *Bangor*, about the year 607, is supposed to have contributed to the population of this island; for not only the brethren who escaped, but numbers of other pious *Britons*, fled hither to avoid the rage of the *Saxons*.

The time in which the religious house was founded, is very uncertain; it probably was before the retreat of *Dubritius*; for something of that kind must have occasioned him to give the preference to this place. It seems likely to have been a seat of the *Culdees*, or *Colidei*, the first religious recluses of *Great Britain*; who sought islands and desert places in which they might in security worship the true God. It was certainly resorted to in very early times; for our accounts say, that it flourished as a convent in the days of *Cadwan* king of *Britain*, coeval with *Dubritius*. It was an abbey dedicated to St *Mary*.

Thomas Pennant, *Tours in Wales*

13. *The Colidei Monks*

Beyond Lleyn, there is a small island inhabited by very religious monks, called Caelibes, or Colidei. This island, either from the wholesomeness of its climate, owing to its vicinity to Ireland, or rather from some miracle obtained by the meriots of the saints, has this wonderful peculiarity, that the oldest people die first, because diseases are uncommon, and scarcely any die except from extreme old age. Its name is Enlli in the Welsh, and Berdesey in the Saxon language; and very many bodies of saints are said to be buried there, and amongst them that of Daniel, bishop of Bangor.

The archbishop having, by his sermon the next day, induced many persons to take the cross, we proceeded towards Banchor, passing through Caernarvon, that is, the castle of Arvon; it is called Arvon, the province opposite to Mon. Our road leading us to a steep valley, with many broken ascents and descents, we dismounted from our horses, and proceeded on foot, rehearsing, as it were, by agreement, some experiments of our intended pilgrimage to Jerusalem. Having traversed the valley, and reached the opposite side with considerable fatigue, the archbishop, to rest himself and recover his breath, sat down on an oak which had been torn up by the violence of the winds; and relaxing into a pleasantry highly laudable in a person of his approved gravity, thus addressed his attendants: 'Who amongst you, in this company, can now delight our wearied ears by whistling?' which is not easily done by people out of breath. He affirming that he could, if he thought fit, the sweet notes are heard, in an adjoining wood, of a bird, which some said was a wood-pecker, and others, more correctly, an aureolus. The wood-pecker is called in French, *spec*, and with its strong bill, perforates oak trees; the other bird is called aureolus, from the golden tints of its feathers, and at certain seasons utters a sweet whistling note, instead of a song. Some persons having remarked, that the nightingale was never heard in this country, the archbishop, with a significant smile, replied, 'The nightingale followed wise counsel, and never came into Wales; but we, unwise counsel, who have penetrated and gone through it.' We remained that night at Banchor.

Giraldus Cambrensis, *Itinerary Through Wales,* 1186

14.   *Ministers denounce 'The Play'*

I was in a little town of some 1,200 inhabitants, to which came a strolling company of players, with a programme of perfectly whole-some and, indeed, edifying pieces. It expected to reap a harvest of sixpences and shillings, and announced performances for four con-secutive evenings. But no sooner were the placards up than in all the seven chapels the ministers denounced 'the play' as a snare of the devil, and warned their congregations to eschew it as a step to damnation. One told an anecdote. A young man with whom he was acquainted went to the theatre, resolved to see a play; but, raising his eyes, he saw written up, 'This way to the pit'. Then, consicence-stricken, he withdrew. 'But,' said the preacher, 'every way — gallery, and stall, and box — lead alike to the bottomless pit.'

The result was that no Dissenters went, no Churchmen either, lest they should offend their 'weaker brethren' of the chapel, and the poor players departed not having pocketed enough to pay their expenses for a single night.

S. Baring-Gould, *A Book of North Wales,* 1903

VII

POETS AND
SCHOLARS

1. *Albert Davies*

Albert Davies, whose life's story may be told, as it illustrates the intellectual and especially the theological bent of the Welsh mind. This mind is speculative and disputive, and it exercises itself by choice in political and theologic fields.

Albert Davies in his early years was a collier in South Wales, a member of a Calvinistic Methodist family, and could speak no other tongue but Welsh. From boyhood his great craving was for books, and, above all, for books that treated of sacred matters. In the dinner-hour it is very general for miners, quarry-men, and labourers to argue points of divinity, and Davies became a strong controversialist against the Unitarian and Socinian notions which were gaining ground among his associates. By degrees an idea germinated in his brain that as Calvin, Wesley, Luther, and other great founders had created organisations to maintain and propagate their opinions, so, in all probability, the great Founder of Christianity had formed a corporate body to carry on His teaching unto the end of time. He had never been brought into direct contact with the Church of England, and had an inherited prejudice against it, as purely English, and as representing Saxon domination over Wales, and he could think of no Body that would answer his requirements but the Roman Church. He accordingly took up the study of its teaching and claims, and became convinced that if Christ did found a community, it must be the Catholic Church, which the Roman Body asserted itself to be; and Davies was received into that communion.

After some years, however, his confidence gave way; he found, as he thought, too much credulity, too great demands made on faith; and he took a study of the Fathers.

Then his faith gave way; he separated from the Roman Communion, and for a while was adrift in his convictions. He left the colliery in which hitherto he had worked, and wandered from place to place in bitterness of spirit, taking up occasional work here and there, unsettled in every way, spiritually as well as temporally.

After a while he settled as a quarryman at Penrhyn, and here for the first time came in contact with Anglican clergy, and found that the Church of England, while not pretending to be the whole Church, considered herself to be part and parcel of the One Body, with the sacred desposit of faith, orders, and sacraments. This gave him what he wanted, and Albert Davies now found his feet on what he thought was solid ground, and the old argumentative spirit reawoke in him, and the dinner-hour was once more the time for theological dialectics.

So years passed, and old age and ill-health crept on. The quarry work that he could do was ill-paid and precarious. He lived in chronic hunger, and often was too poor to afford himself a fire in winter; for every penny he could spare was spent in the purchase of books. He would read none but such as dealt with theology.

At length he became so ill that he had to be taken into the workhouse. He struggled against the necessity as long as he could, and then submitted, saying, 'it is God's will, and I must accept what he desires.'

In the workhouse he received better food, and comforts such as he had not been accustomed to as a poor and failing quarryman. Any little gratuity offered him he accepted to spend on his beloved books, and in time his library was by no means inconsiderable. After his death, by his express wish, they have been divided between Bangor and Beaumaris libraries.

In the workhouse he died peacefully, and content with his solitary lot. He was a man of rugged exterior, with a head and face singularly like those attributed to Socrates.

S. Baring-Gould, *A Book of North Wales,* 1903

2. *Richard Jones of Aberdaron*

Richard Jones of Aberdaron was surely the most prodigious intellectual freak that ever came out of Wales . . . He had certainly the gift of tongues, and a mania for acquiring them under discouraging circumstances, developed to a degree that gives him a place to himself among village prodigies. He was the son of an illiterate carpenter, and the descendant of generations of rude Lleyn peasants. It is more than likely none of his ancestors could even read or write.

But Dick himself died at sixty, the master, more or less, of thirty-five languages, as it is said. Let us for safety's sake reduce the number by one-half, and at the same time remark that he also died as he had lived, a frowsy, dirty peasant, or worse than a peasant: a loafer rather and a stroller, filthy in person, part mendicant part medicine man: one quarter idiot, three quarters genius: the owner of an abnormal brain, if ever there was one. But where did the craving for strange tongues and the capacity for acquiring them come from? The query might well give a physiologist some food for serious contemplation.

Dick fell foul of his parents, or they rather of him, at a tender age. He had no schooling, but hung about the village schoolroom, and by the help of books he found lying about there, and of good-natured boys who had mastered the art, he learned to read in Welsh. Soon afterwards, by the same laborious methods, he acquired English. At twenty he was still a hopeless failure at his father's trade, till, tired of being cursed and beaten, he left Lleyn, and wandered to Bangor and thence to Liverpool. When he came across an Italian or a German pedlar it was his habit to stick to him till he had learned anough of his language to form a basis for future study. It was not, however, the art of conversation in foreign tongues, dead or living, that Dick so much sought after, though even in this he appears to have been glib enough, but grammars and dictionaries were his especial joy. Hebrew he learned from tattered books that chance threw in his way. Latin and Greek he mastered with equal facility and by the same means. French, Russian, Scandinavian, all came in course of time to this road-side, tramp scholar. Patrons in plenty such a man found: bishops, clergymen, and tradesmen. They gave him work in their gardens or stables which he never did, and lent him grammars and dictionaries over which he pored with pen, ink, and paper. He was too filthy in person for the inside of a decent house, and so bizarre in appearance that he was the butt of street boys through his whole long life. He would neither work nor wash. There are plenty of pictures of him extant which show a face and head covered with bushy black hair, from which peered two bright beady eyes. His dress was rugged and uncouth, and he carried his precious library concealed about his person, which gave the latter an inflated and abnormal appearance. The way in which he clung to his books in periods of penury and semi-starvation gives much pathos to a narrative that is otherwise uncanny and unnatural. He had no ambition, except to acquire fresh languages, no thought for the morrow, no regard for money, scarcely

any even for food. At one time he developed a tendency for more pronounced posing, adopting a cast-off blue and silver cavalry jacket as a
dress and a cap of hare's skin with the ears sticking up as a head-gear.
From the ears hung pieces of cloth, on which were inscribed sentences
in Greek and Hebrew, and thus attired he would drone out the song
of Moses in Hebrew to astonished audiences in Welsh village streets.
He carried a ram's horn too, slung round him, and blew upon it lusty
blasts at the most inappropriate times.

Dick was a famous character throughout all North Wales, and he
wandered once as far as Dover, and was for some time in London. He
never begged, nor drank. Hunger compelled him occasionally to
work, but he seemed to think that the public ought to supply his
simple wants, and indeed they did so, after a fashion. His linguistic
accomplishments were useless for any practical purpose. It was the
construction of language — its roots and grammar that fascinated
him. Nor had he the least desire for the information conveyed in their
literature. He was a thorough philologist and scholar of the old
school was Dick in this respect, but his facility was as great as his
ardour. A learned don from Oxford who once sought an interview
with him in Wales put him on to construe Homer, carefully keeping
the breadth of the table between himself and the frowsy bundle of
rags that represented the poor student. Dick, however, proved
himself quite equal to the doctor's tests, but with the unconscious
enthusiasm of a scholar and a purist waxed contemptuously
indignant when his reverend examiner began to question him
regarding the personality of the heroes in the Iliad and touched upon
the story therein contained. Had any one been found to wash and
dress Dick of Aberdaron, and send him to the University, there is no
doubt that it is to the Cambridge of his day that he should have gone!
Though Dick was first and chiefly, according to his rude lights, a
scholar, contemporary authorities entitled to credence declare that he
could speak fourteen languages fluently. He would never ask charity,
though he both expected and accepted it, and had been reduced for
some years before his death to telling fortunes. He was buried in St
Asaph churchyard.

A. G. Bradley, *Highways and By-ways of North Wales,* 1898

3. *Friar's School*

There is also an ancient grammar school (now reconstructed), founded in the 16th century, on the site of a convent of White Friars, and of some repute in bye-gone Wales, and known as the 'Friars' School'. Some of the instructions issued to its masters in the time of Queen Elizabeth give a glimpse of higher education as then known in Wales. 'They shall instruct their scholars,' so runs the ancient ordinance, 'in good nurture and civil manners, as with good literature, with exercise, to speak Latin and other honest discipline. They shall watch the poorest man's child as the richest without partiality. Nor shall any scholars be so hardy as to come to school with his head unkempt, his hands or face unwashed, his shoes unclean, his cap, hosen or vesture, filthy or rent. They *shall use to speak Latin* as well without ye school as within.' The manner in which 'pronunciation and utterance' and 'accent' are insisted on, speaks significantly of the ousting of Welsh as a polite language. Fridays were to be given up to epigrams and verse, while the ordained amusements were cross-bow and running base. The master, moreover, was cautioned 'to use such mildness of countenance and gentleness of speech that he may inflame the dullard, if any such there be, to study.'

S. Baring-Gould, *A Book of North Wales*

4. ACROSTIC

A nne Beauteous nymph ye subject of my Lay
N o Common muse can undertake thy praise
N o not if we conjoined ye Tuneful nine
E ven Cibber could not sing a worth like thine.
L et Maidens Learn thy airs and noble graces
A Beauty far beyond their ugly faces
N ot Helen fam'd in History of old
G reat Venus self could never Look so bold
F -rt for all beauty but what's in thy Eyes
O Lord! how they bewitch us by surprise.
R eader beware Lest you this angel meet
D ull are those blockheads that don't think her sweet.

(Anne Langford was the daughter of the Rev. Simon Langford, M.A., vicar of Rhoscolyn, 1709-1737, and of Holyhead, 1737-1740).

Lewis Morris, *Life and Works,* 1748

5.   *Lewis Morris*

Lewis Morris was born at a place called Tref y Beirdd, in Anglesey, in the year 1700. Anglesey, or Mona, has given birth to many illustrious men, but few, upon the whole, entitled to more honourable mention than himself. From a humble situation in life, for he served an apprenticeship to a cooper at Holyhead, he raised himself by his industry and talents to affluence and distinction, became a landed proprietor in the county of Cardigan, and inspector of the royal domains and mines in Wales. Perhaps a man more generally accomplished never existed; he was a first rate mechanic, an expert navigator, a great musician, both in theory and practice, and a poet of singular excellence. Of him it was said, and with truth, that he could build a ship and sail it, frame a harp and make it speak, write an ode and set it to music. Yet that saying, eulogistic as it is, is far from expressing all the vast powers and acquirements of Lewis Morris. Though self-taught, he was confessedly the best Welsh scholar of his age, and was well-versed in those cognate dialects of the Welsh — the Cornish, Armoric, Highland Gaelic and Irish. He was likewise well acquainted with Hebrew, Greek and Latin, had studied Anglo-Saxon with some success, and was a writer of bold and vigorous English. He was besides a good general antiquary, and for knowledge of ancient Welsh customs, traditions and superstitions had no equal.

George Borrow, *Wild Wales,* 1854

6.   *Suggested Studies of Lewis Morris*

Enquiries to be made by some Ingenious Inhabitant in every Parish, In relation to the natural History, Present state and antiquity thereof.

1. What is the Tradition about the Saint or Founder of the Church? what day the wakes is kept, and if Fairs and Markets. Names of Ruins of Old Churches or Chapels in the parish.

2. What Lands belong to the Church towards its repairs, and what Land and Money to the poor. What Free Schools, Hospitals etc. and by whom founded.

3. Number of Houses, and Inhabitants, distinguished into Males and Females.

4. An account of the most ancient people, Their ages, How Long married and other Circumstances. Of the Distempers most Incident, Food etc., Names common.

5. What monstrous Births happened (the same in Brutes, etc.) and what marks from the mother's Fright. Large Bodies found in Graves, etc.

6. What ancient Superstition, Omens, *Swynion, Coelion*, Remains of Druidism is found among them and what their charms or Lessons are.

7. What Fairy circles, and places reported to have been frequented by Fairies or Haunted by some such Apparitions, Spirits, Devils, Hobgoblins, etc.

8. What Hidden Treasures said to have been discovered by means of these, or by dreams, and where it is said there are some still undiscovered until the D. . .l pleases.

9. What Birds frequent the place by Sea or Land, and their names among the Country people; who hath found the Swallow and Cuckoo's Lodging in the winter? What other Animals, Quadrupeds, by Land or Water or both?

Insects. Serpents such as the water viper, adder etc.

Of the distemper of Cattle, and the Country Cures.

10. What Rivers and their country names? What Fish? and if Bordering upon the Sea, what sea fish and names?

11. What Plants or Herbs? and if noted for particular virtues of uses, what? and their Ancient or Country names? what manures for ground?

12. What medicinal springs or wells, to what Saint dedicated. What distempers they cure? Whether by bathing or drinking? What effect the water hath upon them by Purging, Sweating, etc. What charms or *swynion* used along with the water of in Bottling of it. Whether any of them are Perennial.

13. What Stones and Fossils said to be of use in medicines? What Freestone, what Marble, Black, Gray or White, Slated, Crystalled, or any other valuable stones. Ores of Lead or Copper, or supposed to be such; whether found in Ploughed ground or in a Rock.

What Ochres or Earth for Painting, Yellow, Red, etc.? what fine Red or Blue clays and fine Inland Sands?

What Coals and other Materials for Firing, Bogturf, Peat and Subterranean trees and whether Sulphurous or Resinous.

14. Gentlemen's Seats, old and new names, with noted names of

Farms of Tenements, as are compounded of Bôd, Tre, Caer, Llan, Din, Llys, etc. also the names of Hills that seem old.

15. What Roman Urns, Roman or Saxon Coins, Bullion, Weapons as Flint or Brass axes and arrows, have been discovered and by whom. What Snake Stones or *Glain Neidr*, in whose custody, and the tradition, how made and supposed virtues.

16. What Tumulis commonly called Tommen (Large Mounts) whether opened, what found therein? What other remains of antiquity, such as Coeten Arthur, Cromlech, Meini, Cyttiau Gwyddelod, Barclodiad y widdon, Carnedd, Carn, Ruins of old Towns, old Forts, Dinas or Din, Gwerthyr, Great ditches cast up, Fields of Battle.

Graves of great men in the High road or Elsewhere, Llysoedd or palaces of Princes, Beacons or arwydd eithin, and by what names called by the natives with the Traditions etc.

17. What Ancient Manuscripts on Vellum or Paper, and in what hands? and what ancient British books printed abroad and scarce in Great Britain, such as Dr Roberts Grammar 1st and second col.

18. What Inscriptions upon Stones in Churches and other places, and who they are said to belong to?

19. What Fiery meteors, corpse candles, Rainbow Inverted, night Rainbow, have been seen; and when.

20. What strange appearance of the Heavenly bodies, as 3 Imaginary Suns, etc. and enquire particularly into the names of Stars or of Constellations of Stars, such as *Twrr Tewdws*, cogail y forwyn, etc.

These are the most material Heads (that I can think of at present) that may be serviceable towards making an exact Map, and compiling a Natural History, Present State and Antiquities of a country; Being such a plain method that even persons who never applied themselves to these studies, may be of considerable assistance therein, to direct the compiler to such and such articles.

It will also give gentlemen the Opportunity of having the Curiosities and Antiquities upon their Estates Perpetuated, which otherwise may possibly slip our enquiries.

By such a method as this (which I don't find that anybody ever yet took) a complete Map and History of Anglesey may be had; and also considering the method I would propose to fill up the Outlines of the said Island (already surveyed for the Admiralty) which is, by surveying every River from its mouth to its spring head, and of all the

Roads and by-ways in the County, Boundaries of Parishes and Commote.

Nothing of the Least moment in Antiquity or Natural History can escape our Observation; The Map to be on such a Large Scale, that a mile will take up above Two Inches.

Lewis Morris, *Notebook of Suggested Studies*

7.   *Robin Ddu*

From Vaynol we proceed to the Pwlth bridge, with Bryntirion, the seat of Thomas Jones, Esqr, on our right. In a dingle, through which the stream finds its way to the Menai, on a rock facing the road once stood Ysgubor Robin Ddu, or the abode of Robin the Black, who lived some centuries past, and was, it appears, a prophet. He verified his pretensions to the character by his death. An elder tree near the place is said to be the identical tree on which he foretold that he should be hanged and where for the credit of his function he was hanged. Some refiners, indeed, who dive deeply into human nature, suspect that poor Robin hanged himself to get him and his prophecies a name, as Lycurgus, the great legislator of savageism, cheated his countrymen into an observance of his laws by his absence and death. Absurdities of this kind are scarcely exceeded by the story of Admiral Byng's settling an annuity upon a man to be shot for him. Another of Robin's prophecies was that Bangor Cathedral should stand upon an island, a thing which the nature of the country renders of easy accomplishment by the cutting of a canal along the deep and level valley in which it stands. For many years his credit in Caernarvonshire is said to have been as great as that of the idiot Nixon is in Cheshire, who, if half which I have heard of him in that county be true, was certainly no ordinary fool.

E. Hyde Hall, *A Description of Caernarvonshire*

8.   *A Genuine Anglesey Poet*

'The Red Bard has said that Mona is never to be without a poet — but where am I to find one? Just before I saw you I was wishing to see a poet; I would willingly give a quart of ale to see a genuine Anglesey poet.'

'You would, sir, would you?' said the man in grey, lifting his head on high, and curling his upper lip.

'I would, indeed,' said I, 'my greatest desire at present is to see an Anglesey poet, but where am I to find one?'

'Where is he to find one?' said he of the tattered hat; 'where's the gwr boneddig to find a prydydd? No occasion to go far, he, he, he.'

'Well,' said I, 'but where is he?'

'Where is he? why there,' said he pointing to the man in grey — 'the greatest prydydd in sir Fôn or the whole world.'

'Tut, tut, hold your tongue,' said the man in grey.

'Hold my tongue, myn Diawl, not I — I speak the truth,' then filling his glass he emptied it exclaiming, 'I'll not hold my tongue. The greatest prydydd in the whole world.'

'Then I have the honour to be seated with a bard of Anglesey?' said I, addressing the man in grey.

'Tut, tut,' said he of the grey suit.

'The greatest prydydd in the whole world,' iterated he of the bulged shoe, with a slight hiccup, as he again filled his glass.

'Then,' said I, 'I am truly fortunate.'

'Sir,' said the man in grey, 'I had no intention of discovering myself, but as my friend here has betrayed my secret, I confess that I am a bard of Anglesey — my friend is an excellent individual but indiscreet, highly indiscreet, as I have frequently told him,' and here he looked most benignantly reproachful at him of the tattered hat.

'The greatest prydydd,' said the latter, 'the greatest prydydd that—' and leaving his sentence incomplete he drank off the ale which he had poured into his glass.

George Borrow, *Wild Wales*, 1854

9. *The Shelleys in Wales*

Mr S. promised you a recital of the horrible events that caused us to leave Wales. I have undertaken the task, as I wish to spare him, in the present nervous state of his health, everything that can recall to his mind the horrors of that night, which I will relate. On Friday night, the 26th February, we retired to bed between ten and eleven o'clock. We had been in bed about half an hour, when Mr S. heard a noise proceeding from one of the parlours. He immediately went down stairs with two pistols, which he had loaded that night, expecting to have occasion for them. He went into the billiard room, where he heard footsteps retreating. He followed into an another little room, which was called an office. He there saw a man in the act of quitting the room through a glass window which opens into the shrubbery. The man fired at Mr S., which he avoided. Bysshe then fired, but it flashed in the pan. The man then knocked Bysshe down, and they struggled on the ground. Bysshe then fired his second pitol, which he thought wounded him in the shoulder, as he uttered a shriek and got up, when he said these words: By God I will be revenged. I will murder your wife. I will ravish your sister. By God I will be revenged. He then fled — as we hoped for the night. Our servants were not gone to bed, but were just going, when this horrible affair happened. This was about eleven o'clock. We all assembled in the parlour, where we remained for two hours. Mr S. then advised us to retire, thinking it impossible he would make a second attack.

We left Bysshe and our manservant, who had only arrived that day, and who knew nothing of the house, to sit up. I had been in bed three hours when I heard a pistol go off. I immediately ran downstairs, when I perceived that Bysshe's flannel gown had been shot through, and the window curtain. Bysshe had sent Daniel to see what hour it was, when he heard a noise at the window. He went there, and a man thrust his arm through the glass and fired at him. Thank heaven! the ball went through his gown and he remained unhurt, Mr S. happened to stand sideways; had he stood fronting, the ball must have killed him. Bysshe fired his pitol, but it would not go off. He then aimed a blow at him with an old sword which we found in the house. The assassin attempted to get the sword from him, and just as he was pulling it away Dan rushed into the room, when he made his escape.

This was at four in the morning. It had been a most dreadful night; the wind was as loud as thunder, and the rain descended in torrents. Nothing has been heard of him; and we have every reason to believe it was no stranger, as there is a man of the name of Leson, who the next morning that it happened went and told the shopkeepers of Tremadoc that it was a tale of Mr Shelley's to impose upon them, that he might leave the country without paying his bills. This they believed, and none of them attempted to do anything towards his discovery. We left Tanyrallt on Saturday, and stayed till everything was ready for our leaving the place, at the Sol. General of the county's house, who lived seven miles from us.

This Mr Leson had been heard to say that he was determined to drive us out of the country. He once happened to get hold of a little pamphlet which Mr S. had printed in Dublin; this he sent up to Government. In fact, he was forever saying something against us, and that because we were determined not to admit him to our house, because we had heard his character and from many acts of his we found he was malignant and cruel to the greatest degree.

The pleasure we experience at reading your letter you may conceive, at the time when everyone seemed to be plotting against us. When those whom we had (. . . *manuscript torn* . . .) the horrible suspicion (. . .) from the task when called upon in a moment like that. Pardon me if I wound your feelings by dwelling on this subject. Your conduct has made a deep impression on our minds, which no length of times can erase. Would that all mankind were like thee.

Harriet Shelley, *Letter*

VIII

THE LEADERS

1. *The Kings and Princes of North Wales*

About the middle of the fifth century Caswallon Law Hir (Longimanus, or the Long-handed), grandson of Cynetha Weledig, king of the Cumbrian or Strath-Clwydian Britons, is described to have arrived, either as a voluntary adventurer or a fugitive, in North Wales, of which, after overthrowing some bands of Irish marauders in a great contest, he assumed the sovereignty. His son, Maelgwn Gwynedd, was for his further services distinguished by the title of king of that country, which continued to be the style of the three next princes of his house, Rhun, Beli, Iago, when Cadvan, the fourth in descent from him, was elected King of All Britain. In him, in his son Cadwallon, and in his grandson Cadwalader, this great title rather than possession abided with a continually diminishing splendour until the year 703, when it was finally relinquished by the family as too bulky for the fortunes of this race. The following table will show the series of the North Welsh kings and princes, the miseries of their own condition, and the almost uninterrupted butchery of their subjects:

Names		Year of death	Fate	Enemies with which they were engaged
Son of Cadwalader	Ydwal Ywrch, an exile	720	died	Saxons
	Roderic Moelwyniog	755	died	Saxons and Picts
	Cynan Tyndaethwy	817	died	Saxons, Danes & Civil Wars
Daughter of Cynan, married King of Man	Esyllt Merfyn Frych	843	killed	By the Saxons at a place on the frontiers called Kettil
	Roderic* the Great	877	killed	By Saxons, and harassed by the Danes

	Anarawd	913	died	Civil wars, Saxon, Danes
	Ydwal Foel	940	killed	Irish, Saxons
An usurper Howel Dda (the Good)	948		died	Saxons
Second & third sons of Ydwal Foel	Iefaf & Iago	969 972	de-throned banished	Dreadful civil wars, Saxons, Irish
	Howel ap Iefa	984	killed	Civil wars, Danes English
	Cadwallon ap Iefaf	985	killed	Civil war
Of South Wales	Meredyth	986	ex-pelled	Danes
Anarchy. The true heir descended from Ydwal Foel in 992	Ydwal	933	killed	By Danes; civil wars
Anarchy. Usurper; began to reign in 1003	Aedan ap Blegored	1015	killed	In civil war
Of S. Wales an usurper	Llewelyn ap Seitsyllt	1021	mur-dered	Civil wars
The true heir	Iago ap Ydwal	1037	killed	In civil war
	Gryffith ap Llewelyn	1064	mur-dered	English, Danes, civil war
Brothers and usurp-ers	Bleddyn and Rhiwallon	1073 1068	mur-dered killed	Normans and civil wars
Usurper	Trahaern	1079	killed	At Carno in civil war
True heir	Griffyth ap Cynan	1137	died	Normans and civil war
	Owen Gwynedd	1149		Normans and civil war

Usurper	Howel	1169	killed	Civil war
Second son of O. Gwynedd	David	1194	de-posed	Civil war
The true heir	Llewelyn ap Yorwerth	1240		Civil wars, Anglo-Normans
Second son of Llewelyn	David	1246	died	Civil wars, Anglo-Normans
The true heirs	Owen	1254	deposed	Civil wars
	Llewelyn	1282	killed	At Builth by Anglo-Normans
	David	1283	executed	At Shrewsbury

*He divided his dominions into three parts, Gwynedd, or North Wales; South Wales; and Powis Land, a division productive of lasting and horrible evils.

E. Hyde Hall, *A Description of Caernarvonshire*

2. CARADOC

Have ye seen the tusky boar,
Or the bull, with sullen roar,
On surrounding foes advance?
So Caradoc bore his lance.

Thomas Gray

3. *The Field of Slaughter*

Just above Coytmor bridge by the turnpike the road to Caernarvon along the foot of the hills, branches off, and across it there again goes a mountain road, which, after traversing a considerable space of cultivated ground, enters a large turbary, which at the time of carrying the turf exhibits a lively scene of carriages, horses and men. At other seasons it is desolate and cheerless, and is known, as I am informed, by the name of the Field of Slaughter or of Lamentation. Over the public road, where the second inclined plane is built, hang the remains of an ancient British fortress, which still retains the title of Dinas or Fort. It appears to have covered about an acre of ground, and adapting itself to the form of the hill, to have formed a post of strength commanding the entrance of Nantfranken, and communicating with the general line of forts. Two concentric rows of gigantic stones with the intermediate space filled with earth constitute the rampart, which is stated to have been twenty feet high; but at present the foundation alone remains. The stones seem in some places to have suffered the action of fire, a circumstance of easy explanation, as to burn out an enemy was a common contrivance.

Upon this spot, as upon some others, conjecture has perched in order to make it the scene of Caractacus's overthrow by Ortorius Scapula.

E. Hyde Hall, *A Description of Caernarvonshire*

4. *Caractacus*

The fearless appearance of the Britons, and the spirit which animated their whole army, struck Ostorius with astonishment. He saw a river to be crossed, a palisade to be forced, a steep hill to be surmounted, and every post defended by a great multitude, but the Roman soldiers burned with impatience for the attack. The signal was given. The river was passed with little difficulty. The struggle at the palisade was obstinate, but at last the Britons were forced to give way and fled to the ridge of their hills. The Romans pursued eagerly. Not only the light troops, but even the legionary soldiers, forced their way to the summit of the hills after a heavy shower of darts. The Britons, having neither breastplates nor helmets, could not maintain the conflict. The legions bore down all before them. The victory was decisive. The wife and daughter of Caractacus were taken prisoners. His brother surrendered at discretion. Caractacus fled for protection to Cartismandua, Queen of the Brigantes.

But adversity has no friends, and by that princess he was loaded with irons and delivered up to the conquerors. Caractacus had waged war with the Romans for the last nine years. His fame was not confined to his native island: it passed into the provinces and spread all over Italy. Curiosity was eager to behold the heroic chieftain. Even at Rome the name of Caractacus was in high celebrity. The Emperor, willing to magnify the glory of the conquest, bestowed the highest praise on the valour of the vanquished king. He assembled the people to behold a spectacle worthy of their view. In a field before the camp the pretorian bands were drawn up at arms. The followers of the British chief walked in procession. The wife of Caractacus, his daughter, his brother followed next: he himself closed the melancholy train. The other prisoners, filled with terror, descended to mean and abject supplications. Caractacus alone was superior to misfortune. With a countenance still unaltered, not a sign of fear appearing, no sorrow, no condescension, he behaved with dignity even in ruin. Being placed before the tribunal he spoke in the following manner: 'If to the nobility of my birth, and the splendour of exalted station, I had added the virtue of moderation, Rome would have beheld me, not as a captive, but as a royal visitor and friend. The alliance of a prince descended from a line of illustrious ancestors, a prince whose rule extended over many nations, would not have been unworthy of your choice. A reverse of fortune is now my lot. To you the event is glorious, to me humiliating. I had arms and men and horses; I had abundant wealth; can you wonder that I am unwilling to lose them? Ambitious Rome aspires to universal dominion: must all mankind, therefore, bend their necks to the yoke? I stood at bay for years: had I acted otherwise where would have been your glory of conquest? Where would have been my honour of a brave resistance? I am now in your power. If you are bent on vengeance, carry out your purpose; the bloody scene will soon be over, and the name of Caractacus will sink into oblivion. If you preserve my life, I shall be to late posterity a monument of Roman clemency.' Claudius granted him a free pardon, and the same to his wife, his daughter, and his brother.

Tacitus, *Annals, Book XIV*

5. *Paulinus Suetonius*

Paulinus Suetonius succeeded to the command. He was an officer of distinguished merit. His military talents made him ambitious, and the voice of the people, who never leave exalted merit without a rival, roused him to the highest eminence. By subduing the rebellious spirit of the Britons he hoped to equal the brilliant success of Corbulo in Armenia. With this in view he determined that he would subdue the island of Mona (Anglesey), a place inhabited by a warlike people, and a common refuge for all the discontented Britons. In order to facilitate his approach to a difficult and treacherous shore, he ordered a number of flat-bottomed boats to be built. In these he carried over the infantry, while the cavalry, partly by fording the shallows and partly by letting their horses swim, advanced to gain a footing on the island.

On the opposite shore stood the Britons closely drawn up and prepared for action. Women were seen rushing through the ranks in wild disorder, their dress funereal, their hair loose to the wind, flaming torches in their hands, and their whole appearance resembling the frantic rage of the Furies. The Druids were ranged in order, with hands uplifted, invoking the gods, and pouring forth horrible imprecations. The strangeness of the sight struck the Romans with awe and terror. They stood in stupid amazement, as if their limbs were paralysed, riveted to one spot, a mark for the enemy. The exhortations of the general soon diffused new life through the ranks, and by mutual reproaches the men incited each other to deeds of valour. They felt the disgrace of yielding to a troop of women and a band of fanatic priests. They advanced their standards and attacked with impetuous fury. The Britons perished in the flames which they themselves had kindled. The island fell, and a garrison was established to keep it in subjection. The religious groves, dedicated to superstitious and barbarous rites, were cut down. In these fastnesses the Britons bathed their altars with the blood of their prisoners, and, in the entrails of men sought to find the will of the gods. While Suetonius was employed in making his arrangemments to secure the island, he received intelligence that Britain had revolted, and that the whole province was up in arms.

Ibid.

6.   The Great Army's Field

Now in that place where it is traditionally reported these Romans landed, about a bow-shot from the waterside, is a large field called to this Maes Mawr Gad, or as some call it, *Maes Hir Gad*, viz. 'The great or the long army's field'; from which to the shore of the river *Menai* there yet appear some remains of little works and entrenchments. A little to the East of that, just on the shore, there is a place called the *Rhiedd*, i.e. *Nobilium statio*, 'the chief men's post'; on which place the other day were taken up from under a stone near the sea-shore a parcel of British weapons, a sort those *jacula amentata*, or such like (as appears probable from their loop-holes and sockets) in use among the ancients.

Henry Rowlands, *Mona Antiqua Restaurata*

7. *Cyngen and the Pagans*

Eight hundred and fifty was the year of Christ, and Cyngen was strangled by the Pagans.

853. And three years after that, Mona (Anglesey) was ravaged by the black Pagans. (Danes)

Brut y Tywysogion

8. *The King's Hunt*

The prince had his *Pencynydd*, or chief huntsman. He was the tenth officer of the court. He had for his own supper one dish of meat; and after it, three horns of mead, one from the king, another from the queen,. the third from the steward of the household. He was never to swear, but by his orn and his leash. He had the third of the fines and heriots of all the other huntsmen; and likewise the same share of the *amobr*, on the marriage of any of their daughters. At a certain time of the year, he was to hunt for the king only: at other seasons, he was permitted to hunt for himself. His horn was that of an ox, of a pound value. He had in winter an ox's hide, to make leashes; in summer, a cow's, to cut into spatterdashes.

The king had liberty of hunting wheresoever he pleased; but if a beast was hunted and killed on any gentleman's estate, and not followed and claimed by the huntsman that night, the owner of the land might convert it to his own use; but was to take good care of the dogs, and preserve the skin.

The penalty of killing a tame stag of the king's, was a pound; and a certain fine: if it was a wild one, if it was killed between a certain day in *November*, and the feast of *St John*, the value was sixty pence; but the fine for killing it, a hundred and eighty pence. A stag was also reckoned equivalent to an ox; a hind to a well-grown cow; a roe to a goat; a wild sow to a tame sow; a badger had no value, because in some years it was measled; wolves and foxes, and other noxious animals, had no value, because every body was allowed to kill them; and there was none set upon a hare, for a very singular reason, because it was believed every other month to change its sex.

Thomas Pennant, *Tours in Wales,* 1784

9.   *The Chase*

The Welsh had several animals, which were the objects of the chase; such as, *y Carw*, or the stag; *Haid Wenyn*, a swarm of bees; and y *Gleisiad*, or a salmon. *Yr Arth*, the bear; y *Dring-hedydd,* climbing animals, I suppose wild cats, martens, and squirrels; and *Ceiliog Coed*, or cock of the wood. And the last division was, *y Llwynog*, the fox; *Ysgyfarnog*, the hare; and *yr Ywrch*, the roe. Some of the above come very improperly under our idea of hunting, yet were comprehended in the code of laws relative to the diversion, formed, as is supposed, by *Gryffyd ap Cyann.*

I suspect also, that the otter was an object of diversion; there being a *Cylch Dyfrgwn*, or an annual payment, by the *Welsh*, for the prince's water dogs.

The three first were *Helfa Gyffredin*, or the common hunt. The stag, because he was the noblest animal of chase; and because everybody, who came by at his death, before he was skinned, might claim a share in him. The next animals were, *Helfa Gyfarthfa*, or the animals which could be brought to bay, such as the bear, etc. which were hunted with hounds till they ascended a tree. The bird mentioned here, is the cock of the wood, whose nature it is to sit perched on a bough, where they will gaze till they are shot, as they were, in old times, by the bow, or crossbow.

The third division was *Helfa Ddolef*, or the shouting chase, because attended by the clamour of the sportsmen; and comprehended the fox, the hare, and the roe. The method of hunting was either with hounds, or greyhounds, which they let slip at the animals, holding the dogs in leashes. No one was to slip his greyhound when the hounds were in chase, unless he had a hound in the pack, on penalty of having the greyhound hamstrung; neither was it allowed to kill any animal of chase on its form, or at rest, on pain of forfeiting his bow and arrow to the lord of the manor. When several greyhounds, the property of different persons, were slipped at any animal, the person whose dog was nearest the beast, when last in fight, claimed the skin. A bitch was excepted, unless it was proven she was pregnant by a dog which had before won a skin.

Every person who carried a horn, must give a scientifical account of the nine objects of chase, or else he will be looked on as a pretender, and forfeit his horn. The same penalty attends the *Cynllafan*, or leash; he is never again to wear it round his middle, on pain of forfeiture; but then he is suffered to wear it round his arm.

The ancient *Welsh* held the flesh of the stag, hare, wild boar, and the bear, to be the greatest delicacies among the beasts of chase.

Thomas Pennant, *Tours in Wales*

10.   CONAN

Conan's name, my lay, rehearse,
Build to him the lofty verse,
Sacred tribute of the bard,
Verse, the hero's sole reward.
As the flame's devouring force;
As the whirlwind in its course;
As the thunder's fiery stroke,
Glancing on the shiver'd oak;
Did the sword of Conan mow
The crimson harvest of the foe.

Thomas Gray

11.   *The Youth of Gryffydd ap Cynan*

Gryffydd, as a boy, was well-mannered and gently reared. As he grew older his mother, in whose house and amongst whose kin he lived, daily talked to him about his father, telling who and what manner of man he was, what lands he had inherited, what kingdom he had ruled, and what oppressors now dwelt in it. When he heard these things depression overwhelmed him and he was sad for many days. Then he went to the court of King Murchad and lamented to him chiefly, but also to the other kings of Ireland, that an alien race was lording it over his father's kingdom, and he jestingly besought them to help him in the effort to revcover his inheritance. And the, pitying him, promised to help him at an opportune season. When he heard the answer he was glad and gave thanks to God and to them. And forthwith he went on board a vessel, spread the sails to the breeze, and, crossing the sea towards Wales, found harbour in Abermenai. At the time Trahaearn, son of Caradog, and Cenwric, the son of Thiwallon, were, in spite of truth and right, ruling as kings over Powys and the whole of Gwynedd, which they had shared between them.

Then Gruffydd sent envoys to the men of Anglesey and Arvon, and to the three sons of Merwyd of Lleyn (Asser, Meirion, and Gwgan) and to other noblemen, asking them to come to him in haste. And before long they arrived, greeted him heartily, and told him that he was welcome. Then he besought them with all his might to help him to recover his patrimony (because he was their liege lord), and to take up arms with him bravely to drive out the strangers who had usurped dominion over them . . . After the meeting was over and the council dispersed, he betook himself to the sea again, sailing towards Rhuddlan. Robert, the lord of the castle there, nephew to Hugh, Earl of Chester, was a baron famous, bold, and powerful, and to him Gryffydd prayed for help against the enemies who were in possession of his patrimony . . .

. . . Gryffydd went on board his vessel and returned to Abermenai. Thence he sent a force . . . against King Cenwric, their oppressor. Departing stealthily, they surprised and slew him with many of his men . . . Returning in triumph to Gryffydd, they urged him to follow up his good fortune, and attack Anglesey and Arvon and Lleyn, and the cantrefs of Meirionydd where Trahaearn, his other oppressor, was. The armies met in a narrow valley called in Welsh Gwaet Erw or the Bloody Land, because of the battle there fought, and God gave Gryffydd the victory over his enemies that day, many thousands of them being slain, and the woeful Trahaearn himself hardly escaping with a few of his men. For this cause, Gryffydd was, from that day forth, raised to honour and rightly called King of Gwynedd.

Hanes Gruffydd ap Cynan

12. *Escape of Gryffydd ap Cynan from Prison,* 1094(?)

A young man of Edeyrnion named Cenwric Hir came to Chester with a few companions to buy what they needed. And when he saw Gryffydd shackled in an open place, in the afternoon while the citizens were feeding, he took him on his back, and with his companions bore him to his own house, where he sustained him secretly for a few days. When Gryffydd had grown strong again, Cenwric led him by night to Anglesey.

Ibid.

13. *Invasion of Mona,* 1098

The ensuing year (1098) the French, for the third time, assembled their troops against Gwynedd, conducted by the two leaders, Hugh the Fat and Hugh, Earl of Shrewsbury, as chiefs over them, and they encamped against the Isle of Mona, in the place called Aber Lliennog, where they built a castle. And the Britons having retreated to their strongest places according to their custom, agreed in council to save Mona. And they invited to their defence a fleet that was at sea from Ireland, which had accepted gifts and rewards from the French. And then Cadwgan ap Bleddyn and Gryffydd ap Cynan left the Isle of Mona, and retreated into Ireland, for fear of the treachery of their own men. And then the French entered the island and killed some of the men of the island. And whilst they tarried there, Magnus, King of Germany, came, accompanied by some of his ships, as far as Mona, hoping to be able to take possession of the lands of the Britons. And when King Magnus heard of the frequent designs of the French to devastate the whole country and to reduce it to nothing, he hastened to attack them. And as they were mutually shooting, the one party from the sea and the other party from the land, Earl Hugh* was wounded in the face by the hand of the king himself.

And then King Magnus, with sudden determination, left the borders of the country. So the French reduced all, great and small, to be Saxons. And when the Gwyneddians could not bear the law and judgements and violence of the French over them, they rose up a second time against them, having as their commander Owain ap Edwin,** the man who had originally brought the French into Mona.

* This is Hugh, Earl of Shrewsbury. The arrow pierced the eye, and he fell into the water, his body being recovered only when the tide went down.

** J. E. Lloyd says that Owain and his brother Uchtryd were probably tenants of Hugh of Chester in Tegingl. They had guided the two earls to the shores of the Menai Straits.

1099. The year after that, Cadwgan ap Bleddyn and Gryffydd ap Cynan returned from Ireland. And after they had made peace with the French, they retained part of the country: Cadwgan ap Bleddyn took Ceredigion and a part of Powys, and Gryffydd obtained Mona.

Brut y Tywysogion

14. *The Three Kingdoms of Wales*

Wales was in ancient times divided into three parts nearly equal, consideration having been paid more to the value than to the exact quantity or proportion of territory. They were Venedotia (Gwynedd, now called North Wales); Demetia, or South Wales, which in Welsh is called Deheubarth, that is the southern part; and Powys, the middle or eastern district. Roderic the Great, or Rhodri Maur, who was King of all Wales, was the cause of this division. He had three sons, Mervin, Anarawt, and Cadell, among whom he partitioned the whole principality. North Wales fell to the lot of Mervin, Powys to Anarawt, and Cadell received the portion of South Wales, together with the general good wishes of his brothers and the people, for although this district greatly exceeded the others in quantity, it was the least desirable from the number of noble chiefs, or Uchelwyr, men of superior rank, who inhabited it, and were often rebellious to their lords, and impatient of control . . .

Giraldus Cambrensis, *The Itinery and Description of Wales*

15. *Hospital of St John of Jerusalem*

Descend for two or three miles, and reach the village of *Yspytty Jevan*, or the hospital of St John of Jerusalem; so styled from its having formed, in the then inhospitable country, an asylum and guard for travellers, under the protection of the knights who held the manor and made its precincts a sanctuary. After the abolition of the order this privilege became the bane of the neighbourhood; for the place, thus exempted from all jurisdiction, was converted into a den of thieves and murderers who ravaged the country far and wide with impunity, till the reign of *Henry* VII when they were extirpated by the bravery and prudence of *Meredydd ap Evan*.

Thomas Pennant, *Tours in Wales*

16.   *Llywelyn Fawr's War with John, 1211-16*

Llywelyn, son of Iorwerth, made cruel attacks upon the English, and on that account, King John became enraged, and formed a design of entirely divesting Llywelyn of his dominion. And he collected a vast army towards Gwynedd, with the view of utterly destroying it. And to join his army, he summoned to him at Chester, these princes of Wales: Gwenwynwyn of Powys, and Hywel, son of Gryffydd, son of Cynan of Gwynedd and Madog, son of Gruffydd Maelor, and Maredudd, son of Robert of Cydewain, and Maelgwn and Rhys Gryg, the sons of Lord Rhys. And thereupon Llywelyn moved with his forces into the Perfeddwlad,[1] and his property to the mountain of Eryri,[2] and the forces of Mona, with their property, in the same manner. Then the king with his army came to the castle of Deganwy. And there the army was in such great want of provisions that an egg was sold for a penny half-penny, and it was a delicious feast to them to get horse flesh, and on that account the king returned to England about Whitsuntide, with his errand imperfect, after disgracefully losing many of his men and much property. After that, about the calends of August,[3] the king returned to Wales, his mind being more cruel and his army larger, and he built many castles in Gwynedd. And he proceeded over the River Conway towards the mountain of Eryri, and incited some of his troops to burn Bangor. And there, Robert, Bishop of Bangor[4] was seized in his church, and was afterwards ransomed for two hundred hawks.

Then Llywelyn, being unable to bear the cruelty of the king, sent his wife, who was daughter of the king, to make peace between him and the king, in any manner that she might be able. After Llywelyn had received safe conduct to go to and fro from the king, he went to

---

1   The Perfeddwlad, or four cantrefs between the rivers Conway and Clwyd, a district which constantly changed hands according to the strength or weakness of the Prince of Gwynedd.

2   Snowdonia.

3   It was on 8th July that John started again.

4   On Robert, see Lloyd, *History of Wales*, J. E. Lloyd, ii. 635 note. Though 'consecrated by the Archbishop Hubert at Westminster on 16th March 1197, it would seem, however, that he had never been elected'. He died in 1212, probably as a result of the treatment he had received at the hands of John's rough mercenaries.

him and made his peace with him, by delivering hostages to the king of the nobles of the country, with twenty thousand cattle and forty steeds, consigning also the middle district[5] to the king for ever. And thereupon all the Welsh princes, except Rhys and Owain, the sons of Gruffydd, son of Rhys, made peace with the king, and the king returned victoriously, and with extreme joy, to England. And then the king commanded those princes to take with them all the troops of Morganwg and Dyfed, with Rhys Gryg and Maelgwn, son of Rhys, and their forces, and to go against the sons of Rhys, son of Gruffydd, son of Rhys, to compel them to surrender themselves into his hands, or to retire into banishment out of all the kingdom. And then the seneschal[6] of Cardiff, the man who was the leader of the army, and Rhys and Maelgwn, sons of the Lord Rhys, urged their troops and their strength, and repaired to Penwedig. And since Rhys and Owain, the sons of Gruffydd, could not withstand a power of that magnitude, and there was not a place open for them in Wales to repair to, they sent messages to Falkes to bring about peace. And they made peace with him, and they consented that the king should have the territory between the Dyfi and the Aeron; and Falkes built a castle for the king at Aberystwyth. And then Rhys and Owain, the sons of Gruffydd, went, under the safe conduct of Falkes, to the court of the king, and the king received them as friends.

5   The Perfeddwlad.
6   Falkes de Breauté, one of the worst of John's mercenary captains.

Brut y Tywysogion

17.   Death of Llywelyn, 1240

1240. Then died that mighty man, that second Achilles, namely Lord Llywelyn, son of Iorwerth, son of Owain Gwynedd, then Prince of Wales, having received the monastic habit in the convent of Aberconway with great devotion. His deeds I am unworthy to narrate. For he ruled his enemies with sword and spear, gave peace to the monks, provided food and clothing for those who made themselves poor for Christ's sake, enlarged his boundaries by his wars, gave good justice to all according to their deserts, and by the bonds of fear or love bound all men duly to him.

Annales Cambriae

18. The English King (Henry III) at Deganwy

1245. On the 24th of September, when the king had been staying for almost two months on the farthest borders of Wales at the river flowing between the mountains of Snowdon, building a castle impregnable in its site and fortifications, a certain nobleman of his army, wishing to inform his friends who were anxious about him of this, wrote to them as follows:

'Greeting. The Lord King is staying with his army at Deganwy to strengthen a certain castle which he has now made very strong there, and we live round it in our tents in watching, fasting, and praying, in cold and want of clothing. In watching for fear of the Welsh attacking us suddenly in the night. In fasting because of the lack of food, for a farthing loaf now costs five pence. In cold and want of clothing because our houses are of canvas and we lack our winter clothes.

'But there is a small arm of the sea beneath the castle where we are staying, like a port, where the sea ebbs and flows, into which ships have often come while we have been here bringing provisions from Ireland and from Chester. And this inlet is between us and Snowdonia where the Welsh live now, and, when the tide is in, is about a crossbow shot across. But on Monday before Michaelmas, late in the afternoon, a ship from Ireland, bringing us food for sale, was coming towards the entrance of the port, but being carelessly steered, as the sea receded it remained aground beneath our castle, but on the opposite bank near the Welsh, who, hastening to it, beset it on the dry sand. Seeing this from the nearer bank we sent across the water in small boats three hundred of our Welsh borderers from Chester and Shrewsbury, and with them crossbowmen and armed knights to defend the said ship. When the Welsh saw this, they betook themselves hurriedly to their haunts and well-known hiding-places in their woods and mountains. Our knights, accompanied by their men, followed them for a distance of two leagues, although they were on foot, not having taken their horses across the water with them, and wounded and slew many of the Welsh. Our men, therefore, returned as victors over the enemy, and, like greedy and needy men, spreading plunder, pillage, and fire in the districts across the water. Amongst other sacrilegious deeds they irreverently despoiled an abbey of the Cistercians at Aberconway of all its property, even to the chalices and books, and burnt the buildings belonging to it.

'Meanwhile the Welsh, having collected a large number of their countrymen, suddenly rushed with loud howls on our men, who were laden with booty thus wickedly obtained and impeded by their sins, and put them to flight, wounding and killing many of them as they were fleeing miserably towards the ship. Some of our men, preferring to be overcome by the waves and to die by drowning to being killed at the will of their enemies, threw themselves of their own accord into the sea to perish. The Welsh took some of our knights alive to imprison them, but having heard that we had killed some of their nobles, and particularly, Naveth, son of Odo, a very courteous and brave youth, they hanged our knights, cutting off their heads and dismembering them horribly; and finally they threw their wretched bodies, limb by limb, into the river, in detestation of their wicked avarice in not sparing the church, especially one belonging to monks.

'But there fell in that fight on our side of the retinue of Richard Earl of Cornwall certain brave knights, namely Sir Alan Buscel, Sir Adam de Moia, Sir Geoffrey Sturmay, and a fourth, a certain Raymond, a Gascon crossbowman at whom the King used often to poke fun. About one hundred retainers were killed, beside those drowned, but just as many of the Welsh, or more.

'Meanwhile, Sir Walter Biset with his men was aboard the ship, which he defended bravely until the middle of the night, in constant conflict with the Welsh who attacked fiercely from all sides, and, if our men had not had the sides of the ship for a wall, they would have all fallen into the hands of the enemy. At last the tide rising and the ship floating and becoming inaccessible, the Welsh withdrew, grieving that our men had been snatched from their hands. But on board the ship were sixty casks of wine as well as other much desired and needed provisions, of which we were at that time destitute. So, when morning came and the water retreated, the Welsh quickly returned, trusting to have seized our men in the ship. But, by God's mercy, they had escaped to us in our little boats during the night while the tide was high, before the return of the Welsh, leaving only the ship. So the Welsh came and carried off nearly all the wine and the other things they found in it, but withdrew again as the tide rose, having set fire to the ship and destroyed half of it. The other part is saved with seven of the casks, which we dragged to the near shore.

'But while we have made this stay here with the army, being in need of many things, we have often gone out armed, exposed to many dangers, to procure necessaries, encountering many ambuscades and assaults from the Welsh, bravely bearing losses, but more often, by the changing fortune of war, bringing losses to the enemy. After one fight, we brought back in triumph to the camp the heads of nearly one hundred decapitated Welshmen. At that time there was such a scarcity of provisions and such a lack of all necessaries, that we suffered an irremediable loss of men and horses. There was a time when there was no wine at all even in the King's house, or, as a matter of fact, in the whole army, except one single barrel: a measure of corn cost twenty shillings; a pasture ox three or four marks; and a hen eight pence. So men and horses wasted away and many died from hunger.'

On the morrow of the feast of the apostles Simon and Jude, the king being unable, as well as unwilling, to make any longer stay at Deganwy, owing to the want of provisions and the near approach of winter, after a stay of about ten weeks there, fortified and stored his aforesaid castle of Deganwy which he had built, and made preparations to return to England, in order that he and his army might recover health. He was now thoroughly convinced of the irreparable ruin of his enemies the Welsh; for, on his arrival, the Irish had ravaged the whole of Anglesey, which is, as it were, the protectress and place of refuge for all the Welsh; and at his departure, he cruelly put to the sword and reduced to ashes everybody and everything which remained there; so much so, that the whole country seemed reduced to one vast and uncultivated desert solitude . . . He also prohibited, under pain of death and loss of property, any provisions from being brought, or allowed to be brought, for sale from the English or Irish provinces. This castle of Deganwy, too, well supplied with men, provisions, engines of war, and arms, was, as it were, a thorn in the eye of the wretched, yea, most wretched Welsh, who could not, by any means, pass into England without being intercepted by the castellans . . . nor could they stay in their own country for the famine.

Matthew Paris, *Chronica Masora*

19. *Edward's Second Expedition and end of the Principality*

A.D. 1282, which is the tenth year of the reign of Edward. At the dead hour of night, on Palm Sunday, Llywelyn, Prince of Wales, and David, his brother, surrounded the castles of Rhuddlan and Flint with a large army, and destroyed such other castles of the king as they could effect an entrance into, and having wounded, taken prisoner, and loaded with chains, that noble and illustrious knight, the Lord Roger Clifford, after having first slain all his friends, they sent him across, suddenly and unexpectedly, to the mountain of Snowdon, slaying all they met with, young and old, women and children, in their beds, and devastating afterwards with plunder and conflagration the greater part of the Marches. The king, hearing of this, but scarcely believing it, sent the barons of his Exchequer and the justices of the King's Bench to Shrewsbury to compel the observance of the laws of his kingdom, and having assembled an army, he reduced all Wales towards the mountains of Snowdon under his authority, and he gave large portions of the territory which he acquired there to his earls and barons, and to others of his faithful adherents, to be possessed for ever by them and their heirs. And accordingly, many thousands of soldiers were sent to the assistance of the king from Guienne and the Basque provinces and other foreign countries; therefore the king, wishing to advance farther, and supported by his ships, caused a large bridge to be built over the waters of the Conway,* which flow and ebb near the mountain of Snowdon. Some of the nobles of the king's army, passing over this bridge for the sake of taking exercise, were set upon, and being alarmed by the numbers and the shouts of the Welsh who came against them, endeavoured unsucessfully to effect their return to the island of Anglesey from which they had come, but were miserably drowned in the water. The Welsh ascribed this victory not to English misfortune but to a miracle, and urged their prince to act boldly and fear nothing; because in a short time, according to the prophecy of Merlin, he was fated to be crowned with the diadem of Brutus. Therefore Llywelyn, taking with him a numerous army, descended into the campaign country, leaving the mountainous district to his brother David.

Edmund, the heir of that famous knight now deceased, Roger de Mortimer, with some of the lords Marchers, attacked the army of Llywelyn, and without losing any of his men, slew a great number of the Welsh. In this battle the head of Prince Llywelyn was cut off and carried to London, where it was placed on a stake and crowned with ivy, and erected for a long time on the top of the Tower of London,

* This bridge, which was not over the Conway but across the Menai Strait, was built by Luke de Tany, late Seneschal of Gascony, during Aug-Sept 1282. Edward's idea was that when he advanced to the Conway from the east, Tany and his men should cross from Anglesey by the bridge and take the Welsh in the rear.

from which his father, Gruffydd, had formerly fallen and broken his neck, and so died. The Welsh, alarmed at the death of their prince, and thrown into confusion, surrendered all the castles of Snowdon to the King of England.

Flores Historioarum

20.   *The Death of Llywelyn, Prince of Wales*

Llywelyn, Prince of Wales, was intercepted by the king's troops in South Wales, and lost his life and head on Friday, the 10th December. On the next day his head was sent to the king in North Wales, and he at once sent it to his army stationed in Anglesey, and after the people of Anglesey were satisfied with the spectacle, he ordered it to be conveyed immediately to London. On the morrow of St Thomas the Apostle the Londoners went out to meet it with trumpets and cornets, and conducted it through all the streets of the city with a marvellous clang. After this they stuck it for the rest of the day in their pillory, and towards evening it was carried to the Tower of London and fixed on a lofty pole. As for the body of the prince, his mangled trunk, it was interred in the abbey of Cwm Hir, belonging to the monks of the Cistercian Order.

Florence of Worcester

21.   LAMENT FOR THE DEATH OF LLYWELYN

Cold is my heart beneath a breast stricken with sorrow
For the royal diviner of the court of Aberffraw.
Gold that was not smooth was paid for his hand;
He was worthy of a golden diadem.
Golden horns of a golden monarch, I shall have no joy,
Llywelyn is not living, gracefully to enrobe me.
Woe is me for a lordly hawk free from reproach!
Woe is me of the misfortune which has befallen him!
Woe is me of losing him, woe is me of his destiny!
Woe is me of hearing that he was wounded!
Woe, ye tents of Cadwaladr, that the obstructor of the flood is pierced!
Golden-handed prince, hero of the red-stained spear,

Every winter he distributed rich apparel,
And clothed me with garments from his own person.
Lord of plenteous flocks, our right hand has not prospered,
But he shall enjoy life eternal.
It is my lot to complain of Saxon treachery.
It is mine to complain of the necessity of dying,
It is mine to despise myself because God
Has left me without him.

Gruffydd ab yr Ynad Coch

Stephens' *Literature of the Kymry*

22. *Letter to King Edward I*

December 17, 1282. To my Lord the King.

To his very dear Lord, Edward, by Grace of God, King of England, etc., Friar John, by the permission of God, Archbishop of Canterbury and Primate of all England, greeting in great reverence.

Sire, know that those who were at the death of Llywelyn found in the most secret part of his body some small things which we have seen. Among these things there was a treasonable letter disguised by false names. And that you may be warned, we send a copy of the letter to the Bishop of Bath, and the letter itself Edmund de Mortimer has, with Llywelyn's privy seal, and these things you may have at your pleasure. And this we send to warn you, and not that anyone should be troubled for it.

Besides this, Sire, know that Lady Maud Longespere prayed us by letter to absolve Llywelyn, that he might be buried in consecrated ground, and we sent word to her that we would do nothing if it could not be proved that he showed signs of true repentance before his death. And Edmund de Mortimer said to me that he had heard from his servants who were at the death that he asked for the priest before his death, but without sure certainty we will do nothing.

Besides this, Sire, know that the very day that he was killed a white monk sang mass to him, and my Lord Roger de Mortimer had the vestments.

Besides this, Sire, we ask you to take pity on clerks, that you will suffer no one to kill them or to do them bodily injury. And know, Sire, God protect you from evil, if you do not prevent it to your power, you fall into the sentence, for to suffer what one can prevent is the same as to consent. And, therefore, Sire, we pray you that it may please you that the clerks which are in Snowdon may go hence and seek better things with their property in France or elsewhere. For because we believe that Snowdon will be yours, if it happen that, in conquering or afterwards, harm is done to clerks, God will accuse you of it, and your good renown will be blemished, and we shall be considered a coward. And of these things, Sire, if it please you, send us your pleasure, for we will give thereto what counsel we can, either by going thither or by some other way. And know, Sire, if you do not fulfil our prayers you will put us in sadness, which we shall never leave in this mortal life. Sire, God keep you and all that belongs to you.

This letter was written at Pembridge, Thursday after St Lucy's Day.

Letter to King Edward I, 1282
from Friar John, Archbishop of Canterbury

23. *Aber. William de Breos*

At the entrance of the glen, close to the village, is a very large artificial mount, flat at top, and near sixty feet in diameter, widening towards the base. It was once the site of a castle belonging to *Llewelyn* the Great. Some foundations are yet to be seen around the summit, and in digging, traces of buildings have been discovered. In this place was detected the intrigue of *William de Breos* (son of Reginald, a potent baron in the reign of *Henry* III) with the wife of *Llewelyn*. It seems that *William*, by chance of war, had before fallen into the hands of our prince, at which time probably the familiarity with the princess commenced; but was not discovered till after he was released on a large ransom. The vindictive *Llewelyn*, in the following year (1229) inveigled *Breos* into his power, by an invitation to celebrate the feast of *Easter*; when, after an elegant banquet, the prince reproached him with his crime, and caused him to be dragged from his presence, and hung on an adjacent hill. The tradition of the country is, that a Bard of the palace accidentally meeting with the princess (who was ignorant of the fate of her lover) accosted her in the following manner; and on receiving her answer, shewed him to her, hanginng on a tree.

> Diccyn doccyn, gwraig Llewelyn,
> Beth y roit'i am weled Gwilim?

The princess answers,

> Cymry, Lloiger, a Lhewelyn
> Y rown'i gyd, am weled Gwilim.

Bard —

> Tell me, wife of Llewelyn,
> What would you give for a sight of your *William*

Princess —

> *Wales, England,* and *Llewelyn* to boot,
> I would give them all to see my *William*.

Thomas Pennant, *Tours in Wales*

24. *The Land of Conan*

That night we lay at Llanvair, that is the church of St Mary, in the province of Ardudwy. This territory of Conan, and particularly Merionyth, is the rudest and roughest district of all Wales; the ridges of its mountains are very high and narrow, terminating in sharp peaks, and so irregularly jumbled together, that if the shepherds conversing or disputing with each other, from their summits, should agree to meet, they could scarcely effect their purpose in the course of the whole day. The lances of this country are very long; for as South Wales excels in the use of the bow, so North Wales is distinguished for its skill in the lance; insomuch that an iron coat of mail will not resist the stroke of a lance thrown at a small distance. The next morning, the youngest son of Conan, named Meredyth, met us at the passage of a bridge, attended by his people, where many persons were signed with the cross; amongst whom was a fine young man of his suite, and one of his intimate friends; and Meredyth, obseving that the cloak, on which the cross was to be sewed, appeared of too thin and of too common a texture, with a flood of tears, threw him down his own.

Giraldus Cambrensis, *The Itinerary Through Wales,* 1186

25.   *King Edward I in Wales*

1295. In the year A.D. 1295, the twenty-third of the reign of King Edward, the king entered Anglesey after Easter with seven score ships of war, and showing himself at that time conciliatory with those who hated peace, came to terms with eleven thousand Welshmen.

Then, having built the castle which is called Beaumaris, and appointed custodians for it, he passed through the higher parts of Snowdonia. After that he ordered William, Earl of Warwick, to meet him in the neighbourhood of Merioneth.

*   *   *   *   *

1301. The king gave his son, Edward, the principality of Wales, which was very pleasing to the Welsh, because he had been born in Wales. He also gave him the earldom of Chester.

Annals of Worcester

26.   *Owain Glyndŵr*

Meanwhile the Welsh, seizing the fortunate opportunity of the king's absence, began to rebel, their leader being a certain Owain Glyndŵr. This man was at first an apprentice of the law* at Westminster; then as a squire of some renown he fought for Henry when he was striving to attain the throne. The beginning of the trouble was the taking possession by Lord Reginald Grey of Ruthin of lands which Owain claimed to be his by hereditary right. Seeing his arguments and his dispatches despised, he raised a force and led an expedition against Lord Grey, laying waste his estates with fire, and putting many of his household to the sword cruelly and inhumanly.

When the king heard of this he immediately determined to attack such a disturber of his country's peace. Having collected a multitude of men-at-arms and archers he invaded Wales. But the Welsh with their leader, occupying the mountains of Snowdonia, continually withdrew before him, without fighting. At length the king, having burnt the land and killed such stragglers as fell into his hands, returned to England with a fair booty of carts, cattle, and beasts of burden.

Annals of Henry IV, 1409

* A barrister of less than sixteen years' standing.

27. *Gwilym ap Tudor and Rhys ap Tudor*

Gwilym ap Tudor and Rhys ap Tudor, brothers, natives of the Isle of Anglesey or Mona, because they were unable to obtain the king's pardon for the rebellion of the aforesaid Owain, on Good Friday of the same year seized the castle of Conway, well stocked as it was with arms and provisions. Having slain the two warders through the subtlety of a certain carpenter who pretended to come to his work as usual, and entering with forty other men, they held it as a stronghold.

But being at once besieged by the prince and the people of the countryside, on the 29th of May next following they gave up the same castle through their own cowardice and their followers' treachery; for having secretly bound nine of their number who were most objection-able to the prince as they slept after their night watch, they handed them over on condition of saving their own lives and those of the rest of the garrison. The nine bound and given up to the prince they at once saw drawn, disembowelled, hanged, beheaded, and quartered.

Chronicle of Adam of Usk, 1402

28. *Constable of Harlech warns young people difficult to govern*

This be credence of mouth, that is to say how John Salghall, Constable of Harlech, certified and warned by letter to the Chamberlain of Caernarvon how that a gentleman of Wales that most know was with Med ap Owyn in great specialty and warned him of an accord made between the same Med and men of the Outer Isles and of Scotland, through letters in and out, as he informed him, that they should come and land and arrive at Abermouth and Eye betwixt this and Midsummer night with their power; and that the same Med should privately warn his friends to make ready horses and harness against that time, for which warning the same gentleman dare not pass from the town of Harlech. It does seem to be true because of the way the Welsh are behaving for they sell their cattle and buy horses and harness, saddles, bows and arrows. And reckless men of many counties leave their homes and thrifty governance and assemble in desolate places and wild and hold many meetings privately and though we do not know their purpose the young people are difficult to govern.

Papers of Intelligence — King Henry IV, 1405

29.   *Owain Glyndŵr prepares to assault Caernarvon*

Robert Parys the Deputy Constable of Caernarvon has apprised us through a woman, because there was no man who dared come, for neither man nor woman dare carry letters on account of the rebels of Wales, that Owain Glyndŵr with the French and all his other power is preparing to assault the town and castle of Caernarvon and to begin this enterprise with engines, sowes (hide-covered huts beneath which miners could burrow at castle walls) and ladders of great length; and in the town there are not more than twenty-eight fighting men, which is all too small a force; for eleven of the more able men who were there at the last siege of the place are dead; some of the wounds they received at the time of the assault and others of the plague; so the said castle and town are in imminent danger.'

William Venables, Deputy Warden of the Marshes,
writing to Henry IV

30.   *Letter from 'Hotspur'*

I see much pillage and mischief in the country, that good and hasty measures ought to be immediately adopted by sea as well as by land. All the country is without doubt in great peril of being destroyed by the rebels if I should leave before the arrival of my succesor, the which will be an affair of necessity; for I cannot bear the cost that I am put to without ordering from you.

Henry 'Hotspur' Percy to King Henry IV

31.   OWAIN GLYNDŴR

Here's the life I've sighed for long
Abashed is now the Saxon throng
And Britons have a British Lord
Whose emblem is the conquering sword
There's none I trow but knows him well
The hero of the watery dell

Owain of bloody spear in field
Owain his country's strongest shield
A sovereign bright in grandeur drest
Whose frown afrights the bravest breast.

Iolo Goch (14th century)

32.   Queen Katherine and Owen Tudor

About that time also died Katherine,* King Henry's mother, who was interred at Westminster, in the sepulchre of her predecessors. This woman, after the death of her husband, King Henry the Fifth, being but young in years, and thereby of less discretion of judge what was decent for her estate, married one Owen Tudor, a gentleman of Wales, adorned with wonderful gifts of body and mind, who derived his pedigree from Cadwalader, the last King of the Britons, by whom she had three sons, Edmund, Jaspar and the third, who was a monk of the order of St Benet, and lived not long after, and one daughter who was made a nun. Afterwards King Henry made Edmund earl of Richmond, and Jaspar earl of Pembroke, because they were his brothers on his mother's side.

After the death of Queen Katherine, the said Owen was twice committed to ward by the Duke of Gloucester, because he had been so presumptuous as by marriage with the young Queen to intermix his blood with the noble race of kings, and in the end was beheaded.

Polydore Vergil

---

* Katherine died on 3rd January 1437. According to the Chronicle of London, her marriage was unknown until she died.

33.   Queen Katherine

Queen Katherine being a French woman born, knew no difference between the English and Welsh nation until her marriage being published Owen Tudor's kindred and country were objected to disgrace him, as most vile and barbarous; which made her desirous to see some of his kinsmen, whereupon he brought to her presence John ap m'edyth and Howell ll'in ap Howell his near cousins men of goodly stature and personage, but wholly destitute of bringing up and nurture, for when the Queen had spoken to them in divers languages and they were not able to answer her, she said they were the goodliest dumb creatures that ever she saw.

Sir John Wynne, *History of the Gwydir Family*

34. *Owen Tudor and his Descendants*

Another excursion was to *Penmynnydd*, about two miles south of *Plas Gwyn*, once the residence of the ancestors of *Owen Tudor*, second husband to *Catherine of France*, queen dowager of *Henry* V 'who being,' as honest *Halle* informs us, 'young and lusty, following more her own appetite than friendly counsel, and regarding more her private affection than her open honour, took to husband privily (in 1428) a goodly gentleman, and a beautiful person, garnished with many godly gifts both of nature and of grace, called *Owen Teuther*, a man brought forth and come of the noble lineage and ancient line of *Cadwalader*, the last king of the *Britonnes*.' The match, important in its consequences, restored the *British* races of princes to this kingdom,

No more our long-lost *Arthur* we bewail:
All hail, ye genuine kings; *Britannia's* issue, hail!

These reigned long, under the title of the house of *Tudor*; the mixed race having ceased on the accession of *Henry* VII, grandson to our illustrious countryman.

Owen Tudor himself was unfortunate. He lost his royal consort in 1437, after she had brought him three sons and one daughter, *Edmund, Jaspar* and *Owen*; the last embraced a monastic life in the abbey of *Westminster*, and died soon after; the daughter died in her infancy. It appears, that after the death of their mother, *Edmund* and *Jaspar* most respectfully were placed under the care of *Catherine de la Pole*, daughter of *Michael de la Pole, Earl of Suffolk*, and abbess of *Berking*. A petition from her, dated 1440, appears on record for the payment of certain money due to her on their account. During the life of the queen, the marriage had been winked at, notwithstanding a law had been made after that event, enacting that no person, under severe penalties, should marry a queen dowager of *England*, without the special licence of the king. On the death of *Catherine* all respects ceased to her spouse: he was seized, and committed first to *Newgate*, from which he escaped by the assistance of his confessor and servant. On being retaken, he was delivered to the custody of the Earl of *Suffolk*, constable of the castle of *Wallingford*, and after some time was again committed to *Newgate*. He made his escape a second time. The length of his second imprisonment does not appear. After a considerable period, high honours were conferred on his two eldest sons, half brothers to the king. In the year 1452, they were both created earls; *Edmund* was made earl of *Richmond*, and *Jaspar*, earl of Pembroke. Henry, about this time, was disturbed by the open claim of the Duke of *York* to the succession, and found it prudent to strengthen his interest by all possible means. The *Welsh*, flattered by the honours bestowed on their young countrymen, ever after faithfully adhered to the house of *Lancaster*.

Owen had besides a natural son, called *Dafydd*, knighted by his nephew *Henry* VII who also bestowed on him in marriage *Mary*, the daughter and heiress of *John Bohun* of *Midhurst*, in *Sussex*, and with her a great inheritance. *Owen* was taken no notice of till the year 1460, when, as a patent expresses it, in regard of his good services, he had a grant of the parks, and the agistment of the parks in the lordship of *Denbigh*, and the wodewardship of the same lordship. The year following, he fought valiantly under the banners of his son *Jaspar*, at the battle of *Mortimer's Cross*; would not quit the field, but was taken with several other Welsh gentlemen, beheaded with them soon after at *Hereford*, and interred in the church of the *Grey Friars* in that city.

Notwithstanding the birth of *Owen* was calumniated, he certainly was of very high descent. *Henry* VII early in his reign, issued a commission to Sir *John Leiaf*, priest *Guttun Owen*, and a number of others, to make enquiry into his paternal descent; and they, from our *Welsh* chronicles, proved *incontestably*, that 'he was lineally descended by issue male, saving one woman, from *Brutus* grandson of *Aeneas* the *Trojan*, and that he was son to *Brute* in fivescore degrees.' I shall drop a little short of this long descent. *Owen Tudor* was assuredly of high blood. He was seventh in descent from *Ednyfed Vychan*, counsellor, and leader of the armies of *Llewelyn* the Great, and a successful warrior against the *English*.

Thomas Pennant, Tours in Wales

35.   *Harlech and Edgecote Hill*

My great-great-grandfather, Sir Richard Herbert of Colebrook, was that incomparable hero who (in the history of Hall and Grafton as it appears) twice passed through a great army of northern men alone, with his pole-axe in his hand, and returned without any mortal hurt, which is more than is famed of Amadis du Gaul or the Knight of the Sun.

I shall, besides this relation of Sir Richard Herbert's prowess in the battle at Banbury or Edgecote Hill, being the place where the late battle was fought, deliver some traditions concerning him, which I have received from good hands: one is, that the said Richard Herbert being employed together with his brother William, Earl of Pembroke, to reduce certain rebels in North Wales, Sir Richard Herbert besieged a principal person of them at Harlech Castle, in Merionethshire; the captain of this place* had been a soldier in the wars of France, whereupon he said he had kept a castle in France so long that he made the old women in Wales talk of him, and that he would keep this castle so long that he would make the old women in France talk of him, and indeed as the place was almost impregnable but by famine, Sir Richard Herbert was constrained to take him in by composition, he surrendering himself upon condition that Sir Richard Herbert should do what he could to save his life, which being accepted, Sir Richard brought him to King Edward IV, desiring his highness to give him a pardon, since he yielded up a place of importance, which he might have kept longer upon this hope; but the king replying to Sir Richard Herbert that he had no power by his commission to pardon any, and therefore might after the representation hereof to his majesty safe deliver him up to justice, Sir Richard Herbert answered he had not yet done the best he could for him, and therefore most humbly desired his highness to do one of two things — either to put him again in the castle where he was, and command some other to take him out, or, if his highness would not do so, to take his life for the said captain's, that being the last proof he could give that he used his uttermost endeavour to save the said captain's life. The king, finding himself urged thus far, gave Sir Richard Herbert the life of the said captain, but withal he bestowed no other reward for his service.

---

*David ab Einon. No record of this captain's work in France has come down to us.

The other history is, that Richard Herbert, together with his brother the Earl of Pembroke, being in Anglesey apprehending there seven brothers which had done many mischiefs and murders; in these times the Earl of Pembroke, thinking fit to riot out so wicked a progeny, commanded them all to be hanged, whereupon the mother of them coming to the Earl of Pembroke, upon her knees desired him to pardon two or at leastwise one of her said sons, affirming that the rest were sufficient to satisfy justice or example, which request also Sir Richard Herbert seconded; but the earl finding them all equally guilty, said he could make no distinction betwixt them, and therefore commanded them to be executed together; at which the mother was so aggrieved, that with a pair of woollen beads on her arms (for so the relation goeth), she on her knees cursed him, praying God's mischief might fall to him in the first battle he should make. The earl after this, coming with his brother to Edgecote Field, as is before set down, after he had put his men in order to fight, found his brother, Sir Richard Herbert, at the head of his men, leaning upon his pole-axe in a kind of sad or pensive manner; whereupon the earl said, 'What! doth thy great body' (for he was higher by the head than anyone in the army) 'apprehend anything, that thou art so melancholy? or art thou weary with marching, that thou dost lean thus upon thy pole-axe?' Sir Richard Herbert replied, that he was neither of both, whereof he should see the proof presently, 'only I cannot but apprehend on your part, lest the curse of the woman with the woollen beads fall upon you' . . .

. . . When the said Earl of Pembroke and Sir R. Herbert were taken prisoners in defending the just cause of Edward IV, at the battle abovesaid, the earl never entreated that his own life might be saved, but his brother's.

Lord Herbert of Cherbury, *Autobiography*

36. *Sir Richard Bulkeley, Member of Parliament*

Sir R. Bulkeley served in parliament for the county of Mona, the 2nd and 3rd sessions of Queen Mary, the 3rd of Elizabeth, and the 1st of James. 'He was a goodly person, fair of complexion, and tall of stature. He was temperate in his diet, — not drinking of healths. In the last year of Elizabeth, being then somewhat stricken in years, he attended the council of marches at Ludlow, in winter time. When the

Lord President Zouch went in his coach to church or elsewhere, Sir Richard used to ride on a great horse; and sometimes he would go from his lodging to church, in frost and snow, on foot, with a short cloak, silk stockings, a rapier and dagger, tarry all prayers and sermon, in very cold weather; insomuch that Lord Zouch was wont to say, he was cold to see him. Sir Richard was a great reader of history, and discourses of all estates and countries; of very good memory and understanding in matters belonging to housekeeping, maritime affairs, building of ships and maintaining them at sea. He drew his own letters and answered all letters with his own hand . . . He was a great housekeeper, and entertainer of strangers, especially such as passed to or from Ireland. He nobly entertained the Earl of Essex in his way to be lord lieutenant. He made provision of all necessaries for his table beforehand. He sent yearly two ships to Greenland, for cod, ling, and other fish, which he did use to barter in Spain, for malaga and sherry wines, and always kept good stock of old sack in his cellar, which he called amiable, besides other wines. He kept two parks, well stored with red and fallow-deer, which did afford such plenty of venison, as furnished his table three or four times every week, in the season, besides pleasuring of friends . . . He was an excellent horseman, and an expert tilter, keeping two or three stables of horses, one in Cheshire and another in Beaumaris, and a great stud of mares. His estate in Mona was £2,500, in Caernarvonshire £800, and in Cheshire £1,000 a year, having always a great stock of money lying in his chest. He kept many servants and attendants, tall and proper men. Two lacqueys in livery always ran by his horse. He never went from home without twenty or twenty-four to attend him. He was a great favourite of Queen Elizabeth. He had powerful friends at court, and had the gentry and commonality of the county of Mona at his service, except the Woods of Thosmore, who were always his enemies. Sir Richard being one of the deputy lieutenants of Mona (upon intelligence of the Spanish armada threatening England) was to cesse the country in arms, and cessing Mr Wood of Thosmore, he was highly offended and thought himself too heavily loaden, therefore went up to court to the Earl of Leicester, carrying a false tale with him, that Sir Richard Bulkeley, (a little before the attainder and execution of Thomas Salisbury of Lleweney, and one of the accomplices of Antony Babington, the traitor, 1585) had been in the mountains of Snowdon, conferring with him, and that at a farm of Sir Richard's called Cwmligie, they had lain together two or three nights.

The Earl glad of this information, presently acquaints the queen and council therewith. Sir Richard being called before the council and examined, absolutely denied the whole matter. And afterwards, divers of the lords of the council wrote letters to the justices of assize of North Wales, to publish Sir Richard's wrongs, and to notify to the queen's subjects, his clear innocence. But that Sir Richard might not rest in peace, one Green, belonging to the Earl of Leicester, in the name of one Bromfield, a pensioner, came to him to challenge him to meet Bromfield in the field. "Have you no other errand?" quoth Sir Richard, "No," says Green. Then Sir Richard drew his dagger, and broke Green's pate; telling him to carry that as an answer, he scorning to meet such a knave as Bromfield. This treatment of Green, highly increased the anger of the earl. Bromfield, Green, and others of his retainers, plotted mischief to the person of Sir Richard, but he stood upon his guard, keeping always twenty-four stout men, with swords, bucklers, and daggers, to defend him from their attempts. They hired boats and wherries upon the Thames, with a design to drown Sir Richard as he went from Westminster to London: but he being privately informed thereof, borrowed the lord mayor's barge, furnished with men, muskets, billets, drums, and trumpets, and rowed along the Thames, shot the bridge, and went down to Greenwich, where the queen kept her court at that time; and at the landing place, over against the palace, caused his company to discharge their muskets, to beat their drums, and sound their trumpets. The Earl of Leicester hearing thereof, repaired to the queen, and informed her, that Sir Richard Bulkeley, more like a rebel than a subject, had come with barges, men, muskets, drums and trumpets, and had shot several pieces over against her majesty's palace, to the great terror of her court, a matter not to be suffered. The queen sent for Sir Richard, and after hearing his apology for himself, made the earl friends with him. Within a while after, the earl sent for Sir Richard to his chamber, who coming thither, the earl began to expostulate with him on several wrongs and abuses, he pretended to have received at his hands, and that he had lost £10,000 by his opposition; but the discourse ended in milder terms, and Sir Richard was bidden to dinner, but did eat or drink nothing, save of what he saw the earl taste; remembering Sir Nicholas Thogmorton, who was said to have received a fig at his table. But the Earl of Leicester dying in October, 1588, Sir Richard Bulkeley and his country, enjoyed peace and quietness from his tyrannical oppressions, his devices and wicked practices, and Sir Richard Bulkeley survived to the 28th of June, 1621, when he died, aged eighty-eight. He had attended the coronation of Mary, Elizabeth, and James. His cloak at the last coronation, cost him £500. His second wife, Alice Needham, was implicated with the Goodmans in attempting to poison this "good old knight in a cup of metheglin".

Caerwys and Plas Gwyn MSS

37. *Lord Uxbridge loses his leg*

. . . Just as Sir Hussey Vivian's Brigade were going down to the charge, Lord Uxbridge was struck by a grape-shot on the right knee which shattered the joint all to pieces. I did not see him fall and went on to the charge, but soon missed him and perceived Seymour (Mr Horace Seymour, one of Lord Uxbridge's aides-de-camp) taking him to the rear. He told me immediately he must lose his leg and then began conversing about the action and seemed to forget his wound in the exultation for the Victory. When the Surgeons examined it, they all agreed that it would be at the imminent danger of his life to attempt to save the limb. He only said 'Well Gentlemen I thought so myself and if amputation is to take place the sooner it is done the better'. He wrote a short note to Lady Uxbridge, saying that if he had been a young single man he would probably have run the risk, but that he would preserve his life for her and his children if possible. During the operation, he never moved or complained, no one even held his hands. He said once quite calmly that he thought the instrument was not very sharp. When it was over his nerves did not appear the least shaken, and the Surgeon obseved his pulse was not altered. He said smiling 'I have had a pretty long run, I have been a *Beau* these 47 years and it would not be fair to cut the young men out any longer'; and then asked us if we did not admire his vanity. I have seen many operations, but this neither Lord Greenock nor myself could bear. We were obliged to go to the other end of the room. I thank God he is doing as well as possible. There has been no fever and the Surgeons say nothing can be going on more favourably.

Captain Wildman, 7th Hussars
Letter after the Battle of Waterloo, 1815

38.   The Anglesey Column

Again following the Holyhead road, we soon reach the Anglesey Column, which is worth visiting for the view from its base, or better, its summit. We have the Marquis of Anglesey's effigy in Hussar uniform at the top, but the gallant officer did not bring the whole of his body back from Belgium, and Canning is said to have written the following epitaph on the leg buried at Waterloo:

> Here rests — and let no saucy knave
>   Presume to sneer or laugh,
> To learn that mould'ring in this grave
>   There lies — a British calf.
>
> For he who writes these lines is sure
>   That those who read the whole
> Will find that laugh was premature;
>   For here, too, lies the sole.
>
> And here five little ones repose,
>   Twin born with other five,
> Unheeded by their brother toes,
>   Who all are now alive.
>
> A leg and foot, to speak more plain,
>   Lie here of one commanding;
> Who, though his wits he might retain,
>   Lost half his understanding;
>
> And when the guns, with thunder fraught,
>   Poured bullets thick as hail,
> Could only in this way be taught
>   To give the foe leg-bail;
>
> And now in England, just as gay
>   As in the battle brave,
> Goes to the rout, the ball, the play,
>   With one leg in the grave.

Fortune in vain has showed her spite,
  For he will soon be found,
Should England's son engage in fight,
  Resolved to stand his ground.

But Fortune's pardon I must beg;
  She meant not to disarm;
And when she lopped the hero's leg
  She did not seek his h-arm;

And but indulged a harmless whim;
  Since he could walk with one,
She saw two legs were lost on him,
  Who never meant to run.

Gossiping Guide to Wales

IX

THE LED

1. *The Advantages of North Wales*

As the southern part of Wales, near Cardigan, but particularly Pembroke, is much pleasanter, on account of its plains and sea coast, so North Wales is better defended by nature, is more productive of men distinguished for bodily strength, and more fertile in the nature of its soil; for as the mountains of Eryri (Snowdon) could supply pasturage for all the herds of cattle in Wales, if collected together, so could the Isle of Mona (Anglesey) provide a requisite quantity of corn for all the inhabitants, on which account there is an old Welsh proverb, 'Môn mam Cymbry', that is, 'Mona is the mother of Wales'. Merioneth, and the land of Conan, is the rudest and least cultivated region, and the least accessible. The natives in that part of Wales excel in the use of long lances, as those of Monmouthshire are distinguished for their management of the bow. It is to be observed that the Welsh language is more delicate and richer in North Wales, that country being less intermixed with foreigners. Many, however, assert that the language of Cardigan, in South Wales, placed as it were in the middle and heart of Cambria, is the most refined.

Giraldus Cambrensis, *The Itinerary Through Wales,* 1186

2. *Welsh Saying*

Merchants of Beaumaris, lawyers of Caernarvon and gentlemen of Conway.

3. *Squire Bulkeley's Diary*

. . . to speak to Mr John Lloyd, the Irishman of Hirdrefaig, about my mother's money which he had acknowledged to me, the Session before, to have received and had promised to come himself to pay it to her or send it; having spoke to him whether he would pay it to her he absolutely refused, whereupon having ordered Mr Ambrose Lewis to sue him for it, that man (approving himself a true son of Trysglwyn) went and told him of it whereupon he came to my Lodgings and having called me out, asked me whether I had given Mr Ambrose Lewis orders to sue him. I answered that my mother had given such orders in case he did not pay the money, he then with much fierceness and passion insulted and abused her and me, bawling out and brandishing his stick with G-d d-m her and your soundrely actions and I do not value or regard yours and her scoundrely actions. I replied I hope he would regard the laws and so walked on, leaving him raving for revenge.

Squire Bulkeley's Diary

4. *A Welsh Courtship*

A Welsh courtship is not conducted in the same manner as in England. There is not, or rather was not till recently, any walking-out of couples together; that was denounced from the chapel pulpits as indecorous. But with the consent or connivance of the parents of a young woman the suitor would come at night to the window of the damsel he affected, and scratch at it with a stick or throw at it a little gravel. Then she would descend, open the door, and the pair would spend the greater part of the night together on the sofa in the parlour, with, as a young man who had gone through the experience informed me, a bottle of whisky, a Bible, and a currant cake on the table before them. Some deny the whisky, some the Bible, but all allow that refreshment is necessary when the session is carried on to the small hours of the morning.

S. Baring-Gould, *A Book of North Wales*

5. *The People of Snowdonia*

This mountainous tract scarcely yields any corn. Its produce is cattle and sheep, which, during summer, keep very high in the mountains, followed by their owners, with their families, who reside in that season in *Havodtai*, or summer dairy-houses, as the farmers in the

Swiss alps do in their *Sennes*. These houses consist of a long low room with a hole at one end, to let out the smoke from the fire, which is made beneath. Their furniture is very simple: stones are the substitutes of stools; and the beds are of hay, ranged along the sides. They manufacture their own clothes; and dye their cloths with *Cenn du y Cerrig*, or *Lichen Omphaloides*; and another *Cenn*, the *Lichen Parietinus*; native dyes, collected from the rocks. During summer, the men pass their time either in harvest work, or in tending their herds: the women in milking, or making butter and cheese. For their own use, they milk both ewes and goats, and make cheese of the milk, for their own consumption. The diet of these mountaineers is very lain, consisting of butter, cheese, and oat-bread, or *Bara Cyrch*: their drink whey: not but they have a reserve of a few bottles of very strong beer, by way of cordial, in illness. They are people of good understanding, wary and circumspect; usually tall, thin, and of strong constitutions, from their way of living. Towards winter, they descend to their *Hen Dref*, or *old dwelling*, where they lead, during winter, a vacant life.

Thomas Pennant, *Tours in Wales (Snowdonia)*

6.   *Quarrying for Slate at Penrhyn*

The Penrhyn slate quarries are reached by a branch line from Bangor to Bethesda. The quarrying is carried on upon a vast scale, and the place is interesting to the geologist on account of the presence, in the midst of a great dyke of greenstone, of an eruptive rock which has traversed the beds, and which has been left untouched.

The slates are cut to various sizes. Duchesses are the largest; then come Countesses and Ladies. About the beginning of last century a slate merchant of the name of Docer, going through the quarry with Lord Penrhyn, advised him that the slates should be made of such-and-such a size, and this is the origin of the name of 'Docer'. By this time the skill of the quarrymen and of the slater found some new plan continually. One wanted to do this, and another that. His lordship failed to please everybody. His lady, seeing him in this plight, and in continual trouble, advised him to call the slates after the names of the degrees in the aristocracy. He took up the suggestion, and called the 24 by 12 slate a Duchess, the 20 by 10 a Countess, and the 16 by 8 a Lady.

S. Baring-Gould, *A Book of North Wales*

7.   PENRHYN SLATES

It has truly been said, as we all must deplore,
That Grenville and Pitt have made peers by the score;
But now, 'tis asserted, unless I have blundered,
There's a man who makes peeresses here by the hundred.
By the stroke of a hammer, without the King's aid,
A Lady, or Countess, or Duchess is made.
And where'er they are seen, in a palace or shop,
Their rank they preserve, they are still at the top.
This Countess or Lady, though crowds may be present,
Submits to be dressed by the hands of a peasant,
And you'll see, when Her Grace is but once in his clutches,
With how little respect he will handle a Duchess.

Mr Justice Leycester

8.   *Holyhead Wake*

The following account sheds an interesting light on one of the old customs of Holyhead in the year 1804. 'The evening presented a scene as singular as it was laughable. A collection had been made by the first people of the town, for prizes for different feats of activity; the market place was greatly crowded, and at seven o'clock, four lusty lads, candidates for three prizes, began the sport of eating hot hasty-pudding immediately from the fire. To see the gestures of the boys, the anxious examination of each other's basins, their blowing into their own, now dipping in their fingers, and then applying them to their mouths, and using every method that fancy could suggest, to despatch their contents, would have made a cynic laugh. There was determination in the eye of one lad, who seemed resolved upon triumph; and who, in a few minutes, held up his reversed basin in the air, with a shout that begat a general one from the crowd; which was immediately followed by another, for the success of the second competitor; and, shortly after, the third boy was complimented; and received, with the others, a prize proportionate to his abilities; and the tardy fourth, though not entitled to anything, obtained a small present.'

F. H. Glazebrook, *Anglesey and North Wales Coast Book*

9. *Public Houses*

On my way along the mail road, almost a continued descent between the hills of Bangor, I was surprised by the rapid increase of population and domestic dwellings on the line of the mountain quarries within the last twenty years, and by the marks of improvement and intelligence spreading on every side. One serious drawback alone presented itself, in the endless number of public houses, 'thick as autumnal leaves', strewn over the labouring districts. Every tenth house in some places, Bethesda not excepted, could boast its sign, from 'Uther's Dragon' and 'Prince Llewelyn' to 'Glyndwr's Head' and the 'Meredith Arms', giving a ludicrous and grotesque appearance to the abodes such as could not but excite a smile. In a moral view, at least, these miners' cottages, with their gaily bedaubed lures to intemperance, looked more like 'painted sepulchres' than the dwellings of peace and labour. A mission of one or more of our Temperance Societies would find occupation in many parts of North Wales.

S. Baring-Gould, *A Book of North Wales*, 1903

10. *Funerals*

After a deady body is washed They wrap it in a Linen Shroud or Sheet (if a poor man) or if Rich get him a Coffin. The night before the Burying all the neighbours and Friends of the Deceased come and watch his Body and to say their prayers or Pater nosters as the saying is, padreua i'r wylnos as they term it, and there sit up all night a drinking smoking singing of carols or some ancient odes to the purpose and playing all little comical mountebank tricks as they can think on to keep themselves awake. At their entrance into the house they first go to the room where (the) dead Body lies and say the Lord's prayer kneeling by the dead body, and when they get up one of the nearest relations or masters of the Ceremonies gives each a cup of Ale and they are ordered to sit down. At the dusk of night an evening prayer is read by the clergyman of the parish or if not present by one of the company. The neglect of which they think to be a great slur on the Family. The Singing of psalms if they can, or else fall to singing of carols which are ancient songs containing Reflections upon death etc, and Immortality of the Soul.

Next morning all neighbours home to be dressed in their best, and to the corpse house again, a cup of drink, and if deceased be Rich served with cakes, wine etc. dinner before the Burying, offering on the Coffin. But if poor or Rich when the deceased is carried out of the house he is Laid on the Bier, before the door where they bring Two wooden cups one they fill with milk and the other with ale, over the Body. Some Loaves or Cakes of bread and a cheese, with a piece of money Stuck in the cheese, and this they give to some poor object of charity, first tasting of the milk and ale, the poor tasting likewise, the deceased's name of the cups. Then comes the offering for the coffin maker who is then very busy in nailing up the coffin each offering him a 6d or a shilling etc. or gold if the deceased be a rich person.

Then the parson reads two or 3 sentences up they mount the Bier on their shoulders and carry it to the church singing of psalms most of the way. If they meet a crossroad, the Bier is laid down and they rest. When the sentences of the offertory are read, the Nearest Relations come to the Communion table and there give the parson a piece of money 2/6 or a 1/- or a 6d or sometimes 3d, 2d or a penny. Then come all the parishioners and friends each offering according to his pleasure, when the show is over one of the deceased's Relations commonly counts the money and Returns them to the parson, to what purpose I don't know.

Lewis Morris, *Life and Works*

11.   *Customs in marriages*

The marriage Candle Large and dancing. The dead small and livid. Parson 5s on the book as after They come home from church dinner custards and paying on a plate drinking wooing, dancing, campio, each paying his shot, Fighting; putting the young couple in bed, Throwing the Stocking, drinking posset.

In their way to church Plays fiddles or harps and dance morris dances all the way. The bride handed by two young men, and the Bridegroom by two women, In a very Solemn manner.

Ibid.

12.   *Christenings*

In Christenings, when the Christening is over then the Father Invites home his friends and the parson to drink the health of the woman in the straw, and after dinner this they do for the first part so plentifully till they can drink no more for that day, money to the midwife, to the nurse and to the maid. Home stark drunk.

Ibid.

13.   *Churching Women*

In a week or fortnight's time at most among the poorer sort, The Mother walks to the parish church to be churched and takes along with her her midwife. Offers a 12d or 6d if poor.

Ibid.

14.   *Lesser Customs and Coelion (beliefs)*

Lesser customs and coelion should be handled in Welsh so as not to give other nations occasion to Laugh at us; only Interpreting their Names in English, as for cowsai — cheesing.

Coel (ion).   Gweled oen bach ai din attoch, blwyddyn yn wysg ei thin. To see the first black snail, observe whether on soft or hard ground so your fortune.

A Swallow first seen look in your shoe you'll find a straw of colour of your sweetheart's hair.

To Hau cowarch. Throw 10th top over your head, wrap the rest up in cloth and put it under your pillow, going to bed, without speaking, and shall see your true love.

First Snake seen, if not killed, Loss or Sickness.

3 Shell snails from church wall put under a Leaf on a Table, nos glangaia, will write your sweetheart's name.

What strong effects superstitions have upon men!

Ibid.

15.   *Of the measures of length in Anglesey some of which answer over all Wales*

The least measure is

Modfedd   an Inch, a *Bawd*, a thumb, and meddu, to possess
q.d. Bawdfedd

drynfedd, 4 inches, a Palm, a dwrn, a Fist, etc., dyrnfedd corniog,
   6 inches, a hand and a length of thumb.
   Rhychwant, a pan, a Rhy and chwant.

Troedfedd, a Foot Long, a Troed, a man's foot, 8 Inch 2 Hands breadth.

Elin, a cubit, a Elin, an Elbow, because measured to the Elbow, Hence an Erll or Eln

Llath   Llath is properly the measure
Llathen   a yard
Llathen   the rod we measure with
Lathaid   Llathaid the Cloth or thing measured
   for Llath signifies in Geometry the Radius of a thing as,
   Llath fesur.

Gwrhyd, 6 foot, a Fathom, a Gwr, man and hyd, Length, and it is observed among Mathematicians that the true proportion of a man's Length is what he can fathom, but this meant of a well proportioned man.

Rhwd, a Rod of 8 yards to measure Hedges, which is the pole or Perch for Hedge measure.

Milldir, a Mile or mile pillar or mark, at the end of a Thousand Leaps, or Long Paces, each 9 foot.

Ibid.

16. *The Hiring of Servants*

The hiring of servants is chiefly managed here at a statute fair, and the love of change among these people seems to be so strong and capricious both here and throughout the country, that their services may be said to be almost always in a state of circulation. A disposition to resist a practice attended with so much trouble and inconvenience begins, I understand, to manifest itself, and will, I suppose, prove successful, as in the arts of plotting and combination masters seem hitherto to have very fully maintained their superiority. At this place only within Caernarvonshire I observed the custom of women going about with naked feet to be established and common. The custom may be ridiculed or reprobated or pitied according to the disposition of the persons by whom it is first observed upon their coming out of lands where the use of shoes and stockings is universal; but that it is contributive to cleanliness I have myself no doubt. The practice is for the females coming to market, church, etc. to bring with them in their hands their shoes and stockings until they reach the stream nearest their place of destination. There they sit down, perform their ablutions, and clothe their feet, which have thus the advantage of going to the assembly fresh washed.

E. Hyde Hall, *A Description of Caernarvonshire*

17. *The Farmers of Lleyn*

Nowhere, even in Wales, are there thriftier, harder working and more independent farmers than those of Lleyn. The women milk the cows, make the butter, and look after the marketing of lesser products, and work in the fields in hay and even harvest time. The men do all the outdoor work, only hiring labour, which as elsewhere in Wales is scarce and dear, when absolutely compelled to. Farmhouse fare is of a notoriously Spartan kind all over North Wales, and nowhere more so than here. Fresh meat is rarely tasted. Here, as elsewhere, it is customary to kill the least marketable beast upon the place, a dry cow or a venerable bull, and put it into brine for the year's supply of meat. Pieces are then cut off it from time to time by the careful housewife, and used to strengthen or subsidise the staple dishes of the table. In nine farmhouses out of ten in Caernarvonshire the menu will be much as follows. For breakfast, barley bread and buttermilk; for dinner, potatoes and buttermilk, with a piece of salt meat from the brine pot; for tea, bread with butter or cheese, while porridge and buttermilk are served for supper when the day's work is ended.

S. Baring-Gould, *A Book of North Wales,* 1903

18. *Beaumaris, a fashionable bathing-place*

Beaumaris (or the *Beau Marais* of former days) has been converted into a fashionable bathing-place, where idlers in search of pleasure, and multitudes in quest of health, resort to invent and find perpetual amusement, or to recruit exhausted strength and spirits. When I was contemplating the motley group that sauntered away the morning on what is called 'the Green' — a projecting shore of fine filtrating gravel, covered with short grass, which forms one of the horns of the bay, and has become, from its healthy and attractive situation, the mall of the place — I turned to the waiter of one of the hotels that was standing hard by, with my usual enquiry to such a sagacious and discriminating personage, on like occasions: — 'Why, Sir,' he said, 'this is the place where the *Reg'lars*, as we call them, and the *Short-allowance Gentlemen* turn out, the one to walk themselves into an appetite for the forthcoming-meal, while the latter stand looking upon objects which they have seen for a thousand times before, that they may deceive themselves into forgetfulness of such a thing, and make *one* meal answer for *two*.'

'Well, but, my good friend,' I replied, 'I do not comprehend your distinctions: what do you mean by the terms you apply to those gentlemen, both active and passive?'

'Why, Sir,' he rejoined, 'I suppose you have not been in Blue Morris before, or you would have understood me. You must know, then, that the party before you taking so many Berkeley strides, as if, like the Colonel, they were walking for a wager, are the *Reg'lars*, who pay by the week for all the meals the day will afford, and they are preparing themselves for the bell that will ring them at two o'clock to the dinner table.'

'The *Short-allowance Gentlemen*, on the contrary, are those who pay for each separate meal which they take. These you will always find, at this hour, earnestly contemplating Puffin's island, as if they had discovered some new beauties in the place, and had no leisure left for eating, on purpose that they may make the morning breakfast hold out till supper time.'

Thomas Roscoe, *Wanderings and Excursions in North Wales*

19. WELSH HISTORY

We were a people taut for war; the hills
Were no harder, the thin grass
Clothed them more warmly than the coarse
Shirts our small bones.
We fought, and were always in retreat,
Like snow thawing upon the slopes
Of Mynydd Mawr; and yet the stranger

Never found our ultimate stand
In the thick woods, declaiming verse
To the sharp prompting of the harp.

Our kins died, or they were slain
By the old treachery at the ford.
Our bards perished, driven from the halls
Of nobles by the thorn and bramble.

We were a people bred on legends,
Warming our hands at the red past.
The great were ashamed of our loose rags
Clinging stubbornly to the proud tree
Of blood and birth, our lean bellies
And mud houses were a proof
Of our ineptitude for life.

We were a people wasting ourselves
In fruitless battles for our masters,
In lands to which we had no claim,
With men for whom we felt no hatred.

We were a people, and are so yet.
When we have finished quarreling for crumbs
Under the table, or gnawing the bones
Of a dead culture, we will arise,
Armed, but not in the old way.

R. S. Thomas

20. NANT GWRTHEYRN

Before the bolted breakfast and the rush
To reach the yet unmissionaried depths of home
We had decided, with that instant faith
Which small boys use for certainty, it was a cave.
Stone cliffs as high as sight surrounded us
Along three sides encasing tracts in whose enormity
There surely lodged at least one wizard, several kings
And umpteen elves all reasonably tame.
Sometimes we joined them, feasting on such splendid fare
As boys prepare in the busy kitchens of the mind.

On days of doubt, which always came with cloud,
It could have been some gaping beast which gobbled us,
Though not on purpose, since deep inside his fat, primeval belly
The flesh was sweet and green and smelled of celandines.
And out beyond the flinty jaws he had a mouth of seaside
Stuffed with sand and starfish and such rare snips
As kinder oceans bring for boys on beaches.
Some days the seas brought only stones but none as precious
As the one so big, we hoped, would seal our cave
In final insulation of our faith; it never came.

Much later over milk in classroom without benefit of biscuits
We had deduced our stony confines were a school.
The rock was hard. Ths school was made from rock, and hard.
So was the teacher sometimes, hard as flint.
Especially on Mondays. Secret drinker we were told.
Made his own. And needed to be secret
To drink on Sundays. Regretted Mondays.
But other times he spoke in wondrous recipes which made
Us almost taste the stone, sensing a hint of kin
As though it were some cast, ancestral spawn
Which gave us birth and life and even decoration in our death.
'Stone is a gift from God,' he'd say and turn
To Geography which was all gorse and grit
To which we listened, never quite believed
And knew he never quite expected it.

Was it at lunch when we first felt the stone
Was something which my father called security?
Not just the dumplings, solid though they were
Nor Mam, all aproned and available,
Or Grandad's cough, each quarter hour, like chimes,
Or grace on Sundays when the roast arrived.
It was that through each window of the house
The rock wrapped round us like an overcoat
Buttoned with boulders, pine sewn with heather-hem
Cocooning us from cold and heathen gusts
And winds and storms which other people had.
Inside our private stone, hewn from the mother rock,
We wintered, doubly wrapped and warm.

Or was it in chapel on stiff suited Sundays
When answers came to those confused in pew?
Not preacher's words, which offered nourishment of sorts,
But words of prayer which seem to rise above the stone
Beyond the buzzards, birds of prey.
And louder still the singing till the air
Hung thick with hymn ascending and crescending
Through one great vital chancel whose walls were tall
And true and carved for choirs; in one almighty mixing bowl
Of glorying to God and man and stone and song
All undivided, indivisible, to men whose flesh appeared
To fall from them in dust on doorsteps before tea
And yet who found a kind of worship in their work.
Our fathers, which ate their heaven
Who gorged the stone and spewed it out on strangers' soil
In little geomteric heaps for people to have babies in.
For stone was barter for our bread and bread was stone
And home was stone and familied with children
Quarried from the basalt of their faith
Preserved and sealed with everlasting contract.

It was at supper when they said the stone had died
From something which they felt was lack of need.
No call for it, they said, although the men
Had always listened when there was, responding as they did
More from tradition than tomorrow's custom.
God, in my wisdom, though not his, I thought
Had now removed and found another house
Made out of brick and plastic slate which never knew
The dust of men, somewhere beyond Caernarvon.
And we were moving too, like stone age men
Released from darkness into deeper dark,
Which comes from fear of finding more than loss.

On the beach with furniture and birds in cages
Waiting to be funnelled into lurching boats
I looked back once more at my village rock.
The walls were tall and towered still
But were they greyer, colder than before?
And were the chilly summits curving in?

As though to reunite in roof, enclosing emptiness?
There was no doubting now. It was a tomb,
A silent, songless, fresh vacated sepulchre.
Down in the tide the slowly shoving sea
Still pushed its pebbled debris to the sand
But not the final stone. We knew that would not come.
There was no call for it. The Occupant had gone.
Leaving three lines of print inside a glossy guide
For tourists who descend on Sundays with their sandwiches
And go home hungry.

Geoffrey Newson

Note: In 1960 the last family left the mountain village of Nant Gwrtheyrn and it fell ito ruins. Now it has been renovated as a Welsh Language Centre.

21.　*The Women's Institute*

Canada was the country destined to be the original home of the Women's Institute movement. The first Women's Institute in the world, founded at Stoney Creek by Mrs John Hoodless and Mr Erland Lee, was an offshoot of the Farmers' Institute there, of which Mr Erland Lee, himself a farmer at Stoney Creek, was indefatigable secretary.

It is the pride, but not the boast, of Llanfairpwll that it was the first village in Great Britain to found a Women's Institute.

Llanfairpwll, September 11th, 1915
An open meeting was held at Graig on September 11th, 1915, when it was decided to form a branch of the Women's Institutes. The following committee was elected:

President — the Hon. Mrs Stapleton-Cotton
Vice-President & Treasurer — Mrs W. E. Jones, Graig
Hon. Secretary — Mrs Wilson, Bryn
Committee — 　Mrs Williams, Tremarfon
　　　　　　　Mrs Morris-Jones, Tŷ Coch
　　　　　　　Mrs Edwards, Tyddyn Fadog
　　　　　　　Mrs Jones, Bron Llwyn
　　　　　　　Miss B. Prichard, Menai House
　　　　　　　Miss Watts, Aberbraint
　　　　　　　Miss Roberts, Post Office

September 16th

At this meeting Mrs Watt, of the Women's Institutes, Canada, now with the Agricultural Organization Society, explained the object of the movement.

The following resolutions were put to the meeting and carried:

1. Proposed by Mrs Cotton, seconded by Miss Roberts,
   That we form a Women's Institute in Llanfairpwll, affiliated to the Agricultural Organization Society.
2. Proposed by Mrs Cotton, seconded by Mrs W. E. Jones,
   That it be called the *Llanfairpwll Women's Institute.*
3. Proposed by Mrs Cotton, seconded by Mrs J. R. Williams,
   That regular monthly meetings, of an educational and social character, be held on the first Tuesday in each month, at 2 p.m., in the room kindly lent by Mrs W. E. Jones, until such time as the Women's Institute has its own bulding.
4. Proposed by Mrs Wilson, seconded by Mrs Jones, Bron Llwyn,
   That the membership fee be 2/-, paid in advance, at the annual meeting to be held in January of each year. That new members be proposed by an existing member. That members be not confined to Llanfairpwll parish.

F. W. Wilson, *Hon. Sec.*

C. Davies, *A Grain of Mustard Seed*

22. *The Ghost of Archbishop Williams*

Betty Jones had a shop at Twr, Bethesda, which occupied the site of a house once occupied by Dr John Williams, Lord Keeper under James I and Archbishop of York under Charles I. Dr Williams could not have been as popular with King Charles as he had been with King James; indeed, he spent a period in the Tower of London for 'subornation of perjury' before he became archbishop — but in the Great Rebellion he supported the King and fortified Conway Castle where he was responsible for the safe keeping of certain treasure. When the Scots held the King prisoner, Dr Williams made terms with the Parlimentary forces and surrendered Conway Castle, whereupon one Sir John Owen, acting upon an old letter of the King's seized the Castle and procured the treasure. Dr Williams retired to obscurity and died in 1650.

One day, Betty encountered in her shop an apparition; a seemingly solid figure whom she recognized as Archbishop Williams, and he indicated that she was to dig for treasure at Tyn Twr and remove it so that he could find peace. She went to a certain spot in her garden at the time indicated and there waited, as she had been told, to watch for two stagecoaches to pass over a nearby bridge. Suddenly she heard a voice say, 'Take them!' and in her surprise she fainted and when she recovered, gave up the enterprise.

A day or so later the ghost of the archbishop again appeared to her and told her not to be frightened but to take the money she would find under a pillar in the garden. Summoning her courage, Betty argued with the ghost, saying she did not wish to look for the treasure and someone else could have it. The archbishop's ghost pleaded with her to find the money and eventually she agreed on the understanding that it should go not to her but to her youngest son when he came of age. This was not to be, however, for her youngest son joined the Army and died in India before reaching the age of twenty-one.

But, curiously enough, Betty Jones made no atempt to find the treasure; and it was not until some years later that a father and his son, digging in the garden prior to making alterations to the property, found the treasure referred to by the ghost.

'What it amounted to,' concludes Mr Williams, is this: 'no one outside the family ever knew for succeeding generations who preserved that secret.' The moral seems to be to always act on the advice of a ghost but unfortunately, very few of them speak!

Peter Underwood, *Ghosts of Wales*

23.   The strange fast of Mary Thomas of Barmouth

In a former visit to this place, (Barmouth) my curiosity was excited to examine into the truth of a surprising relation of a woman in the parish of *Cylynin*, who has fasted a most supernatural length of time. I took boat, had a most pleasant passage up the harbour, charmed with the beauty of the shores, intermixed with woods, verdant pastures, and cornfields. I landed, and, after a short walk, found, in a farm called *Tyddyn Bach*, the object of my excursion, *Mary Thomas*, who was boarded here, and kept with great humanity and neatness.

She was of the age of forty-seven, of a good countenance, very pale, thin, but not so much emaciated as might be expected, from the strangeness of the circumstances I am going to relate; her eyes weak, her voice low, deprived of the use of her lower extremities, and quite bed-ridden; her pulse rather strong, her intellects clear and sensible.

On examining her, she informed me, that at the age of seven, she had some eruptions like the measles, which grew confluent and universal; and she became so sore, that she could not bear the least touch: she received some ease by the application of a sheep's skin, just taken from the animal. After this she was seized, at spring and fall, with swellings and inflammations, during which time she was confined to her bed; but in the intervals could walk about; and once went to *Holywell*, in hopes of cure.

When she was about twenty-seven years of age, she was attacked with the same complaint, but in a more violent manner; and during two years and a half, remained insensible, and took no manner of nourishment, notwithstanding her friends forced open her mouth with a spoon, to get something down; but the moment the spoon was taken away, her teeth met, and closed with cast snapping and violence; during that time, she flung up vast quantities of blood.

She well remembers the return of her senses, and her knowledge of everybody about her. She thought she had slept but a night, and asked her mother whether she had given her anything the day before, for she found herself very hungry. Meat was brought to her; but, so far from being able to take anything solid, she could scarcely swallow a spoonful of thin whey. From this, she continued seven years and a half without any food or liquid, excepting sufficient of the latter to moisten her lips. At the end of this period, she again fancied herself hungry, and desired an egg; of which she got down the quantity of a nut kernel. About this time, she requested to receive the sacrament; which she did, by having a crumb of bread steeped in the wine. After this, she takes for her daily subsistence a bit of bread, weighing about two penny-weights seven grains, and drinks a wine glass of water; sometimes a spoonful of wine: but frequently abstains whole days from food and liquids. She sleeps very indifferently: the ordinary functions of nature are very small, and very seldom performed. Her attendant told me, that her disposition of mind was mild; her temper even; that she was very religious, and very fervent in prayer: the natural effect of the state of her body, long unembarrassed with the grossness of food, and a constant alienation of thought from all worldy affairs. She at this time (1786) continues in the same situation, and observes the same regimen.

Thomas Pennant, *Tours in Wales*

24. *The Battle of Beaumaris*

If war hit Beaumaris, it was a glancing blow. When the German planes passed over us on their way to Liverpool, the inhabitants turned out and stood on the Green to view the distant firework display, and when the planes returned the voice of the local school mistress was heard to shrill: 'Don't worry, girls, empty jerries — merely empty jerries.' The dear lady still doesn't know why rude-minded people laughed. If by any chance a stray bomb did drop it was quite an event. and charabanc excursions were taken to view the crater.

In those early days there were no shelters and no air-raid siren: warning of air attack was given by a whistle blown by a certain Councillor. He was a nice little man, small with ruddy complexion and always accompanied by a little terrier dog who obviously adored him. He usually started blowing his whistle outside the White Lion, but being conscientious he would pause to pop his head round the door of 'the snug' to make sure his warning had been heard. Then naturally somebody said: 'Thirsty work, that, Councillor — what about a pint?', and by the time the Sailor's Return had been reached, nobody knew whether the Councillor was blowing the Alert or the All Clear. If Wilfred Pickles asked me who I would pin a medal on, I would award it, posthumously, to that little Councillor. His love of duty cost him his life.

It was an unfortunate mishap, and occurred during the Home Guard invasion exercise. In a small place like Beaumaris, untouched by real war, the mock invasion was an event of tremendous importance. There had been weeks of preparation and on the great day the 'corpses and injured' were carefully labelled and laid out in the car-park behind the White Lion, ready for the ladies of the Red Cross to deal with. The ladies of the Red Cross, led by a local doctor's wife, were a highly efficient body of women. Every Monday and Thursday they made bandages, and as they trooped in, they donned white gowns and white tennis shoes. Even Miss Editha, who was deaf, had to have a special white cover for her ear-trumpet. Cigarettes were, of course, taboo, so several of the ladies abandoned the Sewing Bee to serve in the Red Cross White Elephant Shop, where the smell of smoke was more apt to disinfect the atmosphere than pollute it.

So, on the night of the Invasion, two ladies of the Red Cross, one a smoker and the other a non-smoker, arrived at the car-park behind the White Lion to deal with the injured.

'Send for the Ambulance!' said Mrs Non-Smoker to Mrs Smoker, with authority.

'Ridiculous!' snorted Mrs S., consulting the label on the body. 'This man is as good as dead — we will pass on to the next.'

'Oh, no we won't!' all-but spat Mrs N.S. 'While there is life there is hope — send for the Ambulance.'

'I will do no such thing!' shrieked Mrs S. 'This man is dead — our duty is to the living.'

After a painful ten minutes it was decided to consult the doctor for a ruling on the matter. It was while the ladies had gone to the doctor's house that the Councillor came out of the White Lion. It had been cosy in 'the snug', and he was beautifully warm, both inside and out. Being a compassionate man, his heart bled for the bodies lying on the cold ground of the car-park.

'Wot ye lying there for, ye daft so-and-so's! Get up and b——— off home!'

The bodies needed no further encouragement, and when the ladies of the Red Cross arrived with their Medical Officer — the cupboard was bare!

Fired by the success of his humanitarian action, the Councillor then arrested the Umpire, locked him up in the gaol and lost the key. So until this day nobody knows who won the Battle of Beaumaris. In the commotion that followed, the Councillor was relieved of his duties, and took the matter so much to heart that he took to his bed and died — the little terrier sitting beside him to the last.

Winifred Brown, *No Distress Signals*

25.   *Mr Maddox and the Poet Shelley*

Just short of Tremadoc we pass below the green and well-timbered grounds of Tan-yr-allt, where stands the mansion that the creator of all this prosperity built and occupied, coming here in the year 1791. It seems a trifle ungrateful that the passing stranger as he pauses to gaze with some pardonable curiosity over the park wall, should, in nine cases out of ten, forget all about poor Mr Maddox and think only of the feckless poet who is so curiously and in such a strange manner identified with the spot . . .

. . . Shelley, it may be remembered, came to live here as a friend of Mr Maddox, whose engineering projects had fired his enthusiasm, and whose cause he aided both by money, circulars, and such interest as he possessed.

A. G. Bradley, *Highways and By-ways of North Wales,* 1898

26.   *Porthmadog Embankment*

Mr J. Williams, who had just sat down, would testify to them the sincerity and disinterestedness of his (Mr Shelley's) intentions. That man he was proud to call his friend — he was proud that Mr Williams permitted him to place himself on an equality with him; inasmuch as one yet a novice in the great drama of life, whose integrity was untried, whose strength was unascertained, must consider himself honoured when admitted on an equal footing with one who had struggled for twelve years with incessant and unparalleled difficulties, in honesty, faithfulness, and fortitude. As to Mr Madocks, he had never seen him — but if unshaken public spirit and patriotism — if zeal to accomplish a work of national benefit, be a claim, then has *he* the strongest. The Embankment at Tremadoc, is one of the noblest works of human power — it is an exhibition of human nature as it appears in its noblest and most natural state — benevolence — it saves, it does not destroy. Yes! the unfruitful sea once rolled where human beings now live and earn their honest livelihood. Cast a look round these islands, through the perspective of these times, — behold famine driving millions even to madness; and own how excellent, how glorious, is the work which will give no less than three thousand souls the means of competence. How can anyone look upon that work and hestitate to join me, when I here publicly pledge myself to spend the last shilling of my fortune, and devote the last breath of my life to this great, this glorious cause.

North Wales Gazette, 31 September, 1814

27. CAERNARFON, 2 JULY 1969

Castle to castle —
Is there peace?

Those who came for a song
In Lloyd George's parlour
And for a hooray on the field have gone

The cheer and the boo have gone,
And the proper hats of all the Prince's aunts,
Everyone who said 'lovely', 'love', and 'thanks'.
The velvet cushions have gone:
Five guineas' worth of memories.

The policemen have gone,
And Scotland Yard's fill of suspicious names
And pictures and fingerprints.
The cameras and the microphones have gone,
And the cavalry and battalion of dragons
And the clamour about American tourists
And the cost of the plainclothesmen's Bed and Breakfast
And all the rush for the special stamps
Gone.

On the quay, the soldier has gone
In a fiery chariot like some chapter from the Old Testament,
And the cry of Llywelyn has gone
And of Owain Glyndwr and status and 1282.

The sober signified benches
Have become a hundred thousand planks
What they were before yesterday and long days before.

Another Prince has started on his journey:

Castle to castle:
Is there peace?

T. Glynne Davies

28.   WELSH INCIDENT

'But that was nothing to what things came out
From the sea-caves of Criccieth yonder.'
'What were they? Mermaids? dragons? ghosts?'
'Nothing at all of any things like that.'
'What were they, then?'
                              'All sorts of queer things,
Things never seen or heard or written about,
Very strange, un-Welsh, utterly peculiar
Things. Oh, solid enough they seemed to touch,
Had anyone dared it. Marvellous creation,
All various shapes and sizes, and no sizes,
All new, each perfectly unlike his neighbour,
Though all came moving slowly out together.'
'Describe just one of them.'
                              'I am unable.'
'What were their colours?'
                              'Mostly nameless colours,
Colours you'd like to see; but one was puce
Or perhaps more like crimson, but not purplish.
Some had no colour.'
                              'Tell me, had they legs?'
'Not a leg nor foot among them that I saw.'
'But did these things come out in any order?
What o'clock was it? What was the day of the week?
Who else was present? How was the weather?'
'I was coming to that. It was half-past three
The Harlech Silver Band played *Marchog Iesu*
On thirty-seven shimmerinng instruments,
Collecting for Carnarvon's (Fever) Hospital Fund.
The population of Pwllheli, Criccieth,
Portmadoc, Borth, Tremadoc, Penrhyndeudraeth,
Were assembled. Criccieth's mayor addressed them
First in good Welsh and then in fluent English,
Twisting his fingers in his chain of office,
Welcoming the things. They came out on the sand,
Not keeping time to the band, moving seaward
Silently at a snail's pace. But at last
The most odd, indescribable thing of all,

Which hardly one man there could see for wonder
Did something recognizably a something.'
'Well, what?'
                              'It made a noise.'
                                    'A frightening noise?'
'No, no.'
        'A musical noise? A noise of scuffling?'
'No, but a very loud, respectable noise —
Like groaning to oneself on Sunday morning
In Chapel, close before the second psalm.'
'What did the mayor do?'
                              'I was coming to that.'

Robert Graves

X

THE ROADS

1. *Roman Road*

On leaving the N.E. gate of Segontium the (Roman) road must have run almost direct for some 2¾ miles in a north-easterly direction along the summit of the ridge of land which at first divides the Cadnant valley from the course of the Seiont, and further on forms the north-western boundary of the valley down which flows the stream known as the Cegin. Traces of an old road are said to have been found in the second field to the S.E. of the cottage known as Caegarw, rather less than a mile from the fort, and close to the small post by Bryn glas. Probably the road passed to the S.E. of this post and worked its way in a straight line to the top of the ridge by Erw pwll y glo, thence following the line of the modern road to a point near Glan yr afon, but probably a few yards to the north-west of it and, like it, taking a turn just beyond Glan yr afon. From this point a series of hedges and footpaths carries on in a direct line to the Rectory and the junction of the roads at Llanddeiniolen, five-eighths of a mile N.W. of the important hill-fort of Pen y ddinas, or Dinas Dinorwig. Hereabouts, but apparently a mile and a half S.E. of the hill-fort, among the remains of a group of hut circles near Llys Dinorwig, was found the milestone of Trajan Decius, now in the garden at Pant afon.

The next fixed point is the farm of Tŷ coch by Pant Caerhûn on the W. side of the ravine cut by the Cegin on its way down to the Menai Straits. Just above the house was found the second milestone (of Caracallus) in the year 1806. It had, however, been destroyed by 1810 when Richard Fenton visited the site. There are no obstacles to a direct route between Llandeiniolen and Tŷ coch, and a contributor to *Archaeologia Cambrensis* in 1846 (p. 420) records 'faint indications of a raised way' between Tŷ coch and Segontium along the route here described. Fenton also records signs of a road close to the house. The same writer's suggestion that an old lane leading from the river Ogwen up to Maes y groes, in a direct line between that place and Ty coch, indicates a course for the road is likely to be correct, but the sites of the actual crossings of the Cegin and the Ogwen have yet to be identified.

From Maes y groes to Aber the line is likely to have been almost direct; no actual remains of the road are now to be seen, but it probably ran between the new and old roads, and crossed the river near the Norman castle mount. A short distance beyond this point the ascent of the hills began, not, as is shown on the maps, up the valley, but round the lower face of the hill above Gorddinog, on the western spur of which is the hill fort known as Maes y gaer. The Nant yr eflin fach was probably crossed near the Gorddinog Kennels and the eastern slopes of the valley followed, past the site of the discovery of two more milestones (of Hadrian and of Severus the way probably led almost directly to Bwlch y ddeufaen, joining the 'Ordnance map route' at about a mile from the farm. Fenton is in favour of the route here given from the crossing of the Ogwen, and rejects as improbable the line up the river valleys from Aber.

By the time the road passes through the Bwlch y ddeufaen it has climbed up 1400 feet and it drops down to sea level again in the course of its next four miles to Kanovium (Caerhûn). The latter part of the route it followed here is doubtful, but the probabilities are in favour of its having descended along the S. side of the valley drained by the Afon Roe, after crossing that stream at or near Pont Hafotty Gwyn, and run almost due E. to the fort (crossing the stream again on the way), its entry into which was noted by Fenton.

Sir Mortimer Wheeler, *Segontium and the Roman Occupation of Wales*

2. *Penmaen Mawr. Dangerous road*

In past times it was justly the terror of the traveller; extremely narrow, bad and stoney; and what added to his fears, for a considerable way the danger increased with his progress, by reason of the precipice gaining additional height. Generally it was without protection of a wall to secure him in case of a false step; which might in the loftiest place precipitate him some scores of yards, either on sharp rocks or into the sea, according to the state of the tide. A vein of a crumbling stratum, in one part so contracted the road as to excite new horrors. The *British* parliament eased the fears of the travellers by a generous aid; which, by means of the judicious employment of John Sylvester, about the year 1772, effected what was before thought beyond the reach of art to remedy. The road is now widened to a proper breadth, and near the verge of the precipice secured by a strong wall. The descent towards *Penmaen Bach*, or the Little Penmaen, which before was hardly practicable, is now destroyed; and the road is brought on a level for two or three miles, at a vast height above a return of rich slopes, and the deep bottom of *Dwygyfylchau*, till we arrive at the rude back of that lesser promontory; when we labour up the steep ascent of *Sychnant*, with a horrible and almost precipitous mountain on one side, and hills, with tops broken into most singular crags, on the other. From the top of *Sychnant*, the road is continued about two miles on a perpetual descent to the town of *Conway*.

The breach occasioned by the crumbling stratum, is now effectually repaired by a series of arches; a work the just admiration of travellers, and a high credit to the ingenious contriver. One danger yet remains, which must for ever baffle the art of man: the side of this great rock, above the road, breaks into millions of vast masses, depending often on precarious tenures; which, loosened by the frequent torrents, sometimes (though rarely) descend in stoney streams.

Two or three accidents, which have happened on this road, will remain as miracles. An exciseman fell from the highest part, and escaped unhurt. The reverend Mr *Jones*, who, in 1762, was rector of *Llanelian*, in the isle of *Anglesey*, fell with his horse, and a midwife behind him, down the steepest part. The *sage femme* perished, as did the nag. The divine, with great philosophy, unsaddled the steed, and marched off with the trappings, exulting at his preservation.

I have often heard of another accident, attended with such romantic circumstances that I would not venture to mention it, had I not the strongest traditional authority, to this day in the mouth of everyone in the parish of *Llanvair Vechan*, in which this promontory stands. Above a century ago, *Siôn Humphries* of this parish had made his addresses to *Anne Thomas* of *Creyddyn*, on the other side of *Conway* river. They had made an appointment to meet at a fair in the town of *Conway*. He on his way fell over *Penmaen Mawr*: she was overset in the ferryboat, and was the only person saved out of more than four score. They were married, and lived very long together in the parish of *Llanvair*. She was buried *April* 11th, 1744, aged 116. He survived her five years, and was buried *December* 10th, 1749; was buried close by her in the parish churchyard, where their graves are familiarly shown to this day.

Thomas Pennant, Tour of Wales

3. *Holyhead Road*

Work on the Holyhead road went on for fifteen years, although long before it was finally completed coaches were able to run through to Holyhead. The great expenditure both in money and time was partly due to the high cost of the road-building technique which Telford had perfected in the Highlands. It is because of this high cost that Macadam is better known as a road maker than Telford. Macadam was content to level the ground and lay his road metal upon it without any massive foundation, claiming that a certain resilience in the surface was an advantage and easier on horses. Whether this was true or not, the speed, the ease and the cheapness of Macadam's method led to his widespread employment by Turnpike Trusts throughout the country, whereas the roads to Holyhead from Shrewsbury and Chester are the only noteworthy examples of Telford's road-making south of the Border. But what roads they were! Telford built them in the Roman fashion and it was his boast that, like theirs, they would last for centuries.

Robert Southey, in his diary, tells us how Telford made his roads, and as his account is obviously based on the engineer's own explanation it is virtually first hand. 'The Plan upon which he proceeds in road-making is this,' Southey writes, 'first to level and drain; then, like the Romans, to lay a solid pavement of large stones, the round or broad end downwards, as close as they can be set; the points are then broken off, and a layer of stones broken to about the size of walnuts, laid over them, so that the whole are bound together; over all a little gravel if it be at hand, but this is not essential.' Telford laid great emphasis on the proper grading of the stone, and this graded stone was stored in kists or bins by the roadside for surfacing and for subsequent repairs . . .

. . . Work was begun on the worst and most dangerous sections west of Llangollen and by 1819 sufficient progress had been made for mail coaches to run through to Bangor with safety. Telford had decided that there must be no gradient steeper than 1 in 20 and this, in such mountainous country, involved more than mere side cutting. In places deep cuttings had to be blasted through rock and in others considerable embankments had to be formed or high retaining walls built. Proceeding westwards, the first of these difficult sections was between Berwyn and Glyn Dyfrdwy only a few miles west of Llangollen and there was another on the summit between the valleys of the Ceirw and the Conway. At Bettws-y-Coed the road crossed the Conway by the most notable of the bridges which were put in hand before 1817. This was a single span of iron which, needless to say, was cast by William Hazledine at Plas Kynaston and erected by William Stuttle. It is an extravagant masterpiece of the iron founder's art. The webs of the cast-iron girders consist of the inscription: 'This arch was constructed in the same year the battle of Waterloo was fought' in iron lettering, and the spandrels are filled by elaborate devices incorporating the emblems of the four nations: the rose, the leek, the thistle and the shamrock. It is a display of exuberance rare in Telford's work and unfortunately its proper appreciation involves clambering down to the riverside, so that it is wasted upon the thousands of motorists who hurry over the bridge every year.

The long winding ascent from Bettws-y-Coed to Capel Curig is a splendid piece of road engineering, but undoubtedly the highlight of the whole route is the section which follows — the road past Lake Ogwen and through the pass of Nant Ffrancon. Here, by masterly engineering in a setting of desolate grandeur which rivals anything on his Highland roads, Telford carried his road over the high summit on a ruling gradient of 1 in 22. It remains to this day by far the most easily graded of all the roads which traverse the North Wales massif. As the motorist speeds easily over the pass in top gear he pays tribute to the power which twentieth-century automobile engineering has built into his car, but seldom or never gives credit to the men who surveyed his road 140 years ago. At the head of the pass a cutting blasted through the rock and protected from rock falls by revetments, an embankment and a stone arch carries the road dramatically across the chasm through which the river Ogwen thunders down towards the floor of the valley.

Notwithstanding the dramatic splendours of the Nant Ffrancon pass, however, the most costly section of the whole road, excluding major bridges, was not here but a few miles from Holyhead where a narrow, silted strait separates Holy Island from the mainland of Anglesey. At the village of Valley in Anglesey the old road veered sharply to the south-west to cross this strait at its narrowest point by what is called the Four Mile Bridge. This involved a considerable detour and Telford decided to continue this last lap of his new road on a straight course, a decision which involved building a great embankment across the Stanley Sands reminiscent of the Mound at Dornoch Firth. It was 1,300 yards long, 16 feet high, 114 feet wide at base and 34 feet at top with sides protected against storm erosion by rubble walling, yet the contractors, Messrs Gill & Hodges, completed it in one year. It was opened in 1823.

So much for the Holyhead Road itself; there remained the greatest problem of all which, at the time of the 1815 survey, the Road Commissioners still hesitated to confront. This was the crossing of the Menai Straits. In the sixteenth century the Welsh seer, Robin Ddu of Bangor, delivered himself of the prophecy which appears at the head of this chapter. Translated it reads: 'Two years before tumult there will be a bridge over the Menai.' Like all the best prophets, Robin Ddu combined caution with a splendid dramatic sense. His words have a fine gnostic ring about them, yet even in the sixteenth century the need for a bridge was so obvious that its eventual construction was a fairly safe prediction. And as the affairs of men are such that not a year of recorded history has gone by without some major tumult breaking out somewhere or other in the world, the seer was taking no chances on the date question. However, those who honour such prophets would say that Robin Ddu was very far-sighted, for over two centuries were to pass before his bridge became a reality.

Within the lifetime of Robin Ddu the Menai Ferry rights were leased by Queen Elizabeth I to a certain John Williams, and they descended in his family down to the time with which we are here concerned when an average of 13,000 travellers a year were using this Anglo-Irish route. This traffic yielded John Williams's descendant, Miss Williams of Plas Isa, the not inconsiderable income of between £800 and £900 per annum. When the bridge was eventually built she was awarded at Assizes £26,557 compensation payable by the Holyhead Road Commissioners for the loss of her rights, a nice little nest egg for Sir David Erskine, Bart., whom she shortly afterwards married. The income which the Williams family had for so long enjoyed was derived from the discomfort of innumerable travellers. Notwithstanding all the hazards of the old road through the mountains, it was the crossing of the Menai which travellers most dreaded. The passage was always attended with discomfort and delay, if not with danger. Only in fair weather and calm seas, conditions which occurred seldom in winter, could coaches or carriages be conveyed across. Drovers were accustomed to swim their herds across at low water using the ancient cattle causeway which stretched from the Anglesey shore as far as the rock known as Ynys-y-

Moch (Pig Island) and cattle were not infrequently lost in the process.

Schemes for eliminating these difficulties and dangers by means of a bridge had often been debated. John Golborne produced in 1783 an optimistic proposal for a crossing at the Swilly Rocks which lie some distance south-west of Pig Island. This was to consist of an embankment built out to the rocks and a large lock for the passage of shipping on the Caernarvon side which the road would cross by a drawbridge. In January of the following year William Jessop reported in favour of a wooden bridge at Cadnant and in this case a Parliamentary Bill was promoted though the scheme came to nothing. Next, Rennie examined the Straits in 1801 and expressed himself in favour of a three-arch iron bridge at the Swilly Rocks. The only possible alternative, he thought, was the Pig Island site, but this would require a single arch of so great a span that he did not think it a practicable proposition.

The difficulty which ruled out all these schemes was the insistence of the Admiralty that navigation through the straits must not be obstructed but that vessels of the largest size must pass freely with masts erect. They would ot even countenance the temporary obstruction of the channel by the centering which would be required to build an arch bridge. These stipulations appeared to be crippling, for they called for an arch of unprecedented height and span and at the same time forbade engineers to use their accepted method of building it.

When Telford was first consulted about the Holyhead Road in 1810 he followed Rennie's lead by preparing two designs of cast iron bridges, one of three cast-iron arches of 260 feet span for the Swilly Rock site and the other a single span of 500 feet for Pig Island. To overcome objections to the latter he designed a system of suspended centering for which at that time there was no precedent. He proposed to erect a frame fifty feet high upon each abutment of the bridge. Winch cables would be led over rollers on the tops of these frames and would thus be able to lift the sections of the centering into their places and retain them there. It was really the suspension bridge principle adapted to build a rigid structure. Although it was never employed by Telford, this principle was subsequently used by later engineers, not merely for centering but for the erection of actual bridge spans. For reasons already mentioned, Telford's 1810 proposals came to nothing. In any event his designs allowed insufficient headroom to satisfy the Admiralty.

. . . In 1818 Sir Henry Parnell at last succeeded in forcing the

Holyhead Road Commissioners to face the fact that the Menai must be bridged and Telford was again asked to submit plans. His answer this time was to submit a design for a suspension bridge on the Pig Island site. This provided for a single suspended span of 579 feet with a headway of 100 feet which would satisfy the Admiralty. The two main piers, one standing upon the Caernarvon shore and the other on the island rock, would be extended to form the suspension towers, fifty feet above the roadway and 153 feet above high water in the Straits. These mighty piers, each pierced by arches for the carriage ways, were to be approached by seven lofty masonry arches each of 52 feet 6 inches span, three on the Caernarvon and four on the Anglesey side of the Straits. For the bridge platform Telford adopted the same dimensions as those shown in the Runcorn design, namely two carriageways each 12 feet wide separatd by a central footway 6 feet wide, making 30 feet overall. To support it there were to be sixteen chains composed of composite links each consisting of thirty-six bars of iron half an inch square. These figures may seem conservative when compared with the grandiose dimensions of the Runcorn bridge, yet they far exceeded those of any bridge ever built before and Telford's plan provoked almost as much scepticism and ridicule as had greeted Brindley's proposal for an aqueduct over the Irwell at barton so many years before. Nevertheless, thanks to the energetic championship of Sir Henry Parnell, the Holyhead Road Commissioners approved the design and an initial sum of £20,000 to enable work to begin was voted by virtue of their existing powers.

Carpenters were soon on the site erecting temporary wooden buildings for use as workshops and as accommodation for the men to be employed on the work. This done, blasting operations began on Pig Island to level a foundation for the great western pier. At this juncture, however, three influential local landowners, the Marquis of Anglesey, Owen Williams of Craig-y-Don and Asheton Smith, the owner of the Padarn slate quarries, succeeded in stirring up considerable opposition to the bridge in Caernarvon and work was stopped temporarily while the Commissioners appealed to the Government for special powers. The opposition hoped to win support from the Admiralty, Trinity House and the Menai pilots, but these bodies were satisfied that Telford's high-level bridge would not affect their interests and in 1819 the Commissioners obtained their Act authorising them to proceed with the bridge. Work was then resumed without delay. William Provis was appointed resident engineer,

Messrs Straphen and Hall were awarded the masonry contract and Telford himself went down to Bangor to superintend the start of operations.

A source of good hard grey limestone for the masonry work was found at Penmon on the extreme eastern tip of Anglesey, and this was brought by small coasters down the Strait to quays on both shores. A temporary embankment was built beside the old cattle causeway from the Anglesey shore to Pig Island and on this a railway was laid down to convey the stone for the Pig Island pier. It was here that the first stone was laid without any ceremony by William Provis. It was the middle block of the lowest course of the seaward face of the pier. A rock base for the Caernarvon pier was found on the shore six feet below low-water level. By the end of 1819, 200 men and five coasting vessels were at work.

In July 1823 he reported that the piers were up to roadway height, the towers begun and much of the ironwork ready for installation. In the same letter he mentions that work on the similar, though smaller, suspension bridge which he had designed to carry the Chester road over the Conway was also proceeding rapidly.

In order to provide an immovable anchorage for the great suspension chains, a series of tunnels, each six feet in diameter, were blasted through solid rock on the Anglesey side to a depth of about twenty yards. At this depth the tunnels were united by a single chamber in which was assembled and secured the massive cast-iron frame to which the chains were to be anchored. This frame was therefore securely buried beneath the mass of rock through which the chain tunnels passed. The latter were cut on an appropriate gradient so that the chains would follow a straight path from their subterranean anchorage to the top of the suspension tower. On the Caernarvon shore the procedure was similar, except that earth had to be tunnelled through for some distance before a suitable rock base for the iron frame was found. Here, therefore, massive walls of masonry took the place of natural rock between the chain tunnels, while the distance from tower top to anchorage had to be greater, thus unavoidably destroying the complete symmetry of the bridge.

It was only when these two anchorages had been positively sited in 1821 that Telford was able to settle the lengths and final details of the chains so that a contract for them could be placed with William Hazledine. The links, each a little over nine feet long, were wrought at Upton Forge which stood close by the Shrewsbury Canal near the village of Upton Magna. They were then sent by canal to Shrewsbury where each link was given a tensile test on a machine of Telford's design specially installed for the purpose in Hazledine's Coleham works. John Provis, William's younger brother, was placed in charge of this operation. From the protracted experiments which he had made, Telford had calculated that each link should be able to withstand a strain of $87\frac{3}{4}$ tons before fracture, but in order that there should be no risk of straining them he stipulated that the Coleham test should be limited to 325 tons. As this was equivalent to a load of 11 tons per square inch of cross section, whereas he had calculated that the maximum loading on the bridge would be equal to only $5\frac{1}{2}$ tons to the square inch, this gave the ample safety marin of 100 per cent. To protect them from the corrosive effect of the salt atmosphere the links were heated, plunged in a bath of linseed oil and then stove dried. To ensure accuracy of fitting a steel master link was made through which the three-inch pin holes in each link were bored on a special machine. Today this process would be called jig drilling.

As batches of the links were completed at Coleham they were sent by canal boat (presumably from the Ellesmere Canal wharf at Weston Lullingfields) to Chester, whence they were shipped by sea to the Menai . . .

. . . In building the Menai Bridge, Telford had no precedents to guide him and he therefore proceeded with extreme caution, never trusting to theory alone, but checking every move by practical experiment. Thus notwithstanding the Coleham tests, the first length of chain to be assembled was tested in tension by slinging it across the valley of the Cadnant brook which was near the site on the Anglesey side. At the same time Telford was able to calculate the power which would be needed to raise it into position on the bridge. A quarter-size model of one chain was also made and suspended so that the calculated lengths of the vertical suspension rods could be checked by actual measurement. While these tests were being made and the chains assembled, Wilson was pressing on with the building of the suspension towers. This was slower work than the piers below, for apart from their great height Telford had decreed that each stone must be dowelled to its neighbour by iron pegs. By the early spring of 1825, however, all the masonry work had been completed and all the chains assembled and fixed to their underground anchorages. Everything was therefore ready for the most delicate and dramatic operation of all — the slinging of the suspended portions of the great chains between the two towers.

One of Telford's characteristics which impressed his contemporaries was his imperturbability. The dangers, disasters and unexpected difficulties to which works such as he undertook are always subject he invariably confronted with an unruffled calm which seems to have come naturally to him. When he arrived in Bangor towards the end of April 1825 to superintend personally the slinging of the first suspension chain, if he appeared to his assistants as imperturbable as ever it was a composure sustained only by an exercise of will. For he confessed later that for weeks past he had been suffering from anxiety so acute that he could not sleep. Like every engineer who abandons all safe precedent and takes a bold step forward into the dark, Telford had found himself haunted by the ghosts of all the things which could go wrong despite all his care and foresight. It was imperative that the whole operation of raising the sixteen chains (each suspended portion weighing $23\frac{1}{2}$ tons), should proceed swiftly and smoothly, for the Commissioners had obtained Parliamentary powers to close the Strait to navigation while it was carried out.

The morning of 25 April broke brilliantly fine; the air still and the sea calm. Telford therefore determined to raise the first chain. The waters of the Menai were crowded with flag-bedecked boats and every vantage point on both shores was thronged with spectators as Telford's carefully worked out plan of operation was set in motion. The chain had been laid upon a raft 450 feet long and six feet wide which was moored near Treborth Mill on the Caernarvon shore and at 2.30 in the afternoon, about an hour before high water, this was cast off and swung out into the Menai towed by four boats. The crowd watched in silence while it was manoeuvred into position between the two great piers. On the Caernarvon side it was then attached to the landward portion of the chain which had been laid from its anchorage over the top of the suspension tower and down the face of the pier to within a foot or so of high-water mark. On the Anglesey side the chain had been laid from its anchorage to the top of the Pig Island pier. These passed over blocks on the top of the tower and from thence to capstans mounted on the Anglesey shore which were manned by a force of 150 men. As soon as the end of the chain had been securely grappled the men on the raft sang out 'go along' and a fife band struck up, keeping the time as the capstan gangs swung into action. As the cables tautened the shout went up 'Heave away! Now she comes!' and in a few moments a great cheer sounded from ships and shores as the long raft swung away on the tide and the chain was seen to be hanging free in a low arc over the water.

Slowly, slowly as the men circled their capstans the chain rose higher above the water until, after an hour and a half, its end had been drawn up to the top of the Pig Island tower. Telford had himself climbed to the top of the tower with John Wilson, William Provis and Thomas Rhodes to see the chain united. The crowd craned their necks to watch the small black figures grouped together on the giddy platform 150 feet above the sea. When they saw them lift their hats and wave them in the air they knew that the last link pin had been driven home and another mighty cheer went up which echoed and re-echoed from bank to bank across the Menai. The Welshmen who had laboured to such good purpose at the capstans were at once fortified with a quart of 'Cwrw da' apiece and the general excitement and hilarity was such that three of them, Hugh Davies, a stonemason, John Williams, a carpenter, and William Williams, a labourer, actually walked across the chain to the Caernarvon pier. As the chain was only nine inches wide and the curvature considerable, this was a foolhardy feat worthy of the great Blondin himself. Either they escaped Telford's notice or it was one of those lesser improprieties which, as he had told von Platen, 'he seemed not to know'.

The whole operation had been carried out without a hitch in two hours and twenty minutes from the time the raft had been cast off and it was repeated with the second chain two days later. Therafter a chain was raised whenever the weather served. The lifting of the sixteenth and last chain on the 9th of July was made an occasion for further ceremony. By this time the whole proceeding had become a matter of well-drilled routine, so that only one hour thirty minutes was taken to raise it. As soon as it was home a military band marched down a temporary wooden platform laid over the other chains and halted at the centre of the span where they played the National Anthem. While they played, the navigation through the Straits was formally re-opened by the steam packet *St David* of Chester, Captain D. Sarsfield, which, dressed over-all, steamed down the channel beneath.

While all this was going on at Bangor, work on the Conway Bridge had been proceeding rapidly and when all the Menai chains were in place, men and tackle were transferred to install the Conway chains. With a span of 327 feet between the suspension towers, Conway Bridge was a great work which would have received more notice from contemporaries had it not been overshadowed by the Menai Bridge. It was one of the rare examples (Tongueland and Craigellachie were others) in which Telford departed from that severely functional style which he adopted for nearly all his bridge work. In deference to the proximity of Conway Castle, Telford designed suspension towers in the form of castellated medieval gateways. Like Wolfe Barry's later Tower Bridge where the presence of the Tower of London exerted a similar influence, the romanticism of Telford's Conway Bridge has since been the subject of harsh criticism from architects of the functionalist school. This is a very controversial question. There is truth in the functional argument but it is limited and like all limited truths it can easily be carried to excess. The evidence of this is painfully apparent in too much of the architecture and civil engineering work of today. Such uncompromising functionalism repels us by its arrogant contempt for its surroundings, and if it be said that Telford went to the opposite extreme of false compromise, at least he displayed an intelligent respect for the past which is sadly lacking today. Many would say that he did succeed in his intention of welding bridge and castle into one harmonious composition.

The heaviest work at Conway was not the building of the bridge itself but the formation of its approach embankment over the sands of the tidal river. Two thousand and fifteen feet long and 300 feet broad at the base, this was a work comparable in magnitude with the Stanley Sands embankment in Anglesey. On the site of the bridge the tides run so swiftly through the narrow channel that to use a raft for carrying the chains across as at the Menai would have been a difficult and dangerous undertaking. Fortunately, therefore, thanks to the shorter span, a different and less spectacular method of slinging them was evolved. Twelve of the 6½-inch ropes used for raising the Menai chains were stretched across the river from tower to tower at the correct curvature and upon them a stout timber platform was built on which the chains could be asembled link by link.

Once all the chains had been successfully slung, the building of the suspended roadway platforms was a straightforward and comparatively rapid undertaking and both bridges were opened to traffic in 1826, the Menai at the end of Jannuary and the Conway on 1 July. It is characteristic of Telford, who hated pomp and circumstance, that the opening of the largest bridge in Britain was not attended by any ceremony or officially organised junketing. No major engineering work in history can have had a stranger and less ostentatious inauguration, for it took place in wild weather in the dead of a winter's night. For those few who took part in it, however, the drama of the occasion must have remained with them always.

It was after midnight on 30 January, a pitch dark night and blowing hard, when the Down Royal London and Holyhead Mail came over the Nant Ffrancon Pass. David Davies held the ribbons and the guard was William Read. Waiting for it on the outskirts of Bangor was William Provis and he stepped into the road when he heard above the soughing of the wind the cry of Read's post horn. Davies reined in his horses and in the glimmering light of the coach lamps Provis clambered aboard. The next stop was at the Bangor Ferry Inn. Here quite a party had been keeping vigil, determined to be amongst the first to cross the bridge by coach. There was Akers, the mail coach superintendent, William Hazledine, John Provis, Thomas Thodes, the two young Wilsons and as many more as could find a precarious foothold on the coach. Round the bend of the road the lights of the bridge, special sperm oil lanterns made by James De Ville of London, starred the darkness over Anglesey and threw serpentine reflections on the storm-tossed water far below. So, at 1.35 a.m. on that winter morning while the great chains overhead stirred uneasily and the wind howled through the suspension rods, the first coach rumbled over the Menai and the bridge was opened.

No matter what Telford might think and notwithstanding the fact that daylight brought heavy rain, the local inhabitants were not going to allow the occasion to pass without celebration. Soon after it was daylight a procession of carriages and coaches began to cross the bridge. In the first carriage rode A. E. Fuller, one of the Commissioners, and in the second Telford accompanied by Sir Henry Parnell. Then followed three coaches, the Bangor stage coach *Pilot*, the Caernarvon day coach and the first London stage coach, the *Oxonian*. Next came Sir David Erskine driving himself in a carriage drawn by four splendid greys decorated with ribbons. He headed a seemingly endless procession of vehicles of every kind from the gleaming carriages of the local gentry to farmers' gigs and small pony carts. At mid-day the weather cleared and all that afternoon wheeled traffic and foot passengers moved over the bridge continuously while bands played, cannon crashed out and innumerable flags fluttered in the wind.

It would seem that, having crossed the bridge first thing in the morning, Telford drove straight on to Shrewsbury, for the next day William Provis addressed the following vivid account of the subsequent proceedings to him at the Talbot Hotel. 'The concourse of people who passed over yesterday was immense,' wrote Provis. 'At one time the Bridge was so crowded that it was difficult to move along. Most of the carriages of the neighbouring gentry, stage coaches, Post Chaises, gigs and horses, pressed repeatedly over and kept up a continuous procession for several hours. The demand for tickets was so great that they could not be issued fast enough and many in the madness of their joy threw their tickets away that they might have the pleasure of paying again. Not a single accident nor an unpleasant occurrence took place and everyone appeared satisfied with the safety of the bridge and delighted that they could go home and say 'I crossed the first day it was opened.' The receipts were about £18.

'A good dinner having been provided at Mr Jackson's, a party assembled there to make themselves merry and drink "Success to the bridge". William Hazledine, Esq., having been called to the chair, kept up the life and spirit of the evening with his wit and funny stories; and there being a general feeling to receive all sorts of good things, they were soon as happy and joyous as could be wished.' Evidently William Provis shared this general feeling by consuming his fair share of the good things, for he concludes: 'As far as I can learn, all went off well, but it is difficult today to know what was going on yesterday.'

On the 2nd of July following it was young John Provis's turn to describe to his chief the opening of the Conway Bridge. He wrote: 'Conway bridge was opened yesterday morning between 12 and one o'clock by the Chester Mail with as many passengers as could possibly find a place about it that they could hold by. The horses went on steadily over which was more than I expected they would as the people were shouting and waving by the side of them from the embankment to the pier, the passengers at the same time singing 'God Save the King' as loud as they could . . . I could not hear that the slightest accident happened with the exception of a few broken windows at the public houses . . .' So, amid scenes of revelry and rejoicing which he did not stay to share, Telford's great roads to Holyhead were completed and Robin Ddu's prophecy fulfilled. A month later, Telford celebrated his seventieth birthday.

L. T. C. Rolt, *Thomas Telford*

4. *A Concert in the Britannia Bridge 'Tube'*

Friday evening (18th May 1849), a Concert was given to the whole country round by the Engineering Staff at headquarters connected with the Chester and Holyhead Railway in the great centre tube of the Britannia bridge which was brilliantly lighted up in the centre length, lined with branches at the entrance to resemble a grove, with seats run along the sides for the promenaders to rest on them.

The vocal ability of Caernarvon and Bangor were in full force on this occasion, assisted by Mr Hayden of St Mary's of the former place, who accompanied on the melodium. The 'corps musicale' consisted of 40 or more vocalists and allowing for the diluting effects upon the human voice of a chamber containing from 700 to 800 persons, with an area of upwards 470 feet long, better adapted to the sax-horns of the Distin family — the concert went off with as much eclat as could fairly have been expected . . . We may say all present were struck with the novelty of the thing, while few could have had any previous conception of the brilliant spectacle presented by the illuminated tube and the animated countenances on which its coruscation fell.

North Wales Chronicle

5. *Advertisement for Chester and Holyhead Junction Railway*

PROVISIONAL COMMITTEE

The Lord Vivian
Sir Love Parry, Director of the Porth Dinllyn Railway
The High Sheriff of Anglesey
The Honble. W. O. Stanley, M.P., Director of the Chester and Holyhead Railway
Sir R. B. W. Bulkeley Bart, M.P.
Col. James Hughes
The Mayor of Beaumaris

SOLICITORS

Messrs Scriven, Forward & March, Old Jewry

PROSPECTUS

This Railway will be about 10 miles long, and will commence at the Chester and Holyhead Railway near the Column built in honour of that distinguished and gallant Soldier, the Marquis of Anglesey, and pass through Cerrig y Borth to the Cadnant Brook, from thence a little above High Water Mark, to the picturesque town of Beaumaris, where there will be a Station in the centre of the Green, from thence it will proceed along the Sea Coast to the Church at Penmon.

By this Line the fine Marble and Lime Stone Quarries at Penmon and Trosymarian will be materially served, the supply at each place being abundant, but at present having a scanty sale, owing to the dangerous and unprotected state of the coast.

By recent Surveys it has been ascertained that an extensive Coal Field exists at Lleiniog and the adjoining Lands. A Company has been formed for the purpose of working this Field, which will by this Line be enabled to send their Coal already proved to be of excellent quality into the Market at a cheap rate.

It is also well known that Copper exists in the district between the Cadnant River and Garth Point. These Shafts will be opened and worked without causing the slightest annoyance to the beautiful Marine Mansions of Glyn Garth, Glan y Menai, and Craig y Don.

'There is an old saying of the celebrated Robin Ddu that there is Lead enough at the back of Baron Hill to pave Beaumaris streets with Gold.' The old works which were closed in 1760 have been examined and the prospects are so good that Adventurers have already agreed on a Lease from the worthy owner Sir Richard Bulkeley. It is intended that the Lead raised shall be conveyed to the Station by means of a Tunnel through the Lawn and under the venerable Castle, thus by no means injuring their numerous beauties.

It is also intended in order to avoid any annoyances that may arise to the Residents of the beautiful Marine Villas already mentioned that the Whistle shall not be used and that the Engines shall consume their own smoke. The nature of the Ground is so favourable that the Trains will not be observable from the Windows of either of these Villas.

Immense Summer Traffic is expected from the numerous Visitors who frequent this beautiful Country.

Application for shares to be made to Messrs Preece & Evans, Lothbury, or to John Jones, Esq., Town Clerk Beaumaris, or to the Solicitors.

19th Century advertisement

6.   THE MENAI BRIDGE

I heard him then, for I had just
    Completed my design
To keep the Menai* bridge from rust
    By boiling it in wine.
I thanked him much for telling me
    The way he got his wealth,
But chiefly for his wish that he
    Might drink my noble health.

Lewis Carroll, 'A-sitting on a gate'
from *Alice Through The Looking Glass*

* As a child, Carroll had crossed the bridge on a North Wales holiday with his family.

7.   *Fifty Years Ago* (1933)

A pedestrian toll on the Menai Suspension Bridge was to be scrapped.
Menai Bridge residents planned to form a procession and walk across
the bridge to celebrate the occasion.

North Wales Chronicle, March 31, 1983

XI

THE TRAVELLERS

1. Quaker George Fox preaches at Beaumaris

Having preached the Word at Beaumaris, I bid John get his horse into the ferry-boat, but there having got in a company of wild gentlemen as they called them whom we found very rude men, they with others kept him out of the boat. I rode to the boat's side and spake to them, showing them what unmanly and unchristian conduct it was. As I spoke I leapt my horse into the boat amongst them, thinking John's horse would have followed, but the boat being deep it could not do so, wherefore I leapt out again on horseback into the water and stayed with John on that side till the boat returned. Having crossed we had forty-two miles to travel that evening and when we had paid for our passage we had but one groat left between us in money.

George Fox, Founder of Quakers, *Sermon*, 1657

2. Lord Clarendon travels to Beaumaris

'We are now going to Conway, which is fourteen miles from hence, and will take us up to five hours to go it; we must be there before four in the afternoon, because then the tide serves us to carry us over the ferry.' On landing at Conway Lord Clarendon was met by 'my Lord Bulkeley's son from his father to invite me very obligingly to his house, but when we shall get there God knows.' His fears were well-founded; the tides and the stormy weather kept him at Conway for the next two days; 'and indeed it is a bad place to stay in.' Tiring of the delay he resolved to leave at five in the morning of the 31st, proposing to travel in his coach round the foot of the Penmaenmawr; 'if the tide will not suffer the coach to go under the rocks then my wife shall go in a horse-litter which a gentleman has lent me, and I will ride and so shall her women over the Penmaen ... We passed over Penmaenmawr at the foot of which on this side I met Lord Bulkeley's coach and servants, but they told as they had escaped very narrowly being cast away in coming over the (Beaumaris) ferry, and that the winds were so high that it was not fit for us to attempt that way: so the coach carried us to Bangor where we ferried over (at Porthaethwy) into Anglesey and put my wife into the litter again for never was or can a coach come to that part of the country and then we came safe hither about three in the afternoon without any mischance to our company; and here we are today at my Lord Bulkeley's who makes very much of us and entertains us most nobly.' Lord Clarendon's coaches had been taken over the Penmaenmawr intact: 'by setting the horses in traces one behind the other and keeping three or four men behind that the coach might not slip back; this would scarce have been believed considering it a great heavy coach had it not been at this time of writing in my Lord Bulkeley's yard. My waggon which I left at Conway with orders to be sent back to Chester, there to be embarked for Ireland is this afternoon arrived here, brought likewise over Penmaen with its lading; so we may be said to have introduced a new way of travelling.'

Earl of Clarendon, *Letter to his brother,*
the Earl of Rochester, 1685

3.   *Passage from Conway to Bangor*

Near thirty years ago the normal mode of going betwixt Conway and Bangor was either in boats, or waiting for the departure of the tides, to proceed along the sands at low water. The latter mode was frequently attended with danger owing to the hollows formed by the tide, of the depth of which, when filled with water, the guides could not always be certain. Few carriages at that time were taken between the two towns, but nearly all the travellers were conveyed on horse-back.

Rev. William Bingley
Journal of a Tour Through North Wales, 1798

4.   *Cattle crossing the Straits*

They (the cattle) are urged in a body by loud shouts and blows into the water, and as they swim well and fast, usually make their way for the opposite shore; the whole troop proceeds regularly till it arrives at about 150 yards from the landing-place, where meeting with a very rapid current formed by the tide, the herd is thrown into the utmost confusion. Some of the boldest and strongest push directly across, the more timorous immediately turn round and endeavour to return, but the greater part, borne down by the stream, frequently float to a great distance before they are able to reach the Caernarvonshire shore. To prevent accidents a number of boats well-manned attend who row after the stragglers to force them to join the main body; and if they are very obstinate, the boatmen throw ropes round their horns and fairly tow them to the shore, which resounds with the loud bellowings of those who are landed. Notwithstanding the great number of cattle that annually pass the Strait, an instance seldom, if ever, occurs of any being lost.

Rev. William Bingley
Journal of a Tour Through North Wales, 1796

5. *The Welsh Wars of Edward I*

In the Welsh wars we so continually hear of the embarrassments of armed bodies entangled among forests or enveloped in morasses that a way seems to have been made not found for every fresh movement. That it was the interest of the Welsh nation to multiply rather than to diminish difficulties of this nature is proved not only by the circumstances of various invasions but by the conduct of their great antagonist, Edward 1st, who introduced a very liberal use of the axe into their forests.

E. Hyde Hall
A Description of Caernarvonshire, 1809-1811

6. *The routes from Chester to Holyhead*

Bridleways and cartways, I suppose, succeeded, and, it may be added, were continued as the only routes in the county until the last forty years. The Parliamentary army, indeed, found its way with some few field pieces through the pass of Bwlch-y-daufaen, but until the commencement of the new system of roads, the Lord Lieutenant of Ireland's coach was, I believe, almost the only carriage, with the exception of the above mentioned field pieces, which was dragged by force or contrivance through the admiring country. The first resident coach in the neighbourhood (if the expression may be allowed) was that, I have been told, of Sir Nicholas Bayley, and if my aged informant's memory serves him, most wonderful were the effects of the portentous exhibition. The plough was deserted, the wheel stood still, and the spade was thrown down, until curiosity had been gratified by sight, or still more by touch, of the massive fabric. In those days the inconveniences of passing to and fro between West Chester and Holyhead were so numerous and severe that it is a matter of some surprise how travellers, particularly females, could be induced to repeat the experiment. Guides were to be hired, pillions for the ladies provided, and a long list of anxious questions about fords, tides, etc. etc., to be stored up for use as the necessities of their application occurred.

Of this penury of communication, however, the memory is now lost in our present affluence. We are fully in the circle, and we swiftly revolve round it. Correspondence and commerce increase routes of communication, and routes of communication increase correspondence and commerce. Curiosity also has joined the throng, and in the summer months tends in no ordinary degree to swell the number of passengers by which the roads, turnpike and cross, rough and smooth, are crowded in every direction.

In 1768 the first Turnpike Act was obtained, under the authority of which roads were opened from Tal-y-cafn Ferry through Conway to Bangor, to Bangor Ferry, to Caernarvon and to Pwllheli. From Caernarvon, also, to Pontaberglaslyn by Beddgelert, a road was planned; and in 1776 a second Act was passed for extending the line from Tal-y-cafn to Llanrwst in one direction, and in another, for making a cut to Aber through Bwlch-y-daufaen, or the Pass of the Two Stones. The communication with Llanrwst was established, but the way to Aber still remains in its original condition, a rough bridle road . . .

. . . from Capel Curig to Beddgelert a still more recent turnpike road has been led through some of the most beautiful scenery in the Principality. At the same time the communication was extended from Beddgelert to Pwllheli and to Porthynllaen on the the opposite coast of the peninsula. The last Act which has been obtained abounds with powers for cutting roads in almost every possible direction, but I am not aware of any strong necessity for any new lines beyond those from Caernarvon to Capel Curig by Llanberis, and from Conway to Aber by Bwlch-y-daufaen.

The public carriages which traverse these roads are: 1. A Mail through Conway to Holyhead; 2ly, a second Mail which enters the county by Bettws y Coed and passes by Capel Curig to the ferry on its way to Holyhead; and 3ly, a heavy coach which pursues the same route with the last. An attempt was also made in 1806 to run a coach from Conway to Caernarvon, but the scheme was unquestionably premature, and it failed accordingly. A waggon from Chester arrives once a week by Conway, and a second from Shrewsbury has recently been introduced by the way of Capel Curig. Post chaises may be had at Conway, at Bangor Ferry, at Capel Curig, at Beddgelert, at Tre Madoc and at Pwllheli. The want of one at Clynnog between the last place and Caernarvon may be considered as a desideratum in the accommodations of the county.

E. Hyde Hall, *A Description of Caernarvonshire,* 1809-11

7. *Daniel Defoe in North Wales*

Merionithshire, or Merionydshire, lies west from Montgomeryshire; it lies on the Irish Sea, or rather the ocean; for St George's Channel does not begin till further north, and it is extended on the coast, for near 35 miles in length, all still mountainous and craggy. The principal river is the Tovy, which rises among the unpassable mountains, which range along the centre of this part of Wales, and which we call unpassable, for that even the people themselves called them so; we looked at them indeed with astonishment, for their rugged tops, and the immense height of them. Some particular hills have particular names, but otherwise we called them all the Black Mountains, and they well deserved the name; some think 'tis from the unpassable mountains of this county, that we have an old saying, that the devil lives in the middle of Wales, though I know there is another meaning given to it.

There is but few large towns in all this part, nor is it very populous; indeed much of it is scarce habitable, but 'tis said, there are more sheep in it, than in all the rest of Wales. On the sea shore however, we see Harlech Castle, which is still a garrison, and kept for the guard of the coast, but 'tis of no great strength, but by its situation.

Here among innumerable summits, and rising peaks of nameless hills, we saw the famous Cader Idris, which some are of opinion, is the highest mountain in Britain, another called Rarauvaur, another called Mowylwynda, and still every hill we saw, we thought was higher than all that ever we saw before.

We enquired here after that strange phenomenon which was not only seen, but fatally experienced by the country round this place, namely, of a livid fire, coming off from the sea; and setting on fire, houses, barns, stacks of hay and corn, and poisoning the herbage in the fields; of which there is a full account given in the Philosophical Transactions.

But to return to the face of things, as they appeared to us, the mountainous country spoken of runs away N. through this county and almost the next, I mean Caernarvonshire, where Snowdon Hill is a monstrous height, and according to its name, had snow on the top in the beginning of June; and perhaps had so till the next June, that is to say, all the year. These unpassable heights were doubtless the refuges of the Britains, when they made continual war with the Saxons and Romans, and retreated on occasion of their being over powered, into these parts where, in short, no enemy could pursue them.

There is nothing of note to be seen in the isle of Anglesey but the town, and the castle of Beaumaris, which was also built by King Edward I and called Beau-Marsh, or the Fine Plain; for here the country is very level and plain, and the land is fruitful and pleasant. As we went to Holyhead, by the S. part of the island from Newborough, and came back through the middle to Beaumaris, we saw the whole extent of it, and indeed, it is a much pleasanter country, than any part of N. Wales, that we had yet seen; and particularly is very fruitful for corn and cattle.

Here we crossed the Fretum, or strait of Menai again . . . to Bangor, a town noted for its antiquity, its being a bishop's see, and an old, mean looking, and almost despicable cathedral church.

Daniel Defoe, *A Tour Through the Whole Island of Britain*

8.   HOLYHEAD. SEPTEMBER 25, 1727

Lo here I sit at holy head
With muddy ale and mouldy bread
All Christian victuals stink of fish
I'm where my enemies would wish

Convict of lies is every sign,
The Inn has not one drop of wine
I'm fastened both by wind and tide
I see the ship at anchor ride
The Captain swears the sea's too rough
He has not passengers enough.
And thus the Dean is forced to stay
Till others come to help the pay
In Dublin they'd be glad to see
A packet though it brings in me.
They cannot say the winds are cross
Your Politicians at a loss
For want of matter swears and frets,
Are forced to read the old gazettes.
I never was in haste before
To reach that slavish hateful shore
Before, I always found the wind
To me was most malicious kind
But now, the danger of a friend
On whom my fears and hopes depend
Absent from whom all Climes are cursed
With whom I'm happy in the worst
With rage impatient makes me wait
A passage to the land I hate.
Else, rather on this bleaky shore
Where loudest winds incessant roar
Where neither herb nor tree will thrive,
I'd go in freedom to my grave,
Than Rule yon Isle and be a Slave.

Dean Swift, *Holyhead Journal,* 1727

9. *The Holyhead Packet*

24 September, 1727: 'I dined with an old Innkeeper, Mrs Welch, about 3, on a Loin of Mutton very good, but the worst ale in the world, and no wine, for the day before I came here a vast number went to Ireland after having drunk all the wine.' On the following day: 'The Captain talks of sailing at 12. The talk goes off, the wind is

fair, but he says it is too fierce; I believe he wants more company.' The
26th: 'The weather is fiercer and wilder than yesterday, yet the
Captain now dreams of sailing . . . I should be glad to talk with
Farmers and Shopkeepers but none of them speak English. A Dog is
better company than the Vicar, for I remember him of old . . . The
Master of the packet-boat, one Jones, hath not treated me with the
least civility, although Watt gave him my name. In short I come from
being used like an Emperor to be used worse than a Dog at Holyhead.
Yet my hat is worn to pieces by answering the civilities of the poor
inhabitants as they pass by.' The 28th: 'Tis allowed that we learn
patience by suffering. I have not spirit enough left me to fret . . . Well
it is now three in the afternoon. I have dined and revisited the Master;
the wind and tide serve, and I am just taking boat to go to the ship.'
The 29th, Friday: 'You will now know something of what it is to be at
sea. We had not been half an hour in the ship till a fierce wind rose
directly against us; we tried a good while, but the storm still
continued, so we turned back and it was 8 at night, dark and raining,
before the ship got back at anchor. The other passengers went back in
a boat to Holyhead, but to prevent accidents and broken shins I lay
all night on board and came back this morning at 8. Am now in my
chamber, where I must stay and get a fresh stock of patience.'

Dean Swift, *Holyhead Journal,* 1727

10.   SHALL I REPINE

If neither brass nor marble can withstand
The mortal force of Time's destructive hand
If mountains sink to vales, if cities die
And lessening rivers mourn their fountains dry
When my old cassock says a Welsh divine
Is out at elbows why should I repine?

Dean Swift

11.   *Dr Johnson in North Wales*

We then came to Conway Ferry, and passed in small boats, with some passengers from the stage coach, among whom were an Irish gentlewoman, with two maids, and three little children, of which, the youngest was only a few months old. The tide did not serve the large ferry-boat, and therefore our coach could not very soon follow us. We were, therefore, to stay at the Inn. It is now the day of the Race at Conway, and the town was so full of company, that no money could purchase lodgings. We were not very readily supplied with cold dinner. We would have stayed at Conway if we could have found entertainment, for this mighty ruin, and in all these old buildings the subterraneous works are concealed by the rubbish.

To survey this place would take much time: I did not think there had been such buildings; it surpassed my ideas.

August 20. We went by water from Bangor to Caernarvon, where we met Paoli and Sir Thomas Wynne. Meeting by chance with one Troughton, an intelligent and loquacious wanderer, Mr Thrale invited him to dinner. He attended us to the Castle, an edifice of stupendous magnitude and strength; it has in it all that we observed at Beaumaris, and much greater dimensions: many of the smaller rooms floored with stone are entire; of the larger rooms, the beams and planks are all left: this is the state of all buildings left to time. We mounted the Eagle Tower by one hundred and sixty-nine steps, each of ten inches. We did not find the Well; nor did I trace the Moat; but moats there were, I believe, to all castles on the plain, which not only hindered access, but prevented mines.

August 22. We went to visit Bodville, the place where Mrs Thrale was born; and the Churches called Tydweiliog and Llangwinodyl, which she holds by impropriation.

We had an invitation to the house of Mr Griffiths of Bryn y dol, where we found a small neat new built house, with square rooms: the walls are of unhewn stone, and therefore thick; for the stones not fitting with exactness, are not strong without great thickness. He had planted a great deal of young wood in walks.

August 24. We went to see Bodville. Mrs Thrale remembered the rooms, and wandered over them with recollection of her childhod. This species of pleasure is always melancholy. The walk was cut down, and the pond was dry. Nothing was better.

We surveyed the Churches, which are mean, and neglected to a degree scarcely imaginable. They have no pavement, and the earth is full of holes. The seats are rude benches; the Altars have no rails. One of them has a breach in the roof. On the desk, I think, of each lay a folio Welsh Bible of the black letter, which the curate cannot easily read. Mr Thrale purposes to beautify the Churches, and if he prospers, will probably restore the tithes. The two parishes are, Llangwinodyl and Tydweilliog. The Methodists are here very prevalent. A better church will impress the people with more reverence of public worship.

Mrs Thrale visited a house where she had been used to drink milk, which was left, with an estate of two hundred pounds a year, by one Lloyd, to a married woman who lived with him.

We went to Pwllheli, a mean old town, at the extremity of the country. Here we bought something, to remember the place.

August 25. We returned to Caernarvon, where we ate with Mrs Wynne.

August 26. We visited, with Mrs Wynne, Llyn Badarn and Llyn Beris, two lakes, joined by a narrow strait. They are formed by the waters which fall from Snowdon and the opposite mountains. On the side of Snowdon are the remains of a large fort, to which we climbed with great labour. I was breathless and harassed. The Lakes have no great breadth, so that the boat is always near one bank or the other.

Note: Queeny's goats, one hundred and forty-nine, I think.*

August 29. We came to Mr Myddelton's, of Gwaynynog, to the first place, as my Mistress observed, where we have been welcome.

Note. On the day when we visited Bodville, we turned to the house of Mr Griffiths, of Kefnamwycllh, a gentleman of large fortune, remarkable for having made great and sudden improvements in his seat and estate. He has enclosed a large garden with a brick wall. He is considered as a man of great accomplishments. He was educated in literature at the University, and served some time in the army, then quitted his commission, and retired to his lands. He is accounted a good man, and endeavours to bring the people to church.

In our way from Bangor to Conway, we passed again the new road

---

* Mr Thrale was near-sighted, and could not see the goats browsing on Snowdon, and he promised his daughter, who was a child of ten years old, a penny for every goat she would show him, and Dr Johnson kept the account so that it appears her father was in debt to her one hundred and forty-nine pence. Queeny was the epithet, which had its origin in the nursery, by which Miss Thrale was always distinguished by Johnson. Her name was Esther. The allusion was to Queen Esther.

upon the edge of Penmaen Mawr, which would be very tremendous, but that the wall shuts out the idea of danger. In the wall are several breaches, made, as Mr Thrale very reasonably conjectures, by fragments of rocks which roll down the mountain, broken perhaps by frost, or worn through by rain.

We then viewed Conway.

To spare the horses at Penmaen Rhôs, between Conway and St Asaph, we sent the coach over the road across the mountain with Mrs Thrale, who had been tired with a walk sometime before; and I, with Mr Thrale and Miss, walked along the edge, where the path is very narrow, and much encumbered by little loose stones, which had fallen down, as we thought, upon the way since we passed it before.

At Conway we took a short survey of the Castle, which afforded us nothing new. It is larger than that of Beaumaris, and less than that of Caernarvon. It is built upon a rock so high and steep, that it is even now very difficult of access. We found a round pit, which was called the Well; it is now almost filled, and therefore dry. We found the Well in no other castle.

Dr Samuel Johnson, *Journal of a Journey into Wales,* 1774

12. *J. Huck's pedestrian tour through North Wales,* 1795

Bala is situated upon the borders of a large lake, eleven miles in circumference, and four and a half long. It abounds with pike, perch, trout, and other fish; the country around is grand and sublime, but not interesting; stupendous mountains seem 'to mix their heads with dropping clouds', but with respect to cultivation, or even verdure, they are entirely destitute; every necessary article of life is here more than commonly reasonable; fifty pound at Bala would go as far as an hundred in most parts of England. We were yesterday much diverted with a curious political conversation carried on at the inn, in the room which we in part occupied, at a table by ourselves; at another, were seated the clergyman, the exciseman, the attorney, the apothecary, and I suppose, by his appearance, the barber of the place, etc. these were met upon business over a bowl of punch, which seemed to constitute the chief part of it; whilst in an opposite corner of the room, two more decent looking people were enjoying themselves in a similar manner. The clergyman gave aloud 'Church and King', as a toast, and soon after one of our neighbours at the other table, proposed 'General Washington' to his friend; this created a great commotion amongst the large party; for the clergyman immediately standing up gave as his second toast 'may all *Demicrats* be *gullotin'd*,' when the other filling *his* glass, added, 'may all fools be gullotined, and then I knows who'll be the first'; after this ensued a violent and dreadful battle of tongues, in which these people excel in an extraordinary degree. The clergyman defended his toast, on the grounds that it showed his zeal in a good cause, forgetting that it was necessary first to prove the merit of the sentiment, as united by him, and after that, to show that his zeal was best made known as a clergyman, by his benevolent and truly pious wish. But majors and minors were things which this zealous and humane defender of his church and king had little regard for. The clamour at length became so loud, that we soon withdrew ourselves from the scene of contention, and left the combatants to settle the point in the best manner they could; though it seemed to me that it required more sophistry than the clergyman had displayed, and more wit than the other possessed, to justify or even excuse themselves . . .

The village of Aber Conway, usually called Aber, from whence I dated my last letter, is situated upon the straits of Menai, that at high tide is there about four miles across; but when the water is out, it appears perfectly dry; for the sea retires so far back, that it only leaves a channel of a quarter of a mile, or thereabouts, in breadth: all the rest is a complete flat, and consequently the tide overflows it very rapidly. There are stated times to pass this ferry, which one should be very exact in observing, for ten minutes may be of the utmost conse- quence. The clergyman of the place accompanied us to the boundaries of this wilderness of sand; he gave us the necessary directions for our passage, which were only to keep a white house in view that belonged to the ferryman on the Anglesey shore, and to make what haste we could, since there was no time to lose, for we had four miles to walk over this frightful desert without shoes or stockings, having been advised to pull them off; for being regularly overflowed every twelve hours, great part of the road is necessarily wet and dirty. We had scarcely got half way, before it began to grow thick and foggy. The little village of Aber, which we had just quitted, was no longer perceptible; and nothing behind us was to be seen, but the steep and shaggy mountains of Penmaenmawr, and those known by the general name of Snowdonia, with the dark vapours floating upon their sides; and very soon these became no longer distinguishable, but as one huge mass of clouds. Myself, and another of the party, had considerably outwalked the other two, who had lost sight of their landmark, and were steering their course much too far to the right; when we discovered their mistake they were not so visible to us, that we could tell what they were; all that we could discern was something very dark, moving in a different direction to us; consequently we hailed them, and waited till they came up to us, and we agreed to part company no more. Darkness had now overtaken us in earnest, and we could see nothing, nor hear anything, except the noise which the sea made in its approach, that alarmed us not a little; at length, to our infinite satisfaction, we distinguished the voices of the ferrymen, who were luckily waiting on this side of the passage. When they heard us, they were extremely impatient for our arrival, and continually called to us to make haste, which we wanted no monitor to urge us to do; we therefore made towards the spot from whence the sounds came, which we conjectured to be about the distance of two hundred yards from us, but were unluckily intercepted by a small channel, already filling very fast with the sea. We did not hesitate long, for in fact we had no alternative, and therefore boldly ventured through; it was fortunately only about two feet deep, and rather more than ten yards broad. We congratulated each other upon finding ourselves safe in the boat, though dripping wet, and shivering with cold. Like the Israelites, we had passed through the sea on dry land; but we had run a great risk of experiencing a similar treatment with Pharaoh and his host, from that unmannerly element. When we arrived at the inn at Beaumaris, we made a fire that would have roasted an ox, and ordered a supper sufficient for ten aldermen. Upon opening the window on the following morning, I observed the sea had covered all those immense flats we had so lately, I will not say with dry feet, walked over.

Beaumaris is a dirty sea-faring town; here is another of king Edward's castles built A.D. 1295; it is in tolerable preservation, but the eye is disgusted with new repairs; a fine old tower is frequently patched with modern masonry, in which the workman has barbarously shown his art, in the nice disposition of yellow bricks and mortar; add to this, the inhabitants have made a bowling-green within its walls. The guardian genii of venerable ruins, must surely have been asleep when these impieties were committed.

From Beaumaris we crossed the island, wuth which I felt myself greatly disappointed; I looked around me in vain for those awe inspiring shades and venerable temples where the Druids used to perform their mysterious rites, that filled the wondering multitude with fear, and infused, even into their enemies, a degree of respect and veneration . . .

. . . We dined yesterday at Gwyndn, on the great road to Holyhead, which is called by the natives Caer Guby, on account of St Kybi, a holy man, who lived there A.D. 308; but none of us expressing any inclination to see that place, we left it on the right, and steered our course nearly South, through the centre of the island. Gwyndn signifies, from its name, a place of hospitality at the expense of the lord; and, in truth, it answers, in some respects, to its title even now; nor must I forget to pay my tribute of thanks to the hostess, a fine old lady, who paid us the utmost attention, and appeared particularly solicitous about us; she gave us her blessing at our departure, with a thousand admonitions not to lose ourselves. We left this hospitable inn with regret, and arrived 'post multa pericula', at Moel Don Ferry, a single house, where we were obliged to sleep, or, speaking more accurately, to lie down, for to sleep was totally impossible. It was a miserable hut; but we contrived to procure two beds, though the good woman was for putting us all into one. We crossed the ferry yesterday morning, after a sleepless night, happy to quit this inauspicious island, where fortune had not been over prodigal to us of her favours. The road from this ferry to Caernarvon, winds along the shores of the Menai, and the scenery would have amply repaid me for the fatigue and mortification I had undergone, had I then been in a humour to have enjoyed it; but true it is, that when we cannot enjoy ourselves, we are not much disposed to be satisfied with anything around us; the finest objects lose their beauty; and what at other times would have afforded the highest gratification, are in those hours deprived of their relish. We reached Caernarvon, or Caer-ar-fon (signifying a walled town), to breakfast; and it was not until I had eaten, or rather devoured, a certain quantity of toast and butter, that I began to recover the accustomed tone of my spirits . . .

. . . Beddgelert, situated at the foot of some prodigious high mountains, which seem to encircle it on all sides, whilst the stream or torrent, that had accompanied us all the way from the first lake, here begins to be of more consequence, and forcing its way between these stupendous hills, with a continued and considerable descent, empties itself into an arm of the sea, called Traweth Mawr. As this is the usual place from which travellers make the ascent of Snowdon, we determined to do the same, and in pursuance of this resolution set off at eleven in the evening, though it was quite dark, and a very rainy and stormy night; however, there was a probability that it would be fine in the morning; and that hope was sufficient to make us undergo a few inconveniences; but in attempting to find the guide's house, which was five miles from our inn, and situated quite out of the road, at the foot of the mountain, we became completely bewildered: in this perplexity we were directed by the glimmering of a light to an habitation, which, with extreme difficulty and danger, we contrived to reach. It was a small hut, and its inhabitants, if we might judge from the impenetrable silence that reigned within it, were all asleep. It was some time before we could prevail upon them to open the door, and answer to our entreaties for a proper direction; at length an elderly man appeared, to whom we endeavoured to make known our grievances; but alas! he only spoke his native language, and did not understand a word that we said: However, by frequently repeating the guide's name, 'Ellis Griffith', and pointing to Snowdon, at the same time giving him a glimpse of a shilling, we with much difficulty made him comprehend us; and putting himself at our head, he became our conductor. In about half an hour we found ourselves at the door of another small cottage: our guide vociferated Welsh for some minutes, till we were admitted by a good-looking lad about 17 years of age, who was the person we had been searching for: he remonstrated against our ascending that night, with many weighty reasons, to which we easily assented; but to think of returning to our inn would be madness: we therefore called a council of war, and it was agreed, that we should at all events stay where we were, until morning; when, if it should be tolerably fair, we would ascend. Thus determined, we disposed of ourselves in the following manner: I barricaded myself in a chair, so that I could not fall out; two more reposed themselves on the benches on each side of the fire, and the fourth took up his 'lodgings on the cold ground', with an earthen platter turned upside down for his pillow. As for my part I was not disposed to sleep, but took up the rush-light, which had been placed for security on the ground; and to pass away the leaden hours of time, pored over an old Welsh dictionary (which was the only thing like a book that I could find), till I was scarcely able to see.

I could not help contemplating our singular situation and appearance in this strange place: on one side, around the dying embers of a peat fire, my good friends were enjoying as comfortable a repose as they had ever experienced in the most costly bed: at the other extremity of the room, separated only by a rug, the venerable owners of this humble cottage lay locked in each others embraces: whilst I, like Brutus in his tent at Philippi, sat reading by the midnight lamp, till the light danced before my eyes and the pale spectre of the night appeared to my imagination. . .

. . . Harlech castle is nobly situated, and, like Denbigh, stands upon a lofty promontary, terminating a chain of hills, and commanding on one side a view of the sea, and on the other, a very extensive vale and prospect. From its singular situation, it must have been formerly esteemed almost impregnable; and yet we read in our history, that it was besieged, and taken, in the time of Edward the Fourth, by the Earl of Pembroke, without the assistance of gunpowder. We also here achieved an exploit, which, beyond all doubt, gives us some title to military prowess; for as there did not happen to be anybody in the way, who might open the gates of the castle, and our time not permitting us to wait for the ordinary forms of capitulation, we boldly marched up to the assault, and scaling the walls at four different places, took possession of the garrison, as it were by a coup-de-main. But for this daring outrage, we had all nigh got into an awkward scrape; some of the inhabitants observing our operations, and probably taking us for free-booters, gave the alarm; and mustering a formidable body of forces, marched in military array, to dispossess us of our stronghold. But we soon pacified our opponents, and having convinced them that our intentions were neither predatory nor hostile, they retired to an ale-house to banish sorrow, and indulge themselves, at our expense, in copious libations of ale.

There is nothing interesting in the road to Barmouth, nor has that place itself any striking peculiarities, except that the houses are so whimsically built, upon the side of a steep hill, that the inhabitants may have the advantage, if they choose, of looking down their neighbour's chimneys. The town stands upon the sea shore, and in the season is full of company, who resort thither for the purpose of bathing.

From Barmouth to Dolgellau we were highly gratified; the road wound along a ridge of rocks, that hang over the Avonvawr, an arm of the sea; which, at full tide, has the appearance of a large lake, surrounded with beautiful woods. The mountains on both sides, but particularly on the opposite shore, were strikingly grand; and above all, Cader Idris reared its head into the clouds, which, together with the sombre aspect of the evening, and the hollow murmurings of the sea gave an awful sublimity to the scene that cannot be described.

Dolgellau is a large and dirty town: we took up our quarters at the Golden Lion, a good hospitable inn; and next morning, after breakfast, procured a guide to conduct us to the top of Cader Idris. We armed him with stores, and warlike preparations of all kinds (to wit): ham, fowl, bread, and cheese, and brandy, and began the ascent at nine in the morning, and continued to toil for three hours and a half before we reached the top.

J. Hucks, B.A., *A Pedestrian Tour Through North Wales,* 1795

13. *Marriage Custom*

There is a remarkable custom which the Welsh still continue, that I cannot forbear mentioning: When a marriage is about to take place amongst the middling and lower orders of people, it is usual to invite all their friends and relations of every description, who, when they take leave, present, of one or two shillings, which, however, they have a right to demand again after a certain space of time; the intent of it being probably to enable the new married couple to buy stock, or engage in some business that may allow them soon to repay the small donations of their friends. It is called 'a bidding', and is drawn up in the following form.

'My only son John has lately entered the sacred state of union, and a bidding is fixed on the occasion, on Tuesday the 7th day of October next, in the village of Conwyl, when and where your good company and benevolence are highly solicited, which will be cheerfully acknowledged on a similar occasion, and esteemed a peculiar favour conferred on,
Your most devoted
humble Servants,
John Jones, Senior
John Jones, Junior

Ibid.

14. *The poet Coleridge's experiences in North Wales*
as Huck's travelling companion

From Llanvilling we penetrated into the interior (of) the Country to
Llangunnog, a Village most romantically situated — We dined there
on hashed Mutton, Cucumber, Bread and Cheese and Butter, and
had two pots of Ale — The sum total of the expense 16 pence for both
of us! From Llangunnog we walked over the mountains to Bala —
most sublimely terrible! It was scorching hot — I applied my mouth
ever and anon to the side of the Rocks and sucked in draughts of
Water cold as Ice, and clear as infant Diamonds in their embryo Dew!
The rugged and stony Clefts are stupendous — and in winter must
form Cataracts most astonishing — At this time of the year there is
just water enough dashed down over them to 'sooth not disturb the
pensive Traveller's Ear'. I slept by the side of one an hour and more.
As we descended down the Mountain the Sun was reflected in the
River that winded thro' the valley with insufferable Brightness — it
rivalled the Sky. At Bala is nothing remarkable except a Lake of 11
miles in circumference. At the Inn I was sore afraid, that I had caught
the Itch from a Welsh Democrat, who was charmed with my
sentitments: he grasped my hand with flesh-bruising Ardour — and I
trembled, lest some discontented Citizens of the *animalcular* Republic
should have emigrated. Shortly after, into the same room a well
dressed clergyman and four others — among whom (the Landlady
whispers me) was a Justice of Peace and the Doctor of the Parish — I
was asked for a Gentleman (i.e. to propose a toast) — I gave General
Washington. The parson said in a low voice (Republicans!) — After
which the medical man said — damn Toasts! I gives a sentiment —
May all Republicans be *gulloteen'd* — Up starts the Welsh Democrat
— May all *Fools* be gulloteen'd — and then you will be the first!
Thereon Rogue, Villain, Traitor flew thick in each other's faces as a
hailstorm — This is nothing in Wales — *they make calling one another
Liars* etc. — necessary vent-holes to the sulphurous Fumes of the
Temper! At last, I endeavoured to arbitrate by observing that what-
ever might be our opinions in politics, the appearance of a Clergyman
in the Company assured me, we were all *Christians* — tho' (continued
I) it is rather difficult to reconcile the last Sentiment with the Spirit of
Christianity. Pho! — quoth the Parson — Christianity! Why, we an't
at Church now? Are we? — The Gemman's Sentiment was a very
good one — 'it showed, he was *sincere* in his principles!' — Welsh

Politics could not prevail over Welsh Hospitality — they all except the Parson shook me by the hand and said I was an open hearted honest-speaking Fellow, tho' I was a bit of a Democrat.

We passed over a ferry and landed at Aberconway — We had scarcely left the Boat ere we descried Brookes (sic) and Merdmore, with whom we have joined Parties, nor do we mean to separate. — Our Tour thro' Anglesey to Caernarvon has been repaid by scarcely one object worth seeing. Tomorrow we visit Snowdon — etc. — Brookes, Berdmore and myself at the imminent hazard of our Lives scaled the very Summit of Penmaenmawr — it was a most dreadful expedition! I will give you the account in some future Letter.

Samuel Taylor Coleridge

15. *The prices charged at inns*

Dolgellau, Aug. 19th (1794). Dear Sir, Nothing strikes the traveller who passes through Wales more forcibly, than the extreme reasonableness of the bills at houses of public entertainment. Our supper last night was superb; it consisted of a sole, a trout, and a *gwyniad*, (a delicious fish, somewhat like the trout, and peculiar to Alpine countries) with every proper accompaniment; mutton steaks, vegetables, excellent bread and cheese, and three tankards of London porter.

'With toast embrown'd
And fragrant nutmeg fraught, divine repast!'

Our beds were comfortable, and the breakfast this morning was fit for a monarch. You will scarcely credit me, when I assure you, the charge for this sumptuous fare and admirable accommodation amounted only to five shillings and two-pence; which sum was divided into the following items:

	s.	d.
Supper	2	0
Porter	1	6
Breakfast	1	8
	5	2

This appears the more extraordinary, as the prices of provisions between Wales and England do not differ in anything like the same proportion with the charges at the inns in the respective countries. We have hitherto found good butcher's meat not to be gotten under six-pence per pound; bread full as dear as in the south, and butter little less expensive. These indeed are unnatural prices in Wales, one unfortunate consequence of the war we are engaged in, which has, in the Principality, raised the article of butcher's meat above one hundred per cent. and added in an unprecedented manner to the expense of every article of life.

Rev. Richard Warner, *A Walk Through Wales,* 1794

16. *Fleas in Beddgelert and the ascent of Cader Idris*

Beddgelert, Aug. 19 (1794). Dear Sir, We rose earlier than usual this morning, after a most comfortless night; during which we had been tormented by fleas, and nearly suffocated by the closeness of a room nine feet by five and a half, into which were crammed two beds, a table, and a chair . . .

. . . Arriving at the extremity of the pool, we began to ascend the western summit of Cader Idris, a task not only of labour, but of some peril also, it being a different route from that which travellers usually pursue; six hundred feet of steep rock, covered, indeed, with short grass; but so slippery as to render the footing very insecure. As we approached the top, the ascent became more abrupt, whilst the scene below us, of craggy rocks, perpendicular precipices, and an unfathomable lake, did not operate to lessen the alarm that a person, unaccustomed to so dangerous a situation, naturally feels. Our companion the mountaineer skipped on, the mean while, with the agility of a goat, and whilst C———— and I were dumb with terror, descanted on the beauties of Cader Idris, the excellence of its mutton, and the delicacy of its trout, as coolly as if he had been in the public house where we originally found him. At length, after excessive labour, and repeated efforts, we gained the top of this noble mountain, and were at once amply recompensed for all the fatigue and alarm of the ascent. The afternoon was gloriously fine, and the atmosphere perfectly clear, so that the vast unbounded prospect lay beneath us, unobscured by cloud, vapour, or any other interruption to the astonished and delighted eye; which threw its glance over a varied scene, including a circumference of at least five hundred miles.

To the north-west is seen Ireland, like a distant mist upon the ocean; and a little to the right, Snowdon and the other mountains of Caernarvonshire. Further on, in the same direction, the Isle of Man, the neighbourhood of Chester, Wrexham, and Salop; the sharp head of the Wrekin, and the undulating summit of the Clee hills. To the house we have the country round Clifton, Pembrokeshire, St David's, and Swansea; and to the westward, a cast prospect of the Biritsh Channel unfolds itself, which is bounded only by the horizon. Exclusive of these distant objects, the nearer views are wonderfully striking. Numberless mountains, of different forms, appearances, and elevation, rise in all directions around us; which, with the various harbours, lakes and rivers, towns, villages, and seats, scattered over the extensive prospect, combine to form a scene inexpressibly august, diversified, and impressive. Having refreshed ourselves with the contents of a knapsack carried by our companion, we proceeded, in an eastern direction to the Pen-y-Cader, the highest peak of the mountain, passing on our left the *saddle* of the giant Idris, (from whom the mountain receives its name) and immense *cwm*, its bottom filled with a beautiful lake called Llyn Cair, and its sides formed by perpendicular cliffs at least 1000 feet in height. Here we found the Alpine grasses, the *Aira Caespitosa*, and the *Poa Alpina*; beautiful masses of spar, specimens of pyritae, and a stone much resembling that colcanic substance called pumice-stone. We were now upon the apex of the second mountain in Wales, in point of height, and 2850 feet above the green, near the neighbouring town of Dolgellau.

Rev. Richard Warner, *A Walk Through Wales*, 1794

17. *A Good Bed*

Conway, Aug. 22nd (1794). Dear Sir, No man can justly estimate the value of a good bed unless he have experienced the discomfort of a very bad one. C———— and I were alive to this enjoyment last night, for during the preceding 100 miles, our nocturnal accommodation has been far from tolerable.

Rev. Richard Warner, *A Walk Through Wales*, 1794

18.   *The Menai Ferry*

The ferry was worked by an elderly woman named Grace Parry, better known to her contemporaries as Gras-y-Garth. She had a large conch shell which she used as a trumpet to warn intending passengers when the boat was about to leave . . . She was a short, thick, squat female, who, though upwards of sixty years have passed over her head, is as strong as a horse, and as active as one of her own country's goats. Her excellence in rowing and managing a boat is unrivalled through the coast, which cannot be wondered at, as she served an early apprenticeship to the business, under her father and mother, who lived at the same little cottage as she inhabits, and worked the same passage for the best part of the past century. The prowess of her mother, and the skill of her father, are still the favourite themes of her discourse. She remembers with particular pleasure his ability in swimming, and, as proof of it, relates a circumstance that frequently occurred, even when he had passed his grand climacteric. The ferry was generally plied by the joint exertions of this couple, who, upon the whole, were tolerably loving; but as storms will sometimes happen in the fairest days, so their conjugal serenity was occasionally disturbed; and sometimes an altercation would take place when they were ferrying their passengers across the Menai. In these cases the wife, who was the better man of the two, so completely worsted her spouse in obloquy and abuse that, unable to bear it, he would suddenly cast off his jacket, leap into the Menai, and swim towards his cottage, bidding his dame, with a string of Welsh execrations, to take care of the passengers herself . . . Nothing intimidates this Cambrian heroine, she stands in fear of no human being, and is equally regardless of the rage of the elements. Last winter her boat drifted away in the night, and Grace for some days thought it had been stove to pieces. However as it was her freehold estate, she made diligent inquiry after it, and at last discovered that it had been taken up and carried to Liverpool. Engaging a stout fellow in the neighbourhood to accompany her, she instantly set off for that port on foot, though nearly sixty miles distant, and having recovered her property, embarked on board the skiff (although not more than twelve or thirteen feet on the keel) and, with the assistance of her companion, actually rowed it back to Garth Point, through heavy seas and squally weather, as perilous a voyage as ever was performed. As we found Grace's prejudices against the English rather violent, we thought it necessary for the safety of future Saxon travellers, to reward her labours with double the sum she demanded. This unexpected generosity so gratified the old woman, that she swore most bitterly we were the greatest gentlemen she ever met with, and declared she would always like the English for our sake and insisted on shaking hands with us individually at parting. We indulged her wish, but (whether she meant it as a token of her kindness, or as a proof of her strength I know not) gave us each such a serious gripe, as almost dislocated our fingers.

Ibid.

19.   SUPPER

Up and down through all the day
On the hills of Wales I stray
And at night it is my habit
For to sup on a Welsh rabbit.

Lord Macaulay, A letter to his sisters

20.   Mrs Siddons at Penmaenmawr

We left Conway next morning and ere long crossed Penmaenmawr where like other travellers we alighted from our carriage to look from a bridge that commands the fullest view of the sublime landscape with its rocks and water. Said a lady, 'This scenery makes me feel as if I were only a worm or a grain of dust on the face of the earth.' Mrs Siddons turned round and said, 'I feel very differently.'

Patty Wilkinson, Journal, 1807

21.   Penygwryd Hotel

The old visitors' book at the Penygwryd Hotel was rifled years ago of some of its most precious contents. On one occasion, when Charles Kingsley, Tom Taylor, and Thomas Hughes, the author of 'Tom Brown's School Days' were there, they wrote the following:

T.T.

I came to Pen-y-gwryd with colours armed and pencils,
But found no use whatever for any such utensils;
So in default of them I took to using knives and forks,
And made successful drawings — of Mrs Owen's corks.

C.K.

I came to Pen-y-gwryd in frantic hopes of slaying
Grilse, salmon, 3 lb red-flashed Trout, and what else there's no saying:
Drove me from fish to botany, a sadder man and wiser.

T.H.

I came to Pen-y-gwryd, a larking with my betters,
A mad wag and a mad poet, both of them men of letters:
Which two ungrateful parties, after all the care I've took
Of them, make me write verses in Henry Owen's book?

T.T.

We've been mist-soaked on Snowdon, mist-soaked on Glyder Fawr,
We've been wet through on an average day three times an hour:
We've walked the upper leathers from the soles of our balmorals,
And as sketchers and as fishers with the weather have had our quarrels.

C.K.

But think just of the plants which stuff'd our box — old Yarrel's gift —
And of those which might have stuff'd it if the clouds had given a lift;
Of tramping bogs, and climbing cliffs, and shoving down stone fences,
For Spiderwort, Saussurea and Woodsia Ilvensis.

T.H.

Oh my dear namesake's breeches, you never see the like
He bust them all so shameful a crossing of a dike:
But Mrs Owen patch'd them as careful as a mother,
With flannel of three colours — she hadn't got no other.

T.T.

But can we say enough of those legs of mountain muttons,
And that onion sauce lies on our souls, for it made of us three gluttons.

And the Dublin stout is genuine, and so's the Burton beer,
And the apple tarts they've won our hearts, and think of souffles here!

C.K.

Resembling that old woman that never could be quiet,
Though victuals (says the child's song) and drink formed all her diet,
My love for plants and scrambling shared empire with my dinner,
And who says it wasn't good must be a most fastidious sinner.

T.H.

Now all I've got to say is, you can't be better treated;
Order pancakes and you'll find the best you've ever eated
If you scramble o'er the mountains you should bring an ordnance map;
I endorse all that previous gents have said about the tap.

T.T.

Pen-y-gwryd, when wet and worn, has kept a warm fireside for us:
Socks, boots, and never-mention-ems, Mrs Owen still has dried for us;
With host and hostess fare and ill, so pleased we are, that, going,
We feel for all their kindness, 'tis we not they, are Owin'.

T.H. T.T. C.K.

Nos tres in uno juncti hos feciums versiculos,
Tomas piscator pisces qui non cepi sed pisciculos,
Tomas sciagraphus sketches qui no feci nisi ridiculos,
Herbarius Carolus montes qui lustravi perpendiculos.

T.H.

There's big trout, I hear, in Edno, likewise in Gwynant lake,
And the governor and black alder are the flies that they will take,
Also the cockabundy, but I can only say,
If you think to catch big fishes, I only hope you may.

T.T.

I have come in for more of mountain gloom than mountain glory,
But I'vew seen old Snowdon rear his head with storm-tossed mist
    wreaths hoary;
I stood in the fight of mountain winds upon Bwlch-cwm-y-llan,
And I go back, an unsketching, but a better-minded man.

C.K.

And I too, have another debt to pay some other day,
For kindness shown by these good souls to one who's far away,
Even to this old collie dog, who tracked the mountains oe'r,
For one who seeks strange birds and flowers on far Australia's shore.

Charles Kingsley, Tom Taylor and Thomas Hughes
Visitor's Book

22.   *Coaching on the Holyhead Road*

The fact that the pilgrims travelled in coaches brings me by quite a natural stage from the historical to the coaching side of the Holyhead Road. And it was from all I can learn the coaching road *par excellence*. Celebrated, thanks to the immortal Telford, for its 260 miles of superb surface, so masterfully laid down that, though the last 107 miles from Shrewsbury to Holyhead ran through mountainous country, no horse was obliged to walk, unless he particularly wished it, between Holyhead and London; celebrated too for its coachmen, a long list of historic names shining calmly through many a story of poles snapped; coaches over-turned in the twinkling of an eye; runaway teams nearing closed toll-bars; desperate races for a slight pre-eminence, ending in desperate collisions; celebrated consequently and finally for its time records, which never were beaten.

Not even on the Exeter Road by the Quicksilver or the Telegraph. For though the former covered the 175 miles between London and Exeter in eighteen hours and though the latter covered the 165 miles in seventeen hours, yet on the Holyhead Road, the Holyhead Mail, which ran through Shrewsbury, was timed at ten miles and a half an hour through the whole journey, including stoppages; while the celebrated Wonder did the 158 miles between London and Shrewsbury in fifteen hours and three quarters; and the Manchester Telegraph, travelling some distance at all events on the Holyhead Road, did the 186 miles in eighteen hours eighteen minutes, leaving the Bull and Mouth at five in the morning, reaching the Peacock, Islington, at 5.15, and Northampton at 8.40, where, according to Mr Stanley Harris, twenty minutes were allowed to eat as much as you could, with tea or coffee (of course too hot to drink).

And I think that the performances of these last two coaches are so remarkable that I cannot emphasize them more firmly than by here subjoining their respective time-bills; voiceless proclamations there of great feats in the past, pasted long since most of them into scrap-books of old-fashioned travel, or hanging in melancholy neglect and astounding frames on the smoke-begrimed walls of once celebrated posting houses.

Here then is the time-bill of the Wonder coach from London to Shrewsbury:

Proprietor	Place	Miles	Time Allowed		Should Arrive
			H	M	
Sherman	St Albans	22½	2	03	8.48
J. Liley	Redbourn	4½	0	25	9.13
	(Breakfast)				
Goodyear	Dunstable	8¼	0	48	10.12
Sheppard	Daventry	29¾	2	54	2.15
Collier	Coventry	19	1	47	4.02
	(Business)	—	0	05	—
Vyse	Birmingham	19	1	39	5.46
	(Dinner)	—	0	35	—
Evans	Wolverhampton	14	1	15	7.36
	(Business)	—	0	05	—
	Summerhouse	6½	0	35	8.16
J. Taylor	Shifnal	6½	0	35	8.51
H. J. Taylor	Haygate	8	0	43	9.34
J. Taylor	Shrewsbury	10	0	56	10.30
		158	15	45	

W. Tristram Oultram, *Coaching Days and Coaching Ways,* 1908

23. *The Coachmen*

. . . Dick Vickers, who drove the Mail between Shrewsbury and Holyhead . . . fell a victim to agriculture. That is to say that though in stature he was so little 'that he had to get on to six-pennyworth of coppers to look on to the top of a Stilton cheese' yet the deluded man pined to be a farmer. And he was fond of fishing too, a much more profitable pastime. However a farmer Vickers became, in spite of his friends' entreaties, who after a reasonable interval of anxiety found him *sus. per coll.* This Vickers, not content with the lack of judgement he displayed while on earth, is said to haunt the scene of his indiscretion still. Though the Mail which he used to drive has long ceased to exist, they do say that at times a rumbling is heard — and so on. Mr Birch Reynardson, to get to something more tangible about Vickers, knew him well, as he seems to have known most of the crack coachmen on the Holyhead Road, through Shrewsbury, and has described them as well as he knew them in his *Down the Road*. The ill-fated Vickers, he writes, was a good little fellow, always civil, always sober, always most obliging, and a friend of everyone along the road. And Mr Reynardson had some opportunity of studying his model's characteristics, particularly I should conceive on that one celebrated occasion chronicled, when he sat by him on the box-seat and saw him deal with a team comprised of the engaging attributes of 'Three blind 'uns and a bolter', or in the coachman's own words 'Four horses, but they've only got two eyes among 'em, and it would be quite as well if that horse had not any so far as I know — for he makes shocking bad use of 'em at all times I can tell you.'

A differently organized team was equally successfully coped with by one known to fame as Old John Scott. He drove the Chester and Holyhead Mail, and remarked to Mr Reynardson, who was using all his art to boil up a trot going up Penmaenmawr (thirty-six miles from Holyhead), 'Hit 'em sly — hit 'em sly!' And on being asked the reason for this dark advice alleged that if this particular team heard the whip before they felt it, they would never be got up Penmaenmawr at all.

Of quite a different type was one Winterbottom — who drove the Holyhead Mail four stages out of Holyhead and who on one occasion when Mr Birch Reynardson — the great authority in this part of the world — approached the coach, was described to him by the guard as being 'amazing fresh'. 'Amazing fresh' is not only good in my eyes: it is delicious. And how when Winterbottom presently put in an appearance did he answer to this poetic description? Why, amazingly. 'He approached rolling about like a seventy-four in a calm; or as if he were walking with a couple of soda-water bottles tied under his feet.' The peculiarity of this gait, which might have been much appreciated on the Metropolitan boards as an eccentric dancer's new departure, did not appeal to the teller of this tale as prophetic of safety from the box-seat of a crack coach. So Winterbottom in all the meridian of his freshness was enclosed, a solitary passenger, in the stuffy inside — and Mr Birch Reynardson himself assumed the ribbons. At the change near St Asaph, sixty miles from Holyhead, inquiries were made after Winterbottom's condition. But all his freshness had deserted the cooped-up charioteer! He was however found fairly rational though excessively dejected, and expressed himself thus on a unique experience — 'Well, I think I'd better get outside now! I aren't used to this. Well! This is travelling like a gentleman, and inside the Mail to be sure! Well! I never travelled inside a Mail or a coach before; and I dare say I never shall again! I don't think I like the inside of a coach much; and so I'd better get out now! It feels wonderful odd somehow to be inside the Mail; and I really hardly know how I got there.'

Ibid.

24.   In Search of Wales

It is early in the morning on the day of the opening of the Eisteddfod. I am told that I must rise before breakfast to see the ceremony of the Gorsedd. I have already noticed the druidic circle of stones which officials of the Eisteddfod have planted in a meadow near the road on the slope below the University. When I first saw them I thought that they were as old as Stonehenge!

I dress swiftly and am glad to see that the morning is, although misty, fine. On the hotel landing I collide with someone who appears to be either a female druid or bard. She is swathed in green draperies. She is not quite my idea of an ancient Briton because she wears pince-nez. I did not know that women are admitted to the sacred circle, which I always imagined to be one of the last strongholds of the male. I wonder, as some stray memory of a school primer comes to me, whether she is, perhaps, after all, a burnt offering. Possibly the druids are to place her in a wicker basket and sacrifice her to the Eisteddfod.

I discover in the hall downstairs a number of bards, druids and druidesses. I am told that these green-robed women are novates. The druids are elderly or middle-aged men robed in white. They are distinguished by a benevolence which rules out all theories of human sacrifice. The bards are robed in blue. They are younger than the druids. I am slightly worried by the trousers of bard and druid, which are visible for a few inches below their gowns. Father Christmas has this same trouble with his trousers.

I leave them as they chat together and go through the early morning streets of Bangor, which are already awake and excited.

The stone circle rises from the grass, surrounded by a large crowd. The entrance faces the east. In the centre of the circle is a large altar stone. The waiting moments are enlivened by the expert activities of those young men with a motor-car who broadcast ceremonies to the British Isles. They are just attending to their wires, speaking down telephones to distant colleagues and generally making certain that nothing will go wrong. The wireless van and the druidic circle are an amusing contrast. But something even funnier is to happen. A young man in plus-fours enters the circle, bearing in his hand what appears to be an offering for the high altar. It is a bunch of green leaves. He places it reverently before the altar stone, stands back from it and starts to address it. He might be intoning a prayer, but I know that he is speaking into a microphone which is carefully concealed among the leaves. What a touching tribute from the British Broadcasting Corporation to the age when druids walked the earth.

All is now ready . . .

Soon we see the approaching procession. Men in scarlet gowns bear a litter on which is borne, like the Ark of the Covenant, the enormous Hirlas Horn, or the Horn of Plenty, which is normally to be seen in the National Museum at Cardiff. Behind, two by two, walk the druids in white, the bards in blue and the novates in green. They pause before they enter the circle and form a lane. Between the ranks strides a man in green bearing a great double-handed sword. Behind him comes the Chief Druid. He wears white robes and on his chest lies a replica of the Irish breastplate which Camden illustrated in his *Brittania*.

As the Chief Druid takes his place at the high altar, the attendant druids, bards and novates file in and group themselves round the circle. Now and again the irreverent wind blows aside the robes to reveal trousers of serge and tweed and pin-stripe. It is, alas, unfortunate. I spot one bard who has foreseen this. He alone of the priesthood wears white stockings and sandals. I, greatly daring, tap a druid on the shoulder and ask the name of this bard. He turns and, in the most friendly manner, informs me that the sandalled one is a bard named Cynan. He then adds for my better information:

'The Rev. A. E. Jones, you know . . .'

I conclude that many of the priesthood are Welsh clergymen who are playing at being pagan for a day. But a glance at their trousers reassures me that it is all very respectable!

The ceremony of the Gorsedd begins. The great sword is unsheathed. One by one the druids advance and place their hands on it. The Chief Druid lifts up his voice and cries in Welsh:

'Is there peace?'

He cries this three times. Three times comes a reassuring shout from the crowd:

'There is peace!'

A lady of beauty, who is not a green novate but a red lady who evidently represents the aristocratic laity, advances over uneven grass bearing the huge Horn of Plenty. She kneels before the Chief Druid and offers the relic to him. I expect him to drink from it, or in some way prove its plentifulness, but, as the horn is empty, he merely touches it symbolically and the lady bows and backs gracefully away with her burden.

The Chief Druid, mounted on the altar stone, then delivers a long speech in Welsh. I cannot understand one word of it. But I can tell that it is a good and well-prepared piece of oratory. The crowd love it. The words come rushing out like a stream in flood.

He is followed by other speakers. Some appear to be making epigrams at which the crowd laughs. There are prayers in Welsh. I imagine that the old gods of the Celtic peoples are stirring uneasily in their dim Valhalla. Then one by one, the newly-elected bards are led to the altar stone. These are young men and women singled out during the past year for some work of poetry, music or prose.

The Chief Druid shakes each one by the hand, calls them by their modern names and gives to each one a bardic name by which he, or she, will be forever after known in the Gorsedd.

The ceremony is over. The procession re-forms. Druid, Bard and Novate go their solemn way. The great Gorsedd Sword moves slowly above the heads of the crowd. The Horn of Plenty shines a moment in a burst of early sun. The Eisteddfod is opened . . .

A young man in plus-fours enters the sacred circle and steals out again carrying a bunch of leaves in which is hidden a microphone!

H. V. Morton, *In Search of Wales,* 1932

25. *The Walk*

It was an old custom in Headlong Hall to have breakfast ready at eight, and continue it till two; that the various guests might rise at their own hour, breakfast when they came down, and employ the morning as they thought proper; the squire only expecting that they should punctually assemble at dinner. During the whole of this period, the little butler stood sentinel at a side-table, copiously furnished with all the apparatus of tea, coffee, chocolate, milk, cream, eggs, rolls, toast, muffins, bread, butter, potted beef, cold fowl and partridge, ham, tongue and anchovy. The Reverend Doctor Gaster found himself rather *queasy* in the morning, therefore preferred breakfasting in bed, on a mug of buttered ale and an anchovy toast. The three philosophers made their appearance at eight, and enjoyed *les prémices des dépouilles.* Mr Foster proposed that, as it was a fine frosty morning, and they were all good pedestrians, they should take a walk to Tremadoc, to see the improvements carrying on in that vicinity. This being readily acceded to, they began their walk . . .

. . . The vale contracted as they advanced, and, when they had passed the termination of the lake, their road wound along a narrow and romantic pass, through the middle of which an impetuous torrent dashed over vast fragments of stone. The pass was bordered on both sides by perpendicular rocks, broken into the wildest forms of fantastic magnificence . . .

. . . They now emerged, by a winding ascent, from the vale of Llanberris, and after some little time arrived at Bedd Gelert. Proceeding through the sublimely romantic pass of Aberglaslynn, their road led along the edge of Traeth Mawr, a vast arm of the sea, which they then beheld in all the magnificence of the flowing tide. Another five miles brought them to the embankment, which has since been completed, and which, by connecting the two counties of Meirionnydd and Caernarvon excludes the sea from an extensive tract. The embankment, which was carried on at the same time from both the opposite coasts, was then very nearly meeting in the centre. They walked to the extremity of that part of it which was thrown out from the Caernarvonshire shore. The tide was now ebbing: it had filled the vast basin within, forming a lake about five miles in length and more than one in breadth. As they looked upwards with their backs to the open sea, they beheld a scene which no other in this country can parallel, and which the admirers of the magnificence of nature will ever remember with regret, whatever consolation may be derived from the probable utility of the works which have excluded the waters from their ancient receptacle. Vast rocks and precipices, intersected with little torrents, formed the barrier on the left: on the right, the triple summit of Moëlwyn reared its majestic boundary: in the depth was that sea of mountains, the wild and stormy outline of the Snowdonian chain, with the giant Wyddfa towering in the midst. The mountain-frame remains unchanged, unchangeable; but the liquid mirror it enclosed is gone.

The tide ebbed with rapidity: the waters within, retained by the embankment, poured through its two points an impetuous cataract, curling and boiling in innumerable eddies, and making a tumultuous melody admirably in unison with the surrounding scene. The three philosophers looked on in silence; and at length unwillingly turned away, and proceeded to the little town of Tremadoc, which is built on land recovered in a similar manner from the sea. After inspecting the manufactories, and refreshing themselves at the inn on a cold saddle of mutton and a bottle of sherry, they retraced their steps towards Headlong Hall, commenting as they went on the various objects they had seen.

Mr Escot: I regret that time did not allow us to see the caves on the sea-shore. There is one of which the depth is said to be unknown. There is a tradition in the country, that an adventurous fiddler once resolved to explore it; that he entered, and never returned; but that the subterranean sound of a fiddle was heard at a farm-house seven miles inland. It is, therefore, concluded that he lost his way in the labyrinth of caverns, supposed to exist under the rocky soil of this part of the country.

Mr Jenkinson: A supposition that must always remain in force, unless a second fiddler, equally adventurous and more successful, should return with an accurate report of the true state of the fact . . .

Thomas Love Peacock, *Headlong Hall*

THE FREE LUNCH

THE FREE LUNCH

Al Ramsay

Full Gas Books (Chorley)

Cover design by: Scott Cockerham

To my wonderful sister, Kathryn

1

Felix Haythornthwaite stood by the door to the head teacher's study, pulling nervously on the frayed cuffs of his blazer. His dad had been trying to attract the attention of one of the aged school secretaries, but was having little success.

'No comment!' Miss Catlow bellowed into the telephone. 'It was an unfortunate incident involving youthful high jinks, nothing more… No, Dr Brown is not available.' The moment she put the phone down, it burst into life again.

Felix's dad caught the eye of the second secretary. 'Excuse me, Miss Pomfrett,' he began timidly. 'We have an appointment with Dr Brown, at five-past-nine. The name's Haythornthwaite.'

'Yes!' she snarled over the din, 'I know who you are and I know exactly who *that* is.' She jabbed a finger towards Felix, who recoiled instinctively. 'Dr Brown is busy at the moment. We are *all* busy at the moment and I think you know why.'

Felix did his best to quell the blind panic that was about to run amok in his head. He'd led a blameless, unremarkable life to this point – never excelled at anything but equally, never given cause for concern. And then the *Frecklesall Pen* had come along and given him something to aim for – a purpose to the mind-numbing

1

routine of his daily existence. Becoming editor of the school newspaper had seemed like the best thing that had ever happened to him.

How wrong could he have been?

Father and son watched on in silence as the secretaries fielded the endless stream of calls. When they were together like this you could see they were about the same height, and that meant just shy of six feet tall. But whereas Haythornthwaite senior was built for comfort, his fourteen-year-old son was stick-thin – half-mast trousers revealing too-short socks and spindly white ankles, the sleeves of his blazer creeping up to expose an awkwardness of bony wrist. Felix had been growing at a phenomenal rate over the past eighteen months and his school uniform, together with the rest of his wardrobe, had not kept pace.

His pasty complexion was topped off with a hairstyle best described as unique. Wire wool was the nearest comparable and would probably have been easier to manage. His mousey brown hair didn't grow down – it grew out and up, defying the laws of gravity. And then there were the faint whisperings of a newly sprouting moustache…

A trickle of sweat ran down his back as he studied the brass plaque on the door, which announced grandly:

Dr RC Brown, Headmaster
Frecklesall-on-Sea High School

'Arsey by name and Arsey by nature', his big brother Freddie had always said. It didn't sound quite so funny now that Felix was in the firing line and about to experience his head teacher's arseyness, first hand.

Miss Catlow looked up at them and smiled, grimly. 'Dr Brown will see you now.'

'And put that bloody notepad away,' hissed his dad. 'This isn't one of your stupid stories – this is for real.'

The head teacher remained seated behind his desk, peering at them from over the tops of his half-moon glasses. In his mid-sixties, Dr RC Brown was a tall, thin man. With his long, scrawny neck, hooded eyes and large, beak-like nose, he looked like one of those giant vultures you might see in a wildlife programme, picking over the carcass of a zebra after the lions have had their fill.

'How nice to meet you again, Dr Brown.' Felix's dad broke the strained silence. 'Brian Haythornthwaite – you may remember me? Probably about thirty years since you last gave me a detention, sir.'

Felix sensed the chill wind blowing the tumbleweed across the office floor, but his dad carried on, regardless.

'You'd not been here that long when I started.' He gestured around the grandeur of the study. 'How things change, eh? For the better, of course – and well deserved, too. I always reckoned you'd make it to the top job. I used to say to my mates—'

'Please, Mr Haythornthwaite, this has been a difficult enough morning as it is,' said the head teacher, swivelling around in his chair to point out the message emblazoned across the large, framed poster on the wall behind. 'Do you see that? "Discipline. Personal Organisation. Respect" – the very foundation of our teaching here at Frecklesall High. Did you know that *every* pupil who completes their education with us can

3

make a three egg Victoria sponge sandwich by the time they leave? How many other schools can say that?'

Felix's dad nodded enthusiastically. 'Absolutely. An essential life skill, Dr Brown.'

'This is what happens when discipline, personal organisation and respect are found wanting!' the head boomed. 'Something must be done about it, and mark my words, something most definitely *will* be done about it.'

Felix sensed things beginning to slide away. If only he could turn back the clock – just forty-eight hours would do. He was happy then – well, he wasn't *that* happy, but compared to the way he felt now...

The previous Tuesday at half-past-three, Felix and his team were holed up in the office attached to the school library. A hastily scribbled note had been pinned to the door:

Frecklesall Pen Editorial Meeting
Do not disturb

The *Pen* was, and still is, Frecklesall High's school newspaper:

Run by our students and published every fortnight on the school intranet, the *Pen* presents a lively blend of news, reviews, recipes and human-interest stories, as well as reaching out to cover issues from the surrounding neighbourhood – bringing the school closer to the community it serves.

Well, that's what it says in the school prospectus, sent out to gullible parents in an effort to persuade them that Frecklesall High would be a good place to send their kids. Not that any of them have much choice in the matter, of course.

Half an hour into the meeting, the *Pen's* editor was beginning to lose it. 'There's no way we're running a front-page review of a splatter-fest like *Brain Driller 3 – Zombies' Revenge.* It's a certificate 18 – we've got eleven-year-olds to think of.'

'Yeah, right.' The diminutive figure of Bernie Devaney was having none of it. 'Like, everyone wants to read your Cookery Corner section, Felix, don't they? What is it this week – how to peel an onion without crying… again?'

Felix sighed. Bernie was his best mate but he drove him mad most of the time. At five feet tall, he still had the thin mousy hair, the cheeky grin and the same, round, metal-framed glasses he'd had at primary school. A dangerous-to-know livewire, he was a wind-up merchant who survived on his wit and sarcasm, which was generally just about enough to help him swerve the next pasting.

'It's not my fault we're stuck in a Food Technology Beacon of Excellence College, is it?' replied Felix. 'Anyway, where have Naz and Keira got to? They're supposed to be covering that Blue Pennant story at Slaidforth beach.' He glanced at his watch and groaned. 'They've missed the deadline now, haven't they?'

Bernie laughed. 'You know what Naz is like – "Nervous Nellie" is an understatement. And teaming him up with Crazy Keira isn't exactly the smartest idea you've ever had, is it? Come on mate, you've got a front page to fill. Where better to start than with my most excellent review of *Brain Driller*? Give the readers what they want, for a change.'

'I can't, Bernie – Basil would kill me. The problem is, all we've got left is Naz's lido piece. Y'know, the one I said was too—'

'Too flippin' boring!' shrieked Bernie. 'Like everything he comes up with. No one wants to read about our crummy outdoor swimming pool – it's a dump! What we need is a *real* story, like that Bradley Halfbarrel exclusive. That was a cracker.'

How could he forget?

'Absolutely out of the question,' 'Basil' Brush, Frecklesall High's panic-stricken head of English, had said after reading the piece, which linked the jaw-dropping appointment of the school's one-sandwich-short-of-a-picnic head boy, to the heavily discounted purchase of a school mini-bus from Halfbarrel Motors – his dad's garage. 'I personally guarantee that if even a word of this gets out, you'll all be suspended.'

So much for the scoop of the year.

Felix pulled out his mobile and was jabbing away at the keypad when the door swung open, revealing the slim, scrupulously tidy figure of Naz Hussein. His shorter and considerably more unruly companion, Keira Makinson, stomped in behind.

'Sorry we're late,' said Naz, still catching his breath. 'The traffic was terrible and then the bus broke down on the way back.'

'Did you get the story?' asked Felix.

Naz looked troubled. 'Kind of. I've been writing it up on the bus, but I'm not sure I've pitched it right.'

'It's brilliant, Naz,' Keira chipped in. 'Weren't you saying to him just the other day, Felix – he needs more "punch", more "passion" in his writing? He's totally 'nailed it this time, I've got some crackin' shots, as well.'

'I'm not sure, Keira,' muttered Naz. 'I'm really grateful for your help pulling it together but—'

'Trust me, it's spot on. Not just a scoop – more of a pooper-scooper!' She cackled disturbingly.

There *was* something crazy about Keira, Felix thought – well, something odd at least. He'd been in the same class as her for the best part of three years but was still no closer to understanding what made her tick. The caustic put-downs, the demented look in her eye – it was no wonder most people kept their distance. Still, she took bloody good photographs, and that's what counted.

'Thanks,' said Naz, 'but I'd rather Felix checked it over first, just to be on the safe side.'

Keira rolled her eyes.

'No problem, mate,' said Felix. 'You've missed the deadline for this edition, but file it as a draft on the system and I'll go through it tomorrow. You've still got the front page, though – I'm going with your lido piece this time around.'

Bernie and Keira screamed in unison.

'At least Basil's already approved it,' Felix said defensively, as he pushed back from the table. 'Everything else is boxed off and ready to go. I wouldn't normally do this, Naz, but if I don't get to Doreen's in the next ten minutes, she's going to kill me. Just copy your lido piece onto the Mac and get it over to Basil before five so he can do the final sign-off, will you?'

'No problem, Boss,' replied Naz.

'So long, sucker!' Bernie shouted after him in his shrill tones.

Felix didn't hear – he was already well into his stride, knowing he'd have to go flat-out if he was to avoid the hairdryer treatment from his aunt.

The following morning, Felix was hoicked out of triple food tech by Basil. As he was being marched across the yard towards the main school building, he tried to find out what was up, but the head of English seemed more interested in barking at him.

'Why didn't you show me that article, Felix? You know the rules. I have to approve everything before it goes out.'

'What do you mean?' asked Felix. 'What article?'

'Look lad, you're the editor, so don't tell me you don't know.' The teacher grabbed him by the shoulder and span him around so they were facing each other. 'It's the *Pen*, you moron – your headline story!'

Felix felt the blood drain from his face. 'But it was Naz's lido piece. A bit dull, I know, but you signed it off weeks ago. Don't you remember?'

Basil had turned puce. 'You have to apologise – grovel if necessary. And don't even think of dropping me in it.'

There was no time for further explanation. Waved through the secretaries' office by Miss Pomfrett, the door to the head's study was already open. Felix had barely sat down before Arsey rounded on him.

'And what is the meaning of *this*, boy?' The head slapped a printout of the *Pen's* front page onto his desk.

Felix gave him a bewildered look. And then he spotted the headline.

Slaidforth's Blue Pennant Party Pooper!

There was a photograph, taken on the beach. The backdrop of Slaidforth Promenade was instantly recognisable, complete with the newly awarded Blue

Pennant, fluttering from the flag pole at the end of the pier. But it was the glistening, grey deposit, lying on the sand in the foreground of the shot that almost stopped Felix's heart in mid-beat.

'Well?' demanded Arsey.

'Oh my God, is that a—?' The kick to the shins was enough to drag Felix's attention back to the article:

The cleanest sea front in the north of England? We don't think so! This is what we found stranded on Slaidforth beach earlier today, only moments after the unfurling of the much-coveted Blue Pennant award for beach and sea water cleanliness. Children frolicked in the waves just a few metres away, blissfully unaware of the health hazards posed by this toxic specimen, while the mayor of Slaidforth and his flunkies quaffed champagne at a nearby gala reception. So who's to blame? Is it Slaidforth council, who clearly couldn't care less about visitor safety? Or is it our central government, who allow the water companies to make vast profits while pumping raw sewage into our seas and rivers on a daily basis?

'Speak boy. Explain yourself!' boomed the head.

'I know this looks bad, Dr Brown,' said Basil, 'but I managed to delete it from the intranet earlier this morning. Serious breach of school rules etcetera, but no real harm done.'

Arsey gave the English teacher the blackest of looks. 'Kindly allow *me* to be the judge of the severity of crisis our school now faces, Mr Brush.' He waved a wad of papers at them both. 'Do either of you know what these are?'

Basil exchanged glances with Felix, who shrugged.

'Then permit me to enlighten you,' Arsey continued. 'Each and every one is a media enquiry – the *Sunday Scorcher*, the *Bugler*, *Cookery Today,* even *Lancashire Life*… who profiled me last year. You may have seen it, Mr Brush? A fine piece.' He gazed wistfully into the middle distance for a moment.

'But that's impossible,' mumbled the English teacher. 'The *Pen* only runs on our intranet. It can't get outside the school. Miss Sidhu told me all about it – there's a firewall or… or something like that.'

'Wrong, wrong and wrong again!' snapped Arsey. 'This so-called 'article' appeared on the school's website last night, readily accessible to all and sundry. And worse, much worse – someone has taken it upon themselves to circulate it to every media agency in the region, and beyond!'

Felix sat there with his mouth hanging open.

'I don't need to tell you what this could do to my reputation,' the head continued. 'And in case it had slipped your mind, Mr Brush, we also have the trivial matter of our new governor – the recently elected mayor of this town – who just happens to be making his first official visit to the school next week.'

Basil buried his head in his hands.

'Fortunately for both of you, the Misses Pomfrett and Catlow have been working tirelessly to put a stop to this nonsense. Most of the journalists who've contacted us have been sent packing.'

'Most?' asked Felix, hopefully.

'Most, but sadly not all. I'm sure you'll be familiar with *It's Grand Up North!,* that dreadful regional roundup programme they put on after the national news?'

Felix and Basil nodded in unison.

'In which case,' added Arsey, 'you'll be aware of a roving reporter going by the name of Marjorie Spangles.'

Basil immediately perked up. 'Of course, Dr Brown – I never miss "Marje at Large!". I'm a huge fan!'

'Ah, then dreams really do come true, Mr Brush.' Arsey offered up a grim smile. 'By which I mean, Miss Spangles will be conducting a live television interview with the two of you, on Slaidforth beach this very evening.'

'Awesome!' Basil rubbed his hands together, eagerly.

Felix could hardly believe his ears. 'It wasn't me,' he mumbled. 'I didn't do anything wrong.'

The head's words reverberated around the room. 'Allow me to remind you of the facts, boy. *You* are the editor of the *Pen*, so like it or not, *you* take full responsibility for all content contained therein. Be there, on the beach – quarter-to-six, sharp. An apology is owed – to the council, to the good people of Slaidforth Sands and to anyone else foolish enough to be watching. And be warned, both of you – if there are any slip-ups, anything at all, you can expect the remainder of your time at this school to be very, very limited.'

Back at 21 Scundale Chase, Brian Haythornthwaite was not a happy man. 'What the hell have you been up to now, Felix?'

His son shrugged. 'I'm innocent, Dad, I didn't do it. I've spoken to Naz and he says he typed up his Blue Pennant piece and saved it on the system for me to review, like I told him to. I've been stitched up.'

'Man, you're *so* busted!' Felix's big brother, Freddie, guffawed from the depths of the settee. 'Interview on the beach? That's a sphincter-factor ten, Bumfluff!'

Felix felt self-consciously for his top lip.

His dad groaned. 'For God's sake, I can't be doing with this now.'

'There'll be someone there from the Slaidforth tourist board and *It's Grand Up North!* – Marje Spangles I think her name is. And we're going to be interviewed on live TV and...' Felix babbled away, like he always did when he was in a corner.

'Hang on a minute.' His dad's tone softened in an instant. 'Do you mean, "Marje at Large!" Spangles?'

Felix nodded, fearing the worst, but the effect was remarkable, his dad's face instantly transforming from darkest thunder to the brightest sunshine.

'Marje Spangles!' his dad let out a sigh. 'Well, we need to be sure we're there in good time. Christine, love!' he shouted through to the kitchen. 'Can you keep the tea warm until we get back? I'm just off to get changed.' And with that, he disappeared upstairs.

Felix was puzzled – perplexed, even. 'What's going on?' he asked his brother, who was smirking, knowingly.

'It's that Marje Spangles chick,' replied Freddie. 'Every dad's dream girl. Wait 'til he comes down – you'll see.'

And sure enough, their father descended the stairs a man transformed. He looked scrubbed and polished, and unbelievably, Felix caught a distinct whiff of aftershave as he brushed past to pick up the car keys.

'Lookin' sharp there, Brian,' Freddie remarked.

'Just my normal evening get-up,' his dad replied, defensively. 'Come on Felix, get your skates on, lad, or we'll be late.'

Felix was dragged out to the Haythornthwaites' vintage Ford Fiesta. His mum blew him one last kiss, before scurrying back inside to phone all her friends to tell them to watch her baby on that evening's edition of *It's Grand Up North!*.

A sizeable group of middle-aged men had gathered near the centre of Slaidforth beach, forming a huddle around a large *It's Grand Up North!* golf umbrella, their balding heads glinting in the late afternoon sunshine. Sheltering in the shade, a well-groomed lady was signing autographs for a long line of admirers, smiling with the sincerity of a budget airline flight attendant.

Father and son joined the crowd and as they edged forward, Felix caught his first proper glimpse of the object of his dad's affections. Marje was attractive, in a smart, middle-aged kind of way. Her shoulder-length blond hair framed an orange, perma-tanned face, the suspiciously ultra-smooth gloss of her expressionless forehead, contrasting with the deep wrinkles creasing the corners of her eyes and top lip. Wearing a well-tailored khaki safari suit and brandishing a leather-bound clipboard, she looked like a woman who meant business.

An uncharacteristically spruced Basil was more than a little relieved to see him. 'Thank God! I was worried you weren't coming. Look, here's the drill – whatever she asks, just say this: terrible mistake... humble apology... time to move on. Think you can manage that?'

Felix sensed a sudden urge to go to the toilet.

Standing next to Basil was a short, red-faced man sporting a Blue Pennant T-shirt and matching baseball cap. Wearing a skimpy pair of white tennis shorts and a disappointed expression, Slaidforth council's Executive Director of Absolutely Awesome Visitor Experience did not look like he was having a good day.

'Live in five!' the cameraman shouted. A ripple of excitement ran through the crowd as he counted down. 'Four, three, two... and *action*!'

The roving reporter sprang into life as if someone had just flicked a switch on her back. 'Good evening viewers,' she began. 'This is Marje at Large, live, for *It's Grand Up North!*.' She stared thoughtfully into the camera for a second. 'And tonight, we're here in Slaidforth Sands, Lancashire's premier holiday destination. *Not*, as you might expect, to celebrate the award of the region's first Blue Pennant for beach cleanliness - alas, *no*! We're here this evening to investigate a bitter row that has broken out between this top resort and its second-rate, down-at-heel neighbour, Frecklesall-on-Sea.'

Marje swept the hair from her face, like a model in a shampoo advert, and then she was dashing across the sand, her camera crew in hot pursuit. Felix and his dad were left jostling for a view of the action on the TV monitor.

In no time, Marje had landed her first victim. Bending forward, she shoved a microphone into the face of an unsuspecting sunbather, while the camera zoomed in on her ample backside, revealing the 'Marje at Large!' slogan plastered across the seat of her trousers. Felix sensed the excitement of those around him, but there was little time for her fans to enjoy the moment. Seconds later, she was up and running again.

In the space of just two, short minutes, Marje had cajoled vox-pops from a handful of innocent bystanders. With the exception of one man who'd fled the scene with a towel over his head, wailing, 'The missus'll kill me if she finds out I'm 'ere!', everyone said the beach was nice and clean, and Slaidforth Sands was a grand place to come for a holiday.

And then she was back. Waving a printed copy of the *Frecklesall Pen* at the camera, she launched straight into the main event. 'And I'm joined here this evening, live, by Alan Turbot, Slaidforth Sands' Executive Director of Absolutely Awesome Visitor Experience; Vernon Brush, head of English at Frecklesall High School, and the villain of the peace himself – Felix Haythornthwaite, the editor of the *Frecklesall Pen,* which published the offending and frankly, offensive article, earlier today. Alan Turbot – this was supposed to be your big day and it's ended in total and utter calamity. Tell me now, how much damage has been done to the resort's reputation by this scurrilous piece of nonsense?'

The tourism chief looked like he was about to burst into tears. 'This is nothing short of a kick in the teeth for Slaidforth Sands, the north of England's premier holiday destination,' he said. 'We're completely and utterly gutted.'

Marje shook her head, sympathetically, but beside her, Basil was hopping from foot to foot.

'Miss Spangles, it's such a pleasure to meet you at last,' he blurted, before she'd even had the chance to ask him a question. 'And can I add, without seeming too forward, how lovely you're looking this evening?'

Out of the corner of his eye, Felix spotted a familiar face in the crowd. Not his dad, who was standing on tip-toes, trying to get a better view of the action, but someone else – someone who was crawling, commando-style, through the forest of legs, a small blue rucksack strapped to her back, frizzy hair falling forward over her face. It was Crazy Keira Makinson and she was making a bee-line for the roving reporter, a white Tupperware box clutched in one hand.

Hmm – looks like she's brought some sandwiches with her, thought Felix.

'No evidence!' Alan Turbot screamed into the microphone for the third time. 'Some people will do anything to spoil the absolutely awesome things we've achieved here in Slaidforth Sands… No evidence at all. Put up or shut up!'

Marje thrust the microphone into the young editor's face. 'Felix Haythornthwaite,' she began. 'Given the damage and upset you've caused today, don't you think this would be a good time to offer an unreserved apology – to Mr Turbot, as well as all the decent, hard-working folk of Slaidforth Sands?'

'Err…' And for a moment, time stood still. Felix tried to speak but no words came from his mouth. Paralysed by nerves, he gawped into the camera like a terminally ill goldfish.

Before he could pull himself together, Keira had jumped up and was waving her sandwich box in the tourist chief's face. 'No evidence?' she yelled. 'Get a load of this! We scooped it up from the beach the other day. And there's plenty more where it came from.'

In a flash she'd flipped the lid off the box to reveal… the Turd. Felix caught only a fleeting glimpse, but to his untrained eye it looked very much like the same revolting piece of faecal matter, pictured in glorious Technicolor on the front page of that morning's *Pen*.

There were gasps of horror, and then all hell broke loose. Basil lunged forward to try to wrestle the container from Keira's grasp and in the ensuing struggle, its contents were catapulted high into the air. Felix could only watch, open-mouthed, as the glistening stool arced over their heads... before landing with a sickening Splat! onto the shoulder of Marje's jacket. Sliding down her left sleeve, it left an awful, slug-like trail in its wake.

'Oh my goodness! Is there a doctor in the house?' the English teacher shouted as Marje swooned into his arms. 'Or a dry cleaner, perhaps?'

Within moments both he and the roving reporter had been engulfed in a stampede – the umbrella, the TV monitor and the camera crew, disappearing under an almighty ruck as a dozen middle-aged men scrambled forward to try to rescue their beloved Marje from what was clearly some kind of terrorist attack. In the midst of it all, Felix was grabbed by his dad and the two of them made their escape.

They dashed back to the Prom to the accompaniment of wailing sirens and screeching tyres, a handful of policemen brandishing riot batons, running past them onto the beach. Seconds later, they'd jumped into the Fiesta and were chugging away from the scene of the crime.

'Gimme five, Bro!' Freddie yelled, gleefully. 'Respect!'

Felix was in no mood. 'Shut it, you numpty.'

Their mum was sitting in the lounge beside a half-empty bottle of red wine, her head in her hands. 'You were supposed to be looking after him, Brian!' she wailed. 'It was nothing short of a riot and *you* let it happen. And all because you were too busy ogling that Spangles woman. How am I ever going to show my face at the badminton club again?' She started to sob.

Before her husband could marshal his defences, the landline rang.

Freddie picked up the call. 'Yo, Arsey! Howzit hangin', my man?'

His dad snatched the phone from him and the seriousness of the situation immediately hit home.

'Yes indeed, Dr Brown... Deeply regrettable...' he mumbled into the handset. 'Yes, we'll be there. Tomorrow morning at five-past-nine – your office.' He turned to Felix, a grim look on his face.

Sentence had been passed with typical pomposity. Suspended, heading for permanent exclusion if Arsey had his way – it was touch and go, dependant on a school governors' meeting set up to hear the case in a few days' time.

His dad broke the strained silence as they drove away from school. 'You're off to your aunt Doreen's – make yourself useful for a few days while this gets sorted. I'm not having you bouncing around at home, winding up your brother.'

'But that's not fair, Dad,' pleaded Felix. 'I didn't put that story in the *Pen*. I didn't throw that *thing* over Marje Spangles!'

'Guess what, lad? Life, isn't fair,' his dad replied, drily. 'You're going to Doreen's and that's that, OK?'

It wasn't OK. It was a million miles from OK, but there was no point in arguing.

2

The old adage, 'First impressions are lasting impressions', has long challenged those seeking to promote the attractions of Frecklesall-on-Sea, at the northern end of Lancashire's Irish Sea coastline. On the drive along the single main road into town, visitors are confronted by the weed-ridden Big Lamp roundabout and its rusting, triple-lamped, art deco lighting standard. Positioned immediately in front of this once grand landmark, is a large, faded sign featuring a picture of a couple in fulsome 1950s swimwear, gaily throwing a beach ball to each other. The slogan above it, proclaims boldly:

YOUR Welcome to Frecklesall-on-Sea

The jewel of the Lancashire Riviera
(Home of Frecklesall's Famous Donkeys)

The dodgy graffiti had been added back in the 1980s but no one had ever bothered enough to paint it out, let alone correct it.

Alas, the town's days as a holiday destination are long gone. The scabby beach, the decrepit 1930s lido, the Famous Donkeys – the oldest donkey attraction in the north (allegedly) – well, that's about all there is on offer. The usually mild-mannered *Holidays in England – Your Essential Guide* dismisses Frecklesall in just a single sentence:

An unremarkable place. Don't bother visiting.

*

'Gerramoveon! Gerrup there!' yelled Felix's great-aunt Doreen as she marched off in front of her donkeys – Dave, Dee, Beaky, Mick and Titch. Passers-by paused to watch the spectacle meandering along the high street, public humiliation being just one the many punishments Felix had been forced to endure since his exile had begun, five long days earlier.

'Come *on*, lad!' she bellowed at her great-nephew, who was grappling with a half-full bucket, a brush and a shovel. He'd had to stop to clear up donkey muck on a couple of occasions already, and was on the verge of landing his hat-trick.

'Why can't we just leave it?' he whined. 'Why do I have to pick it up?'

'Would you like a dirty great pile of shite dumped outside your front gate?' she shouted back at him. 'Would you 'eck as like! Now shut up and get weaving.'

Doreen was well known in Frecklesall – notorious might be a better way of putting it. Looking like an old bag-lady, with her grubby, crumpled skirts and dishevelled grey hair, opinions of her varied from the kindly ('eccentric') to the vindictive ('stark raving bonkers'). But as the guardian of one of the town's few remaining visitor attractions, she didn't have to take

20

stick from anyone, and those foolish enough to have a go would get it back – with interest.

Struggling to keep up, Felix threaded the broom stick through the handle of his bucket, before slinging the pungent cargo over a shoulder, seven dwarfs' style. It seemed to do the trick but he hadn't reckoned on the split in the bucket's side, which resulted in an unpleasant brown stain, seeping down the middle of his back.

'For God's sake, lad!' Doreen bawled at him on their arrival at the Paddock, the run-down bungalow and acre of land where she and the donkeys lived. 'I told you to put it *in* the bucket, not smear it down your shirt.'

Stomping around the back to stow the tack, she left him to go inside and tidy up, on the basis that 'things had got a bit out of hand'. *Understatement of the year*, Felix thought as he surveyed the chaos of her living room. Damp and dingy with the smell of animal, everywhere, the place was a jumble sale of dirty clothes and books, with a few platefuls of mouldy sandwiches and half-eaten biscuits, thrown in for good measure. The bedroom he shared with Freddie was a tip, but this was something else, altogether.

Having laboured for the best part of twenty minutes, he was searching for a place to stash some old newspapers when he spotted a narrow door in the corner, tucked away behind an old standard lamp. Rattling the brass door knob, he edged his way into the tiniest of rooms – shelves, groaning under the weight of ancient-looking papers and photo albums, the walls crammed with black and white photographs from way back. A framed collection of postcards from the 1950s and 60s caught his eye. The caption on the first one read: 'Greetings from Frecklesall-on-Sea!', above a picture of a beautiful young woman, her long curly hair cascading over a one-piece bathing costume. She was holding onto the reins of a couple of glum-looking donkeys.

Opening up one of the albums he found more photos of the same woman – this time at the lido – looking curvaceous and glamorous in her swimwear. There were a couple of shots of her standing by the diving boards, next to an older, dopey-looking guy in a baggy suit, who was gurning into the camera, clutching what looked like a miniature guitar. On the next page she was pictured with a handsome young man, the two of them walking, arm in arm together, along Frecklesall Prom. There were more shots of the same man a few pages later, sitting astride a sleek racing bike, complete with drop handlebars and narrow wheels – the name 'Hill Special' stencilled onto its crossbar and down tube. Wearing all the proper cycling gear, he looked like he knew what he was doing.

Felix wondered who they were. The donkeys had been in the Haythornthwaite family for years, so he was probably related to them in some way. It would be interesting to find out.

The sound of his aunt crashing around in the kitchen jolted him back to reality. Heart in mouth, he crept towards the narrow door that had led him to this secret place, and eased it open.

'What the hell are you doing in there?' she yelled. 'You're supposed to be clearing up out here, not poking your nose into my private life!'

'Sorry,' he mumbled. 'I was putting some stuff away and I saw these old pictures. Actually, I was just wondering—'

She held up the palm of a hand. 'They're *my* memories. I don't want to talk about them with you, or anyone else for that matter.'

He sat down on the settee, hands pressed either side of his face, knees crammed up to his chin.

Doreen glanced around the room with a critical eye. 'You need to buck your ideas up, lad – this place looks worse than it did half an hour ago.' And with that, she marched off to her bedroom.

Still muttering about the injustice of it all, Felix was on his third sink of pots when relief came in the form of a knock at the back door. His great-aunt reappeared, clearly in no mood for small talk with his dad.

'What are you after, Brian?' she asked abruptly.

'We've just had a phone call from the school,' he replied. 'They've reached a decision, at long last.'

'Come on then, put the lad out of his misery.'

'It was one of the school secretaries who phoned: Miss Catlow – says she knows you, Doreen. She asked me to pass on her regards.'

She rolled her eyes. 'Get on with it, will you? Sometime today would be good.'

'Right. Well, it was a long meeting, apparently – a lot of back and forth, to and fro, edge of the seat stuff. But at the end of the day, they've decided…' He paused, like they do when they're announcing who's being kicked out of the *Bake Off* tent. '…They've decided to reinstate you, Felix! You're back on Monday – final warning and all that, but hey!'

Doreen laughed and gave her great-nephew the briefest of hugs. 'I knew tha'd be reet, lad,' she said quietly.

The sun was shining and all was well with the world, Felix's spirits not even dampened by his dad's outrageous offer to 'lend' his youngest son to help out with the donkeys over the next few Sundays – 'Just to get the season going, Doreen. It's the least we can do after the support you've given him these past few days.'

Support? Slave labour, more like, Felix thought. But he didn't care – it was a small price to pay.

The following Monday morning, at the end of English, Basil asked him to stay behind.

'If it was down to Dr Brown, you'd be out on your ear by now. It was the mayor who stuck up for you – God knows why. You've a lot to thank him for.' The English teacher began wringing his hands. 'And... well, I'm sorry about this, Felix, but it turns out that you can't be the editor of the *Pen* any longer. Dr Brown was most insistent on that point. I'm sure you understand.'

Felix groaned – he'd guessed this was coming. 'So, who's it going to be?'

Basil looked down at his shoes. 'Well, not an obvious choice, really.'

'Don't tell me it's Bernie. I know he's a mate of mine but...'

The English teacher chuckled. 'Not Bernard – that would never work, obviously.'

'Who, then?'

Basil grimaced. 'Actually, it's *me*, Felix. Dr Brown says he wants me to run the *Pen* until the end of term. He's determined to keep a firm grip on proceedings, and with a responsible adult at the helm he knows there'll be no more slip-ups.'

'But that's ridiculous! It's our paper – we don't want you standing over us, telling us what to do. Anyway, this whole thing's a stitch-up and when I find out who's behind it—'

'Now hang on a minute.' Basil nudged the classroom door shut with an outstretched foot. 'Don't think for one minute that I'm any happier with this arrangement than you are. You're bloody lucky you're still here, so be warned – if I get even a sniff that you're not giving me your full support, you'll be off the team for good – no second chances.'

And so it was that the following Wednesday, after school, the *Pen's* new sports correspondent found himself teamed up with the paper's photographer, watching the school rugby league team in the semi-finals of the Lancashire Coast Challenge Cup.

Felix viewed the action with disinterest – twenty-six lummoxes blundering around, chasing a funny-shaped ball, the Frecklesall half of the equation being subjected to a torrent of motivational abuse from their head of PE and proud Welshman, Mr Gareth Llewellyn-Evans.

'Gazza', as he was known to the inmates, was the man who put the 'pug' into pugnacious. With his wonky, rugby player nose, flattened features and mad, staring eyes, he was no oil painting – although that wasn't quite the way he saw it when he gazed into the mirror (something he spent rather a lot of time doing). An arrogant bully – what he lacked in height, he made up for in muscle, taking every opportunity to show off his honed physique to the girls, while making absolutely sure that the boys were in no doubt as to who was 'top dog'. And of course, as a PE teacher, he was contractually obliged to wear all the latest sports gear, all the time.

The lads running around on the pitch were the school's sporting elite – the 'jocks' who occupied an altogether separate and more glamorous universe than Felix and his friends. As if to prove the point, a cluster of year ten and eleven girls were giggling on the touchline, checking out the boys in their shorts.

To make matters worse, there was a new face on the team that day. The notorious Sean Spugley had somehow crawled his way into contention following some last-minute no-shows, and was making his debut. The earring, the intimidating dead-eyed stare and the ten-a-day habit were all enough to send Felix running for the hills. Frecklesall High's number one psycho had had a go at him a couple of months earlier, and he was keen to avoid a rematch.

By the second half, the game had degenerated into a series of bone-crunching collisions and floundering tackles. The players' shirts were so muddy, it was difficult to tell the teams apart – a detail which made precious little difference to Felix, who hadn't got a clue what was going on. Mind wandering, he completely missed Spugley wading into a challenge, fists and boots flying. The referee was a tad more observant, however, and after a finger-wagging lecture, the disgraced debutant trudged off the pitch to take up a position ominously close to where Felix was standing. The novice sports reporter shuffled a few paces to his left.

The dour struggle continued, Gazza working himself into a red-faced frenzy, the veins bulging from his neck, his flat cap all but falling from his head as he kicked out at every ball and intercepted every wayward pass. And somehow, it seemed to be working. An improbable victory was on the cards, until one of the Frecklesall players screamed out in agony from the depths of a multi-player pile-up.

'Bloody Hell, Noblett!' the PE teacher bawled as the casualty was being hauled off the pitch in tears. 'Why go and dislocate your shoulder now, boy? 12-10 up with five minutes left – we can't hold on with just eleven men, they'll murder us!'

Heroic failure now looked a certainty for the home team, whose regular substitute was revising for his GCSE maths exam the following morning ('Let himself down, let the team down. It's all about priorities' – Mr G Llewellyn-Evans). Felix was reflecting on revised headline options for his match report when he was snapped from his torpor.

'Spugley, get your kit off and give it to Haythornthwaite,' barked the PE teacher.

Felix sensed the ground rippling beneath his feet. It took him a moment to find his voice. 'I'm sorry, Mr Llewellyn-Evans, sir. Only… rugby isn't really my thing, so if it's all the same with you—'

'Shut UP!' bellowed Gazza. 'Which part of that simple instruction did you not understand? You!' He pointed at Spugley. 'Get your kit off, NOW – all of it, mind. And you, boy…' His finger jabbed back towards Felix. 'Put it on and get yourself onto that bloody pitch before I kick you so hard, you'll have to have my boot surgically removed from your arse!'

Muttering obscenities, Spugley pulled off his shirt and boots, dropping them into the mud at Felix's feet. After a further glower from the PE teacher, the shorts followed suit, leaving him shivering on the touchline in his underpants.

And then the heavens opened.

The referee ran towards them, pointing at his watch. Still in a daze, Felix handed his blazer to Keira and, unable to bear the embarrassment of exposing his

27

emaciated frame to an audience of giggling fifteen-year-old girls, opted to wear Spugley's shorts and shirt over the rest of his school uniform. Nothing fitted, but the boots were a particular nightmare. Even tying them as tightly as he could, it felt like he had a pair of clown shoes strapped to his feet.

Gazza barked some final instructions to the emergency substitute, who did his best to look like he understood what he was being told.

'Go to full back and keep out of the way. If one of their guys breaks through our line, you stop him – OK? If they kick over the top, you catch it, then kick it into touch – OK? Catch and kick. KISS!'

Felix was taken aback. 'I'd prefer a handshake if you don't mind, sir. That's not really my kind of thing.'

'No, you idiot – KISS. Keep It Simple, Stupid!'

The rain was coming down in stair-rods but despite the drenching, players from both sides roared with laughter at the sight of the unlikely substitute, stumbling onto the pitch. Glancing back over his shoulder, Felix saw the coach muttering a silent prayer. He also spotted Sean Spugley, arms clasped around his body, suddenly springing into life to chase after Keira, who'd taken some snaps of him shivering in his pants.

The hands of the clock turned with agonising slowness but despite the odds, Felix's team-mates somehow managed to hold it together, the action occurring exclusively in the Slaidforth half. But when a XIII becomes a XII and one of those XII is a gangling beanpole, weighing in at a hefty nine stone (wet through), with boots three sizes too big and not even a basic understanding of the rules of the game, there can only be one outcome.

A minute to go and, alone in the Frecklesall half, Felix had slipped back into daydreaming mode. Gazing across the school field towards the old lido building, he spotted a couple of men in HiViz jackets, wrestling with a tripod. It looked like they were trying to take some shots of the town's decrepit outdoor swimming pool. The summer season was due to start at the weekend, so at least Freddie, who had a job there as a lifeguard, would be out of his hair for a while. Lifeguard? That was a laugh! His big brother had been acting like a total plank since he'd come back from that surf-rescue course in Newquay. The whole thing was pointless – it wasn't as if there were any waves at the lido, or even down on the beach most of the time. And on top of that, just the other day in the bathroom he'd—

'WAKE UP, HAYTHORNTHWAITE!' a Welsh voice screamed from the touchline.

Wiping the rain from his eyes, Felix peered through the deluge, and to his horror, spotted the ball spinning crazily over the heads of his stranded team mates. To add to his woes, the fearsome heavyweights of the Slaidforth forward line were heading straight for him, and it didn't look like they were planning on an exchange of pleasantries about the weather.

'Catch and kick, you idiot. CATCH AND KICK!'

Gazza's cries barely registered as Felix blundered towards the oncoming threat, more in hope than expectation.

He didn't get very far.

After a few faltering steps, one of his oversized boots caught on a divot. Toppling forward, he threw out his arms in a desperate bid to make the interception. The ball, untroubled by his efforts, splatted down hard onto the turf before ricocheting up to catch him, square on the forehead. He face-planted into the mud, barely aware of the flashes coming from Keira's camera as she recorded the moment for posterity.

The Slaidforth front line steamed in, like a runaway truck slamming into a group of elderly nuns on a zebra-crossing. Grabbing the ball, they charged up the pitch to score the winning try.

The final whistle blew and Felix's lifeless body was dragged to the touchline. He tried to sit up but suddenly felt dizzy and was promptly sick all over Gazza's new rugby boots. Leaping high into the air to avoid the worst of it, the PE teacher's whistle flew from his top pocket and landed with a splat, in the middle of the steaming mess. Spugley, who was standing nearby, made the mistake of snorting with laughter.

Gazza let out a stream of expletives. 'Pick up that whistle, Spugley, you idiot, and be sure to give it a bloody good clean before you hand it back to me. And get some clothes on – you're frightening the girls.'

'Nice one, donkey boy,' Spugley growled at Felix. 'You just cost us the match.'

Keira was standing nearby. 'Shut it, Captain Underpants!' she yelled. 'Do one, before I decide who's going to see these lovely shots I've taken of you in your frillies.'

Felix managed a faint smirk. From the look of utter fury on Spugley's face, it was something he instantly regretted.

'Mild concussion', the doctor had said, which was why Felix found himself at home that Thursday afternoon. A day off school seemed like scant reward for the trauma he'd suffered, but with Freddie in the lounge, overdosing on daytime TV, and the fourth slice pinging from the toaster, things could have been a lot worse. And then his big brother discovered a letter on the doormat. It was from the council.

'"The opening of Frecklesall lido is delayed for essential health and safety works",' he read out loud. '"Lifeguards need not report for duty on Saturday and should await further instructions". Man, that's such a bummer.'

Felix's response wasn't exactly sympathetic. 'Yeah, well ever thought of looking for a proper job, Fred?'

Freddie bounded into the kitchen to confront him. 'Any more lip from you and I'll send you back to the hospital with an even bigger headache.'

'Seriously though, you've got to start doing *something*, Fred. You can't spend the whole summer hanging around the house like this – it's pathetic.'

'It's not my fault they closed the lido, is it? You can stick your stupid newspaper thing 'cos. I've got myself a *real* job – saving lives. It's a tough gig, but the rewards…'

'Yeah!' Felix laughed. 'Admit it – you're only in it for the girls.'

He'd been down to the lido a few times the summer before and knew how it worked – Freddie and his mates strutting around in their 'baggies', shirts off, administering sun lotion to the most 'bootilicious' of the 'chicks' – '*Aloha* babes, get a squirt of this… Don't wantcha getting any hotter that you already are, do we?'.

'Well, you got me there, Bro!' exclaimed Freddie. 'Sunny day down the lido – wall-to-wall bikinis! What's not to like? Hey, I know that's not really your thing but...'

Their conversations always seemed to go this way. Felix had never had a girlfriend – he'd had friends who were girls, of course, but on the few occasions he'd plucked up the courage to try to move things on to the next level, he'd blown it, in awkward, tongue-tied embarrassment. The only thing more painful than his abject failure with the opposite sex was the effortlessness of Freddie's success. Felix would never have admitted it, but deep down, he knew his brother had the looks. He also knew, for a fact, that he was an obnoxious, egotistical idiot with the mental capacity of a sheep, but for reasons he'd never been able to fathom, these glaring deficiencies didn't seem to put the girls off. Admittedly, none of them ever hung around for very long, but there were always more waiting in the wings, and it drove him mad.

'Yeah right,' said Felix. 'Remind me again, Fred – how did those GCSEs go for you?'

Freddie's chair clattered aside as he grabbed his brother by the throat and shoved him up against the wall.

'Violence won't get you anywhere,' croaked Felix.

They both froze at the familiar sound of the Fiesta's unhealthy rattle, signalling their dad's return from his morning shift at Marty's Mart – Slaidforth's premier second-hand caravan sales showroom.

'If you hadn't just got out of hospital, you'd be dead meat,' hissed Freddie, relaxing his grip as the back door opened.

3

The usual weekend-starts-here buzz was decidedly lacking as Felix and Naz trudged home from school that Friday afternoon.

'I can't do this any longer,' moaned Felix. 'First they dump Basil on us and now we've got to sit there like stooges and read out their stupid questions. I'm going on strike.'

'Come on, mate,' said Naz. 'It's just so Arsey can keep everything under control. He doesn't want another "Turd" on his hands, does he?'

'What if someone else wants to ask something? What about freedom of speech?'

Naz looked at him in disbelief. The mere suggestion that anyone at Frecklesall High would willingly ask their new school governor a question in the special assembly scheduled for the following Monday morning, was clearly beyond ridiculous. 'I'm off now,' he announced, sounding more than a little relieved. 'The cycling's on Sky Sports. Me and Saj watch the highlights every day after school. Come round, if you want?'

'Thanks, but it's not really my thing. I'll see you later.'

Felix kicked out at an old beer can, spilled from a nearby bin. He hadn't realised quite how much being the editor of the *Pen* had meant to him, until the job had been snatched away. And now, his dream of becoming a journalist was fading, fast.

'Yow!'

Snapped back to reality, his arms were pinned from behind as the sneering figure of Sean Spugley loped into view.

''Ow do, Thwaitey lad,' Spugley greeted him. 'Your nerdy friend cleared off, then?'

'And 'is bird as well! Felix Haythornthwaite and Crazy Keira Makinson – who'd have thought, eh?' Felix immediately recognised the grating voice of year ten's, Ricky Sowerbutts, the obnoxious son of his Dad's boss, Marty. 'Just smack 'im, Spug – come on, mate, get on wi' it!'

'Wait yer 'urry, Butty lad. No reason to rush things, is there?'

'No… no reason at all,' pleaded Felix as Ricky tightened the grip on his arms. He glanced up and down the deserted street in the forlorn hope that a random passer-by might come to his rescue. 'Look Sean, I'm really sorry about the other day, but you saw what happened. It was concussion – I could die if you hit me.'

Grinning, Spugley came up close. 'Yeah right, Thwaitey. I reckon you should have thought of that before you started laughing at me.'

'You got it, Sean,' chimed his dim-witted accomplice. 'It's bang out of order, that's what it is. I even heard some people have been calling you Captain Un—'

'Shut UP Butty, you moron!' screamed Spugley. He gave his friend a dirty look, then turned back to Felix. 'So, this is how it goes, Haythornthwaite. No one makes a fool of the Spug and gets away with it – understand?

Felix nodded, enthusiastically. 'I… I totally get it, Sean, I really do. Message received, loud and clear.'

'Excellent. And just so's you don't forget, I'm gonna give you a little reminder.' He span around, his right fist a blur.

The punch landed with a sickening crunch… square into the face of Ricky Sowerbutts, who was struggling to hold the wriggling captive still.

'Owww!'

The lock on Felix's arms loosened for just an instant and he broke free, scrambling off up the road. He'd got a decent head start but he was a lousy runner and knew he wouldn't be able to stay clear for long. Flapping around the corner onto Marine Drive, and out of sight for just a few seconds, he threw himself headlong into the depths of the overgrown laurel bushes at the front of the old lido complex.

Heart hammering away, he curled up into a ball and held his breath. He heard Spugley and Sowerbutts thunder around the corner, shouting and cursing. And then… silence.

He had no idea how long he'd been hiding there amidst the rotting chip papers and stale cat shit, but after what seemed like an age, he uncurled his lanky frame and began crawling towards the footpath. Just as he was about to break cover, the sound of footsteps sent him diving back into the depths. They were nearly on him when he caught their voices and realised, to his immense relief, that he was safe. One was a clipped, home counties accent – quite well-to-do – the other, the slow, baritone drawl of an American from the Deep South. To

Felix's ear, it sounded a bit like an exchange between Prince William and Elvis Presley.

He was itching to see what the two characters looked like, but something kept him glued to the spot. Ever the journalist, he pulled out his trusty notepad.

'So that's us, home and hosed. What say you, my friend?' asked Wills.

'Y'know, it makes me kinda sad, in a way. Almost a shame to have to take this place out,' replied Elvis. 'But I guess nothing stands in the way of the mighty US dollar, huh? Say, what's that heap of garbage over there? Looks kinda interesting.'

'Sorry old chap, no can do. That's the local school. Look at the state of the place! It's no wonder our education system's in such a bally mess.'

The American laughed. 'So, remind me – are we good to go, here?'

'Yah. The levels came through and the desktop is clear. It was greenfield before they built this, way back in the 1930s. Developed and owned by the council, of course – must have thought it would help them get one over on Slaidforth Sands, all those years ago.'

'Hell, yeah!' chimed Elvis. 'And those guys are still at each other's throats! Did you see that crazy fight on the bulletin the other day?'

'Gosh, absolutely! Nothing like a bit of good old argy-bargy between some ghastly northern seaside towns to spark a bit of publicity. But that Marje Spangles is a rather special lady, don'tcha think?'

What was it with Marje and middle-aged men? Felix thought, as he scribbled away in the subterranean gloom.

Elvis got the conversation back on track. 'OK, Roop, so we've gotten the levels, S.I.s and services. Herb's signed-off the design – pretty much standard template, of course. Planning follows when the legals are wrapped up, and God help anyone who tries to stand in our way. Let's wash up here, why don't we?'

Prising himself out of the mud, Felix breathed a sigh of relief. He hadn't a clue what they'd been talking about, he was just relieved to still be in one piece. But with Sean Spugley after him, how long was that going to last?

And then his phone went off.

Wrenching the mobile from his pocket, his fingers fumbled across the keypad.

'What in tarnation?' roared the American.

'My goodness!' Wills joined in. 'Someone's been spying on us. Look, Isiah – over there!'

Surfacing, waist high in the foliage, Felix blinked in the glare of the late afternoon sunshine.

'I say!' yelled the floppy-haired, red-faced Englishman. 'What the hell d'you think you're doing, eaves-dropping on our private conversation, like that?'

'I wasn't. Honest!' shrieked Felix. 'I was just tying my shoelace.' It was pathetic, but it was all he could think of.

'Y'know, he looks kinda familiar,' said the older, square-jawed, silver fox in the sharp grey suit. 'I've got this crazy feeling I've seen the guy someplace before.'

Felix thundered onto the path and was hurtling off along Marine Drive before either of them could even think of giving chase.

Racing home, his mind was in turmoil at what he'd just heard. It was unbelievable… devastating… disastrous, even! How could that idiot Sowerbutts think Keira was his girlfriend? If word got out, he'd never live it down.

*

After a boring Saturday, stuck at home, and a Sunday of hard labour with the donkeys, Felix wouldn't normally have been too disappointed at the prospect of heading back to school. But the mere thought of bumping into Sean Spugley turned his legs to jelly, while the imminent arrival of the new mayor and school governor had done nothing to improve his mood.

Trudging in that Monday morning, he knew his best hope of survival was to keep the drama of the previous Friday to himself – the less people who knew about it, the better. Sadly, that boat had already sailed. Within minutes of his arrival, it was clear that news of his epic fist fight had already been leaked (thanks, Bernie!) and was spreading like wildfire.

The entire school had been crammed into the hall. As befitted their senior status, the year nines, tens and elevens were lined up on chairs at the back, while the rest of the rabble were shoe-horned in, close to the stage. Normally, assembly was split between seniors and juniors but with everyone press-ganged into attendance there wasn't room to swing a hamster, let alone a cat.

Somewhere in his mid-forties, the new school governor and recently elected mayor of Frecklesall-on-Sea, was a short, podgy man. Wearing a navy-blue suit and white, open-necked shirt, he carried most of his excess weight on his top half. Ballooning out from the waist up, he looked like a barrel on legs – solid, round and with no neck to speak of. The small, neatly-trimmed beard, stranded in the middle of his face, merely accentuated the chubbiness of his ruddy cheeks.

'Boys and girls,' he began, in his faint Geordie twang, 'for those of you who don't know me, my name is Mayor Troy Wiseley MBA, and like it says on the tin,

I'm the democratically elected mayor of Frecklesall-on-Sea. I also happen to be your new school governor - but let's park the formalities for a moment, why don't we? You can just call me, The Boss!' He paused, waiting for a laugh that never came.

'Oh... right.' His hesitation echoed around the hall. '... Anyway, I'm so thrilled to have the opportunity to reach out to you all this morning...'

The speech was a long one, although not half as long as it seemed to the bored, fidgeting audience, who showed no interest whatsoever in the mayor's ramblings about wellbeing league tables, place-shaping paradigms and world-beating plans to turn Frecklesall into an 'aspirational destination'. Time slowed to a snail's pace as he droned on and on, until mercifully, after twenty excruciatingly dull minutes, things seemed to be edging towards a close.

'Let's cut to the chase!' enthused Wiseley. 'Change is *good* and it's long overdue, here in Frecklesall, so I know how keen you'll all be to hear my *mission critical* announcement – the one that signposts the real-time upload of my blue-sky, visioneering programme.'

There was a hush of anticipation, or more likely, indifference, broken only by the huge yawn coming from head boy, Bradley Halfbarrel, who was hanging off his chair, next to Arsey at the side of the stage.

The mayor's beaming smile crumpled into a pained expression of dismay. He stepped back, slapping the heel of a palm against his forehead. 'Oh no, I got ahead of myself, there. I *do* apologise. I've just remembered – there's a strict embargo on this bulletin. I'd *so* love to step you guys through the moving parts of my integrated change roadmap, but if you're looking for a deeper dive into how I'm gonna jump-start this town back into life with a transformative agenda that will *quite literally* blow your minds, you'll have to get yourselves down to the mayor's ball, this Saturday night.' He smirked. 'Actually, it's a complete sell-out, but hey!'

He placed his hands together in a prayer-like gesture. 'In all seriousness, though, it's been my absolute pleasure, keynoting you this morning – a truly humbling experience. You guys really are the future of Frecklesall so I'm gonna leave you now with this big, hairy, audacious question. Direction of travel-wise, do you want our home town to limp along as the dead-end, no-hope dump it is now? Or will you grasp the opportunity and join me, Mayor Troy Wiseley MBA, on a game-changing journey to transform Frecklesall-on-Sea into… A Happening Place for Happening People?'

The slogan popped up in huge capitals on the screen behind him, above a cheesy, thumbs-up shot of the town's first citizen.

Frozen in mid-flourish, his final words echoed emptily around the hall. A couple of seconds passed before Arsey jumped to his feet and started clapping, the other teachers eventually joining in, more out of relief than anything else.

'Thank you so much, Mayor Wiseley. Inspirational words, indeed,' gushed the head. 'And now, boys and girls, I'm sure you have lots of questions you'd like to ask our esteemed civic leader, whilst he's with us today.'

A few hands went up. Unsurprisingly, they belonged exclusively to the editorial team of the *Frecklesall Pen*, Arsey's planted questions resting uncomfortably in their sticky palms.

Naz was first up. 'Your Worshipfulness,' he began, trying to ignore the sighs and groans coming from all around. 'Thank you for that excellent insight into your vision for our town. And can I ask, Mr Mayor…'

And spookily, it all went more or less as planned: greatest political influence? Nelson Mandela ('I had the honour of meeting him once – such a humble man'); favourite football team? Newcastle United ('Howay the Toon!'); top tip for a young person thinking of going into politics? Some guff about being true to yourself and the people who voted for you.

'I think we've just got time for one more!' announced Arsey as he searched for Felix's hand amidst the mass of glum faces.

Felix considered his options. Surely it wouldn't matter too much if he didn't ask the question? But then he caught Basil's imploring eye and knew instantly that resistance was futile. Straightening out the crumpled piece of paper from his blazer pocket, he braced himself for yet more humiliation.

But at exactly the same time he raised his hand, so too did year seven pupil, 'Little Dennis' Crangle, who was sitting up front, close to the stage.

The head teacher wafted a bony finger in Felix's direction, but before he could say anything, Little Dennis had jumped in.

'Mayor Wiseley,' he began in his shrill soprano. 'My mum likes to take an early morning dip down at the lido, but we just found out it's closed. She wants to know when it'll be open again.'

A look of confusion flashed across Wiseley's face. 'Oh… thank you for that, young man. But I think what you *really* meant to ask me was, what will Frecklesall be like in five years' time?' The cheesy smile crept back onto his face. 'Awesome question – and under my leadership it's a total no-brainer. Quite simply, my mission is to shift the dial and ramp-up performance to top-quartile—'

'That's not what I asked!' shrieked Little Dennis. 'When's the lido going to open? You're the mayor, aren't you? You must know.'

Wiseley looked panic-stricken. 'Well, yes... I understand there have been a few problems down there,' he replied, hesitantly. 'We had hoped to open last Saturday but some, errm... last-minute investment, I mean... planning issues, have cropped up.'

The mini-inquisitor had his arms folded across his chest. 'When's it happening, then? And why won't you give me a straight answer?'

Beads of sweat glistened on the mayor's brow. 'The lido site is, errm... it's a highly valuable asset for Frecklesall – central to our plans for the town's renaissance. It's a total no-brainer. Think, low-hanging fruit, or... or shooting the crocodiles nearest the canoe. Rest assured, everything is on track. You can expect an announcement very, very soon.'

'But when—?'

'Fascinating! I think we'll wrap it up there.' Arsey cut Little Dennis off as the year seven was dragged, protesting, from the hall.

That lunchtime, Felix was in the canteen with the *Pen* team, flicking through the pages of his notepad. 'Something's going on down at the lido,' he said quietly. 'Did you see how Wiseley reacted to Little Dennis's questions?'

Keira laughed. 'You did well there, mate.'

Felix ignored her. 'As soon as he mentioned the lido, Wiseley just freaked out. I mean, he must know what's going on, mustn't he?'

'Absolutely,' chimed Naz. 'Since the council signed up to that local empowerment initiative, Wiseley is in charge of all our local services. He runs just about everything.'

Bernie sighed. 'You lot are barking up the wrong tree, as usual. The guy's a politician. You know what they're like – they never answer the question and if they do, well, they're probably lying anyway!'

'Very good, smart-arse,' said Felix. 'Little Dennis caught him off-guard, didn't he? Listen to what he said.' He flicked through his notes again. 'There was something about the lido not opening "for investment reasons" and the site having "a high asset value… central to plans for the town's renaissance". What's that all about, then?'

Bernie stifled a yawn. 'How should I know? I slept through the whole thing – other than the bit about shooting crocodiles, which sounded quite a laugh, actually.'

Keira shrugged. 'Don't look at me, Felix.'

But he wouldn't let it lie. 'The thing is, the other day, when Spuggie was after me—'

'Yeah - I think we might have heard that one, mate,' said Bernie. 'About a million times, already.'

'Just listen to me for once, will you? When I was hiding out, I overheard these guys talking about the lido.' He eventually found the right page in his notepad. 'They were going on about a building coming down and planning permission. It didn't mean anything at the time, but it kind of fits now.'

'Yeah right,' said Bernie, snatching the notepad from his friend's hand. 'It kind of fits with you being a complete and utter dick!'

'Hey! Give it back!'

'Hang on a minute.' Bernie's face broke into a beaming grin. 'What's this you've written – Prince William? Elvis Presley? Have you lost your marbles, mate?'

'They sounded a bit like them,' Felix pleaded. 'I couldn't see what they looked like, so I wrote down the names, just in case.'

'In case what?'

'Well, you never know.'

'You never do!' Bernie laughed. 'I saw Elvis on the bus t'other day. And Wills often takes his hols in Frecklesall, round this time of year. Him and Katie were down the chippy last night, apparently. And what's this?'

Felix made an unsuccessful grab for the notepad.

'Hey, you gotta see this, guys!' Bernie roared with laughter as he pointed at the words, scrawled across the mud-spattered page:

Felix H ♥ ♥ ♥ Keira M

Felix sensed his world spiralling away. He looked around for Keira but she'd gone, disappearing into the crowd shuffling out from the canteen.

He spent the rest of the week ducking and diving, desperate to avoid an encounter with Sean Spugley. And as if that wasn't enough, he now had to contend with the stories of his supposed infatuation with Keira. The sensible thing would have been to get together and talk it through, but that was never going to happen – it was all too awkward. Two days had passed and while they'd had a few classes together, somehow, when the bell rang, one of them was always late arriving or first out the door.

And now, on Thursday afternoon at half-past-three, Felix was dragging his heels towards the library for the weekly editorial meeting, filled with the dread certainty that she'd be there. He hung around outside the office for an age, before eventually plucking up the courage to sidle in. And when he did… there was no sign of Keira!

Then, to his horror, in swaggered Sean Spugley.

'Hi, Sean – pull up a chair.' Basil greeted the newcomer, unenthusiastically. 'Sorry everyone, I forgot to mention – Sean's joining us for the rest of term, seeing as PE and games aren't an option any longer.'

'Banned again, Spug?' asked Bernie.

'Yeah! Bit of "afters" following the match t'other day,' grunted Spugley. 'Had it coming to him, mind you.' He fixed Felix, with a particularly mean stare.

Basil called them back to order. 'So, I've written up the mayor's speech, which is going to be our lead, obviously.' He passed a couple of sheets of paper around the table. 'Check it out if you must, but I won't be making any changes – Dr Brown's already signed it off. I have to say, I found the whole thing rather inspiring. Exciting times ahead, eh? And the mayor's comments about his big announcement on Saturday were more than a little intriguing. I don't suppose any of you are going to the ball, are you?'

'As if!' snorted Bernie.

Felix barely glanced at the article, but Naz was reading it from top to bottom.

'What about Little Dennis?' he asked, looking up a short while later. 'There's no mention of his lido questions. Have you heard Felix's theory?'

'Well?' asked Basil.

'It was a stupid idea,' mumbled Felix. 'Not even worth talking about.'

'No, it was good stuff,' said Naz. 'Felix reckons something's going on, there – like the council are planning to redevelop the site.'

Spugley, who by this time was slumped, face-down across the table, suddenly lifted his head. 'Actually, I've always fancied getting a job down the lido,' he grunted.

'Really?' Naz sounded surprised.

'Yeah, I'd like to work there – knocking it down. I hate the bloody place.'

Basil interrupted the exchange. 'That's not a particularly constructive comment, Sean. And I have to say, I'm surprised at you, Felix – considering how the mayor went out of his way to support you after what happened last week. And while we're on the subject, what the hell happened with your question in assembly? Dr Brown was *not* amused.'

The meeting eventually came to a close, but it was as Felix was attempting a rapid exit that he caught the English teacher's final, devastating announcement.

'Oh, and Sean – I've decided to buddy you up with Felix on the sports page. After all, you're the athlete amongst us and Felix, well, he's more of a writer. So, between the two of you, I'd say it's something of a dream team.'

4

As Felix chomped his way through a second bowl of cornflakes that Saturday morning, the traumas of the week began to seem just that little bit more manageable.

After a cursory wash, he got dressed, pulling on the brand-new pair of undies he'd found in his drawer. As usual, he hadn't removed the cardboard label that was attached to them and it immediately started digging into his backside. *Have to do something about that*, he thought, squirming around in an attempt to get comfortable. Heading into the kitchen, he found his little sister, Flo, engrossed in a newspaper.

Felix was in awe of Flo. While she looked like any normal nine-year-old girl, with her brown hair cut into a neat bob, her preference for anything pink or sparkly and the ever-present trainers with the flashing lights in the soles – compared to her brothers she was from another planet. Blessed with more common sense than the rest of the family put together, if she wasn't reading a high-brow novel or a broadsheet newspaper, she'd be into something educational on the web.

'Just checking my virtual share portfolio,' she said. 'It's for a school project. The Footsie took a bit of a pasting yesterday.'

'Footsie?'

She rolled her eyes. 'Financial Times Share Index, stupid.'

He was prevented from making a bigger fool of himself by the arrival of an even bigger fool. Stumbling into the kitchen, Freddie threw open the fridge door and glugged half a pint of milk, straight from the bottle.

'Yo, Sis – sold your soul yet?' he asked, wiping his chin with a sleeve.

'You seem perky today, Freddie,' she replied, without even looking up from the paper.

'Damn right! Scorcher out there by the looks of it.' He flexed his biceps. 'Sun's out, guns out! Might even take a stroll down the beach in a bit – check out the vibe.'

Sightings of Freddie before midday were as scarce as Y-fronts under a Scotsman's kilt, and on the few occasions he was up and about before lunchtime, he'd generally be in such a foul mood it was best to steer clear. But Felix knew the signs – his brother always acted like this when he'd landed a new girlfriend.

'So, who is the unlucky lady, Fred?' he asked.

Freddie chuckled. 'Ah, you know me so well, my little gay friend. We hooked up at OT's last night. She's only here for the week but that's long enough for the magic to work.'

'Are you sure you're ready for a new relationship?' asked Felix, drily. 'From an emotional perspective, I mean? It must be all of three days since your last one dumped you.'

Freddie pulled him aside and Felix thought he was in for another battering, but it turned out his brother had a special request.

'Listen up, doofus,' he said in a low voice. 'Mum and dad are out tonight – Badminton Club rave, or some such. I'm bringing Amber back here and I'm not having you hanging around, cramping my style.'

'No way.'

'Come on, Bro! I'd do the same for you, if you ever... well...' He snorted. 'Like that's ever gonna happen!'

Felix's heart sank – Freddie would make his life hell if he didn't give him a clear run. 'Look, I'm off to Naz's in a bit. I'll see what he's up to. No promises, but if I do go out, you'll owe me.'

His brother's face lit up. 'Awesome, Bro! *Mucho obligado.*'

Clunking along the high street on his battered old mountain bike, later that afternoon, it was clear that things were not quite as unremarkable as usual in his home town. Preparations for the mayor's ball were at fever pitch, with caterers, DJs and party decorators scurrying in and out of the town hall like their lives depended on it. Unsurprisingly, Felix had never actually been to Frecklesall-on-Sea's society event of the year, and had no plans to break the habit of a lifetime. But somewhere buried deep down, the journalist within him was niggling away, telling him that maybe, just maybe, there might be something in the mayor's speech that evening, that could be worth listening to.

His thoughts evaporated the instant he turned the corner of the old building. A huge image of Marje Spangles gazed down at him from the side of a gigantic *It's Grand Up North!* outside broadcast lorry. Her dazzling white teeth, Tango-orange glow and expressionless forehead was enough to send any number of red-blooded males, over a certain age, into a tremble.

But it didn't stop there – the car park was rammed with a veritable Eurovision Song Contest of foreign vehicles: French, Dutch, German, Italian – even a campervan all the way from Spain.

What the heck was going on?

Felix locked up his bike and strolled across to the Hussein's DVD shop. After a quick chat with Naz's dad, he was ushered through to the back room where Naz and his younger brother, Saj, were sitting in the gloom watching one of the sports channels.

'Cycling – *Giro d'Italia*,' said Naz, in hushed tones. 'We get all the national tours on satellite: the *Giro; La Vuelta*, and the *Tour de France* – that's the big one, of course.'

'Have you seen what's going on outside?' asked Felix.

Saj shushed him. 'They're almost over the climb. Krankel's going to hit them any moment now. He usually sits tight until they get close to the top, then just as everyone else is easing off – Bang!'

'Zapatista, Frisson, Klanger, Gonzalez!' The commentator worked his way through the list of exotic-sounding names as a cluster of cyclists crawled up an impossibly steep mountain pass, cheered on by a mass of fans, crammed in against the roadside.

'Great!' said Felix. 'I come down here to see you and all you're interested in is watching this rubbish.'

Sighing, Naz turned to face his friend. 'Sorry, mate.'

'It's like the flippin' United Nations out there. And that Marje Spangles is back again. Don't tell me it's just for Wiseley's stupid ball.'

Naz shrugged. 'I… I really don't know…'

He was gawping at the screen again and Felix eventually got the hint, only remembering why he'd called, on his way out the door.

'You're not free this evening, are you?' he asked. 'Only Freddie's on a promise with his new girlfriend and I need to keep out of their way.'

'My dad's out tonight as well,' Naz replied, glumly. 'So I'll be stuck here, doing the shop with my mum. You're welcome to come round if you want but you know how it is on a Saturday night.'

Felix groaned. He'd tried it before and it wasn't worth the hassle – loads of drunks staggering in, giving them a hard time because all the best films had long gone. 'Thanks,' he said, 'I think I'll leave it.'

'Not my problem,' hissed Freddie. 'I don't care what you do or where you go – just be out of my face by eight.'

'Come on, Fred,' pleaded Felix, from the midst of his fish fingers and beans. 'I'll keep out your way.'

'No chance! I'm heading up for a soak and when I come down it's gonna be like you never existed. And if you *are* still here, you'll just *wish* you'd never existed – geddit?' He sloped off upstairs.

Felix's mum was up in her bedroom, getting ready for her big night out, while Flo was mounting a one-girl campaign to avoid having to accompany her parents to the evening's festivities. Felix didn't blame her for trying – he'd been to the badminton club 'do' a couple of years earlier and had had a miserable time, rounded off nicely by Freddie getting drunk, then chucking up in the car on the way home. He winced at the memory.

'Mum!' he shouted up from the hallway. 'Would it be alright if I came with you tonight? Only, I've not much else on and there's nowt on telly.'

His mum came to the bedroom door in her dressing gown, a towel wrapped around her head. 'I suppose so,' she replied, less than enthusiastically. 'There'll probably be a few spare tickets going on the door. But what are you going to wear?'

Felix reviewed his current ensemble – anti-fit jeans (Freddie's hand-me-downs, actually, but who would know?), a pair of scruffy old trainers and a pale blue sweatshirt, freshly stained by a wayward forkful of beans. He thought he looked fine, but as his mother explained – in no uncertain terms – he did not look fine, he looked a million miles from fine. So he was despatched upstairs with instructions to have a wash, use some deodorant and find something 'nice' to wear.

Freddie was still wallowing in the bath, so the wash, while desirable, was out of the question. Pulling the soiled sweatshirt off over his head, Felix considered his options. There was a 70s disco track playing on the radio and he found himself dancing around the bedroom, catching a glimpse of his scrawny physique in the wardrobe mirror. Gangly, hollow-chested, milk-bottle white – what girl could possibly resist? He struck a bodybuilder pose just as Flo came to the bedroom door. She shielded her eyes from the terrible sight.

'Felix, you've got a visitor,' she announced. 'You'd better get some clothes on.'

'Thank God!' he shrieked. 'That'll be Bernie.' Barging past her, he jumped down the stairs, three at a time. Hearing voices from the lounge, he bounded straight in.

'Hey! Bernie...'

The words died on his lips as his eyes took in the scene. His mum, dressed up to the nines for her night out, was offering a plateful of chocolate digestives to their highly uncomfortable-looking visitor, while his dad turned and offered him a surreptitious wink.

'Felix!' oozed his mum. 'Why didn't you tell us *Keira* was coming over?' The syrupy smile disappeared the moment she saw her son's state of undress. 'For goodness sake lad, you'll frighten her off looking like that!'

Felix crossed his arms over his bare chest. 'Sorry Mum… err... Hi, Keira.'

Sitting at the far end of the settee, she gave him a pained smile.

'Oh, don't get me wrong, Keira,' his mum continued. 'It's so lovely to meet you – it's just that if we'd known you were coming…' She turned to her son. 'And will you go back upstairs and dress yourself properly. Keira's looking as pretty as a picture and you look like you've been camping out in the garden all week.'

Felix had to admit that Keira did look nice – really nice. In her short, sparkly, electric-blue dress with matching camouflage-pattern leggings, he reckoned she must be heading out on a date. But it was her hair that was the real turnaround – tied back and straight, so you could actually see her face. She was still wearing the old trainers, though, and still clutching that rucksack. Some things didn't change.

Felix scrambled back upstairs. Flinging open the wardrobe door, he grabbed one of Freddie's white shirts and a pair of oversized black school trousers, bought in the sales on the basis that he'd 'grow into them'. Under normal circumstances, these were the last things he'd have dreamt of putting on, but they were clean, not too badly creased, and there was an emergency situation developing downstairs.

He pulled on the trousers, noticing the card still flapping from the back of his new undies. Ripping it off, he stuffed it into a trouser pocket before hurtling down to the lounge, catching snippets of Keira's interrogation on the way.

'You know, I always look forward to the *Pen*,' his mum was saying, 'especially Cookery Corner. I usually get Felix to print me off a copy. I have to say, it was all a lot more interesting when he was in charge.'

Felix landed back in the room. 'Mum, Dad – if it's alright with you, I'll not bother with the badminton club thing tonight. Me and Keira have got some *Pen* stuff we need to sort out.'

The parents exchanged wary glances.

'Hmm,' mused his mum. 'I'm not sure it's the proper thing to leave you two here on your own. Well, I suppose Freddie's around – he can always keep an eye on things, can't he Brian?'

Felix's dad nearly choked at the suggestion, but he had other, more pressing matters on his mind. 'Christine, I'm sorry darling, but if we're going to get that table near the buffet, we need to get going.' He started fidgeting with his car keys.

Felix's mum gave her husband a withering look. 'Keira love,' she said warmly, 'I'm so sorry but we really do have to leave now. Felix, when you've finished talking about your newspaper thing, I want you to treat Keira to something special. Brian, give him some money, please. We can't have these two all dressed up with nowhere to go.'

Grimacing, Felix's dad prised a ten-pound note from his wallet. Following a stern look from across the room, he produced an additional fiver and handed it over.

Felix's mum called back as she made for the door, dragging a protesting nine-year-old behind her. 'And no funny business, mind. We'll be home just after eleven.'

His dad rushed past, adding grumpily, 'I'll be having my change back from that, as well.'

The front door slammed behind them, leaving the house in silence, save for the rasping sounds of the Fiesta's exhaust. Keira, who'd maintained an admirably calm demeanour for Felix's parents, was now slumped lifelessly across the settee.

'Bloody hell!' she exclaimed. 'What was that all about, then?'

Felix sat there for a few seconds as it dawned on him that he was going to have to explain himself, after all. 'Err, just my mum really – she's a bit bonkers. Anyway…' His voice moved up a semi-tone, 'I'm glad you called round, Keira, because I wanted to talk to you about that thing that's been going on at school.'

'What thing?' She looked up at him, disarmingly.

'Y'know, the stuff I wrote in my notebook. It was something that idiot Sowerbutts said when Spuggie was having a go at me. So now, everyone thinks I've got a crush on you. But that would be ridiculous, wouldn't it? You and me, together like that? Not that it would be ridiculous, mind – anyone would be pleased to go out with you, but…'

Seemingly stunned into silence, Keira had turned bright red, but it was nothing to do with the nonsense Felix was spouting.

'Well *aloha*!' Freddie greeted her as he bounded into the lounge. Fresh from his bath time excesses, he was sporting an unfeasibly short towelling robe. It was enough to frighten anyone – one false move and… well, it didn't bear thinking about. 'Hey Bro – how about some *introducciones*?'

'Oh, right,' mumbled Felix. 'Freddie, this is my friend, Keira. We're on the *Pen* team together.'

'Cool! Forgive the current state of undress, Keira babe, but I've been working the beach this afternoon – lifeguarding, surf-rescue – tough gig, obviously.'

'Fred, hadn't you better get some clothes on?' pleaded Felix.

Freddie raised his hands as if in surrender. 'Keira, I can't tell you how excellent it is to see a pretty little thing such as your good-self, hanging with my esteemed Bro. It's about time he nailed his colours to the mast, so to speak.'

He made a bee-line for their guest, and suddenly, things got a whole lot worse. Somehow, the back of his shorty bathrobe had got caught up in its towelling belt, revealing his large hairy backside for all to see. Well, Keira hadn't clocked it yet, because he was still facing her, but it was only a matter of time.

'Fred!' Felix tried to warn him, but he wasn't listening.

Keira recoiled as Freddie knelt down, grabbed one of her hands and planted a slobbering kiss on it.

'If you ever need anything, and I mean *anything*,' he crooned, 'all you gotta do is call, you dig?'

He sprang to his feet, turned, and strutted back towards the door. Felix barely noticed – he was too busy watching Keira cramming the corner of a cushion into her mouth, tears of mirth rolling down her cheeks.

Freddie headed upstairs, leaving the two of them alone again.

'What an arse!' she shrieked, almost exploding with laughter. Catching the look of dismay on Felix's face, she realised he'd got the wrong end of the stick. 'No, what I meant was – what an idiot! Are you really related to him?'

''Fraid so,' he replied, glumly. 'Listen, do you fancy heading out somewhere? Fred's bringing his new girlfriend back and I promised… kind of.'

'I may have something on tonight, actually,' she said, delving into her rucksack and pulling out her phone. 'I wanted to show you these, first.' She opened up the 'Gallery' app, clicking on one of the action shots she'd taken of Felix floundering around at the rugby match.

He groaned. 'Very funny.'

'*Big soft lad*,' she muttered, dismissively. 'It's not you – it's what's going on in the background that's important.'

He looked at her, blankly.

'You said something put you off when you tried to catch that ball… There!' She pointed to what looked like a couple of yellow dots and a small white blob, far away in the distance.

'Oh, yeah - that was it, said Felix. 'There were these two guys in HiViz jackets, taking some pictures with this old-fashioned camera. They distracted me. I'd have caught it but for that.'

'Yeah, right!' Keira sniggered. 'I'll zoom in a bit. Shout out when it makes more sense.'

Before he knew it, he was studying a close up of the Hi-Viz guys. 'Like I said, they had this vintage kit…'

The image was crystal-clear now. The two men were framed against the back wall of the lido, one grappling with a tripod, the other standing a short distance away, propping up a full-height stick, one end resting on the ground.

Keira pointed at the tripod. 'That's no camera, Felix – it's a theodolite.'

'You what?'

'They use them to check out the levels when they're setting up building sites.'

He was struggling to see where this was going.

'And that fits as well,' she continued, pointing at the image of the white van, which had 'GeoTec S I' emblazoned across its side. 'You said that Prince William guy mentioned it. 'S I' is short for site investigations. That's where they drill holes in the ground to work out the kind of foundations they're going to need.'

Something in the cobwebbed recesses of Felix's brain began to stir into life: the lido not opening; the site investigation stuff; the conversation between Prince William and Elvis… 'Wiseley!' he shrieked. 'He's up to something down there, isn't he? Do you think it's to do with the big announcement he's making at the ball, tonight?'

'Dunno,' Keira replied, almost casually, 'but we're gonna find out, aren't we?'

5

Felix realised he was heading way beyond his comfort zone, when Keira dragged him up to his bedroom, evicting Freddie, who they'd found sprawled – now mercifully dressed – on his bed, listening to some music. She said the mayor's ball was 'black tie', which was code for a black suit, white dress shirt and a bow tie. Felix was already halfway there, settling on the trousers and shirt he was already wearing, topped off with his school blazer.

Keira sat on his bed, looking him up and down with a critical eye. 'The kecks and the shirt work – kind of. You might just about get by with that blazer, but it needs a few adjustments.'

She grabbed the breast pocket – the one with the Frecklesall High badge embroidered onto it – and pulled, violently. There was a sickening rip of stitching and suddenly the whole thing was in her hands.

Felix went into shock.

'That'll do,' she said. 'Now – bow tie? You got one?'

He gave a nervous laugh. 'As if!'

'We'll come up with something,' she said, scrutinising the excuse for facial hair decorating his top lip. 'You've just about time for a shave if you get a move on.'

'I can't,' wailed Felix. 'I've never had one before. I don't know what to do.'

Rolling her eyes, she turned her attention to the much bigger challenge of his hair. She pulled a tube from her bag and squirted a massive splodge of something gooey onto her hands. After climbing up onto a chair she began rubbing it into his scalp.

'Oww! What're you doing? It hurts!' he shrieked. He'd not come across Iron Grip Radical Hold Hair Gel before and hoped he never would again. Apart from the cloying, perfumed smell, his head felt like it had changed shape, the comforting warmth of his frizz now cruelly replaced by the chill wind of despair.

It was eventually agreed that the bow tie should be fashioned from cardboard, coloured in with a black felt pen and stapled to his shirt. Felix's school shoes were being re-soled at Timpson's, so the best he could muster was a pair of grubby grey trainers.

At the end of those TV makeover shows, the unfortunate victim, having been subjected to any number of humiliations – such as having to parade through the streets of Milton Keynes in her frillies – is revealed in her fully transformed glory, to gasps of amazement from friends, family and the nation as a whole.

It wasn't quite like that for Felix.

It would be nice to say that the reflection in the mirror cut a dash in the James Bond mould. It would be nice to say that, but sadly, it would also be untrue. The petrified figure staring back at him was an awkward, white-faced freak – hair plastered tightly over a distressingly small head, big white ears sticking out like trophy handles. Loose threads hung from the former site of his breast pocket while the oversized trousers necessitated a triple pleat in the 1980s New Romantic style. The wonky cardboard bow tie was the icing on the cake.

Felix couldn't have looked more like someone who'd escaped from an institution for the criminally insane, if he'd tried.

Keira bundled him down the stairs and out of the house, stopping briefly to demand money from Freddie to keep out of his way for the next few hours (a further five-pound donation, received with thanks).

They headed off into town together, Felix feeling surprisingly chipper, under the circumstances. He was out on a date – at least, that's what he thought was happening – and was so excited, he'd all but forgotten about the big story they were chasing down.

Not for long, as it turned out.

The entrance to the town hall was a hive of activity as guests, in a variety of splendid and not-so-splendid outfits, made their way into Frecklesall-on-Sea's, normally unremarkable society event of the year. The two of them observed the scene from their vantage point in the bus shelter, directly opposite. After a couple of minutes, they ambled along the side of the old building to the chaos of the multinational car park. Keira stuck two fingers up at the Marje Spangles truck, and they both laughed.

'Look at the cards in the windscreens of those cars,' she said, pointing at a battered blue Fiat estate. '*Gazzetta dello Sport*, and that French one – *L'Equipe.* They're sports newspapers.'

'How d'you know that?' asked Felix, but when he turned, expecting an answer, she'd disappeared.

'*Someone coming – get down*!' she hissed, from beneath a grubby-looking Citroen. Felix dived to the tarmac – he wasn't sure why.

And then a huge, silver Mercedes purred into view. Navigating around the abandoned vehicles, it pulled up just short of the town hall's rear entrance.

The doors to the building were flung open and a trio of official-looking flunkies rushed out, smoothing their black suits in preparation for what looked like the arrival of some very important guests. One of the three was shorter than the others – a huge barrel of a man, his massive shoulders merging into a neck that was far wider than his bullet-like head. With his squashed features and chubby, jowled chops, he looked like a bulldog. While the other two suits stepped forward to greet the new arrivals, he stayed put, checking up and down the car park.

'Security,' said Keira, peering out from her hiding place.

Two similarly dinner-suited men emerged from the back of the limo. There was a brief moment of confusion as they tried to embrace their hosts, leaning forward to kiss them on the cheek. Rebuffed, they were offered more manly handshakes instead.

'Europeans,' added Keira. 'Kissing… and look, they've all got man bags.'

Felix had never seen anything like it in Frecklesall, or anywhere else for that matter.

Misunderstanding over, the men waited while the car door opened on the other side and a third figure stepped out. Slim and athletic, he looked the picture of Mediterranean sophistication, a granite jawline and deep suntan accentuating his dazzling smile. His eyes were concealed by a pair of wraparound mirror-lens shades.

'So good you could make it, Modesto!' one of the suits said as they headed inside. 'Having you here for the launch is really fantastic.'

'*Si, prego – capisco*,' the stylish European replied. 'Ees my pleasure. *Grazie*.'

Italian? Spanish? Felix couldn't quite place the language.

'That does it,' said Keira. 'We're going in – whatever it takes.'

Felix nodded, the smile fixed on his lips as the magnitude of what he was getting into finally hit home.

They walked along the Prom to buy some chips, then sauntered back to the bus stop. It was getting close to ten o'clock and the entrance to the town hall was deserted, save for a couple of police officers, chatting at the top of the steps. Keira told Felix to stay put while she paid a quick visit to the toilets, just up the road.

He skulked around in the bus shelter, listening to the disco hits filtering out from the ballroom. Under normal circumstances he'd have made his excuses and headed home, but tonight was different. He was out on a date *and* he was chasing an exclusive. Life just didn't get much better than this!

Creeping up on him from out of nowhere, Keira slapped him hard on the back.

'Oww!'

Spinning around, he was stunned by what he saw. It wasn't Keira… Actually, it was, but this was another version of Keira – one he'd never seen before. She'd done something with her hair, which now came down past her shoulders, looking sleek and soft. Her dress had grown – it was still the same blue, sparkly number, but now it was full length, like a proper evening gown. And her face was different, transformed with lipstick, mascara, eye shadow – the works. But the biggest mystery of all was that she was about seven inches taller than the last time he'd seen her.

'Is… is that you?' he asked, rubbing his eyes in disbelief.

She threw her head back and laughed.

'You look… different.' He wanted to say she looked amazing but checked himself at the last moment. 'What have you done to yourself?'

'Oh, you know, a bit of slap, Velcro dress extension, and then these.' She lifted the hem of her dress to reveal her shoes. The battered old trainers had gone, replaced by ultra-high platform wedges – orange, with purple stars on the side. 'They used to be my gran's.'

'You sure you can walk in them?' he asked. 'You'll break an ankle if you're not careful.'

'No problem – I can handle it. Now, come here.'

Felix bent forward while she stabbed away with a mascara brush to touch up his weedy moustache.

'You'll do,' she said. 'Come on Cinderella, you *will* go to the ball!' And with that, she marched off across the road, Felix scurrying up the town hall steps after her without the faintest idea how this could possibly end well.

'Have you got your tickets, sir, madam?' The grizzled old sergeant with the grey walrus moustache, bulbous nose and pock-marked complexion, gave Felix a withering look.

'No – we're Press, actually,' Keira announced, much to Felix's surprise.

'Got your accreditation then – your passes?'

'Certainly.' She reached into her bag and pulled out her *Pen* press pass – the one they used at school to get into dinner early if they had a lunchtime meeting. She nudged Felix and after an agonising search, he eventually found his, buried in the depths of a blazer pocket.

'Hmm…' The sergeant studied the cards, carefully. '*Frecklesall Pen*, eh? I don't recall seeing that name on the list. Just hold them here, PC MacCruiskeen. I'll go back and check.'

'No problem, Sergeant Pluck!' replied the younger policeman.

Felix felt like he was about to have a heart attack, but Keira didn't seem the least bit fazed.

'How you doing Steve?' she said, smiling sweetly at the constable.

'Blimey! Keira? I didn't recognise you for a moment, there.' The policeman blushed. 'I'm fine, thanks. Be glad when this is over, though.'

'Yeah,' she chimed. 'Nicole sends her regards, by the way. She told me she had a really nice time with you last Saturday. I think you made quite an impression.'

'Honestly?' He sounded surprised. 'Only looking back on it, I'm not sure *Brain Driller 3* was the best choice for a first date.'

'Nah, you're wrong there. It doesn't matter what film you see if you're with the right person, does it? She hasn't stopped talking about you all week.'

The policeman's face lit up. 'Wow! That's brilliant.'

'The thing is, Steve,' she continued, 'we're with the school newspaper – the *Pen* – and Wiseley's our new school governor. We wouldn't normally be seen dead at something as lame as this, but we were told we had to turn up. Apparently, he's making this big announcement, which we've got to report on. The secretaries at our place are a joke, so we're probably not even on your list.'

'No worries, Keira.' PC MacCruiskeen glanced over his shoulder to check no one was looking. 'Be sure to send that lovely sister of yours my regards. Tell her I'll give her a ring, tomorrow.' And with that, he stepped aside and ushered them in.

Felix was stunned. 'Amazing! I didn't know you were on first name terms with the police.'

'Not me,' she corrected him. 'It's our Nic. She loves a man in uniform. Not that loser, though – she said if she never sees him again, it'll be too soon. She's going to be *so* pleased when he calls her up!'

They walked across the lobby and through some double doors, arriving at the top of a handful of stairs leading down into the town hall's main function room – the Lancastrian Suite. The scene below was breathtaking. They'd stood at the bus stop watching the cream of Frecklesall society filing into the town's event of the year, and now, just over an hour later, they were looking out over a scene reminiscent of a drug-fuelled rave at one of those *Holiday Resorts from Hell* TV documentaries – but for old people.

There were bodies all over the place – slumped across tables, one or two even lying unconscious on the floor. Unlikely looking couples were locked in clinches, like it was going out of fashion while those not too drunk, molesting each other, or plundering the buffet, were dancing in long lines to the *Time Warp*, pelvises thrusting away in hideous synchronisation.

Dragging his eyes from the debauchery, Felix spotted Marje Spangles up on the balcony. It looked like she was running through some kind of technical rehearsal with her crew. But it wasn't just every dad's dream-girl, up there. Felix counted at least fifteen bored-looking hacks lounging about, as if waiting for something to happen.

The two of them navigated their way around the edge of the dance floor and as a passing waiter wafted by, carrying a tray loaded with glasses of red wine, Keira grabbed a couple, handing one to Felix.

'Told you we'd get in,' she said.

Felix winced at the sour taste, then downed it in one – after all, he needed to blend in and this seemed like as good a way as any. They headed on, stepping over comatose bodies and dodging past entwined couples, but the odd thing was that even though Felix was rubbing shoulders with people he saw on a daily basis, not one of them seemed to recognise him.

They found a quiet table, Felix plonking himself down onto a chair, only to spring out of it, moments later as if it had been plugged into the mains. There, sitting directly opposite them, were Dr RC Brown and an elderly lady, who Felix could only assume was his wife. Panic-stricken, he 'accidentally' knocked a paper plate to the floor and dived off his chair to retrieve it.

Cowering beneath the table, he had to shout to make himself heard over the music. 'That's it, Keira – we're stuffed!'

'What's your problem?' she yelled back.

'Are you blind or something? It's *him* – Arsey!'

Grabbing him by the scruff of the neck, she hauled him back to table-top level. 'You didn't look in the mirror properly before we left, did you?'

'Oh…well, it was a bit of a shock, to be honest.'

'*Lightweight*,' she muttered under her breath. 'Listen, Felix – no one is ever going to recognise you in that outfit, and even if they did, they're all too drunk to remember. Look at the state of them.'

He turned to check out the antics of the middle-aged swingers, and it suddenly hit him. She was right – there was no way he was going to be spotted. He could do anything he wanted, with no comeback. His mind raced at the possibilities while Keira tottered off, returning a few minutes later with more wine. He was developing quite a taste for the stuff.

'We're not here to have a good time, we're here for the story,' she said. 'I was talking to one of the waiters just now and he reckons Wiseley's on stage at eleven. The place is stuffed full of his cronies – some of them are bound to know what this is about. We should split up – see what we can find out.' She gestured across to the far side of the room. 'I'll meet you over there by the exit sign, as soon as he comes on.'

Felix gulped down his second glass, bowed with a flourish to Mr and Mrs Arsey, and wandered off to check out some nearby tables. He quickly lost Keira in the crush, but he wasn't that worried. For some inexplicable reason his nervousness had disappeared and he was even beginning to enjoy himself – so much so that he almost missed the DJ's important announcement.

'Boys and girls, we're gonna slow things down a little for you now, with some up-close-and-personal vibes: The Commodores – *Three Times a Lady*... Enjoy!'

The dance floor was suddenly awash with improbable-looking pairings shuffling around to the slow rhythm of the music. Felix surveyed the scene with a mixture of dismay and disbelief. Seconds later, he was sent sprawling by a hefty whack to his shoulder.

Spinning around, he was confronted by a large, elderly lady with a glint in her eye. Wearing a migraine-inducing, black and white, diagonally-striped ball gown, her dazzling orange hair had been piled into an impossibly high beehive. She looked like a wobbly zebra crossing come to life.

'Young man, would you do me the honour?' she asked, smiling alluringly.

'Err… No thanks,' he replied, starting to feel a bit dizzy. 'This isn't really my kind of thing.'

'Oh, come now! We can't have you stood there like a wallflower – not when there's *ladies* who'd like to dance.' She grabbed his arm and began dragging him towards the dance floor. He struggled to break free but she was a big woman, just a few inches shorter than he was, although much, much wider. Hips straining at the seams of her overly tight dress, her gigantic cleavage rippled menacingly.

'No… please… I really don't want to…'

A small crowd had gathered around to gawp at the scene. Even in his confused state Felix knew he had to close this down, quickly.

That's when he spotted the bulldog man they'd seen out the back, steaming across the dance floor towards him.

6

He was out of options. The woman gave one final, almighty heave and as Felix dropped his resistance, they catapulted forward, ploughing into smooching couples and knocking one lot over altogether. It worked like magic and once the cursing and dirty looks had faded away, they were just another anonymous pairing, shuffling around to the music.

Held in a rib-crushing embrace, he was being shunted about the dance floor by his new-found companion, fighting for air over the overpowering smell of her hair spray. He looked up from his partner's chubby shoulder, the one his chin had been resting on for the last minute or so… *Phew*! *No sign of Bulldog Man.* But having jumped from the frying pan, he was only too well aware that he'd landed slap-bang into the middle of the fire.

Zebra Crossing Woman looked lovingly into his eyes. 'There, that wasn't so awful, was it? Ooh, I do like a man with a moustache.'

Before he knew it, her lips had locked on to his. Puckering up, he tried to pull his head back.

'Come on, gorgeous,' she slurred, turning her attentions to his right ear and all but chewing it off in the process. 'Just one little kiss.'

Sliding a hand down his back to grope for his rear-end, she loosened her grip ever so slightly, and he seized his chance. One hefty shove later, she was tottering backwards.

Felix glanced over his shoulder as he darted away, wincing at the sight of the black moustache smeared onto her face from the mascara on his own top lip. The floor shuddered as she lost her footing and landed, with an almighty Thud! onto her substantial backside.

Cannoning around the dance floor like a pin-ball, he paused only to glug down a half-full pint of beer, snatched from a nearby table in a desperate bid to wash away the taste of cheap white wine and perfumed lipstick. After a frantic search, he eventually found sanctuary at the far end of the room, slumping, exhausted, into a chair. But his relief was to be short-lived.

Moments later, two men wearing well-cut dinner suits sat down opposite him.

They looked vaguely familiar.

'I say!' The younger man with the floppy hair attracted Felix's attention. 'Mind if we join you?'

Struggling to focus through the gloom and the alcoholic haze, Felix instantly recognised the fruity English accent. It was Prince William! He sat there, aghast, as the enormity of his latest predicament hit home. He hadn't been recognised, but that was surely going to change the moment he opened his mouth. If only he'd just legged it when they'd spotted him in the bushes outside the lido, rather than coming up with that pathetic shoe-lace excuse.

And then something rather odd happened.

'Och aye – no problemo, lads!' The words were coming from his own mouth, but it was as if someone else was speaking them… in a fabulously realistic Scots' accent! Felix had lots of Scottish relatives who visited from time to time, and could only guess that somewhere, deep in his subconscious, he'd unwittingly absorbed their speech patterns and now, in this moment of crisis, his brain had clicked onto this bizarre, self-preservation strategy.

There was an awkward silence.

'Allow me to introduce myself, gentlemen,' he continued. 'The name's, err... Thistle, Patrick Thistle, by the way.'

'Isiah J. Wolfe,' said the older man, grasping Felix's hand and shaking it firmly. 'Mighty pleased to make your acquaintance, sir.'

Prince William held out his hand, limply. 'Rupert Fudgeley-Smythe – a pleasure.'

'Forgive me, Pat,' drawled the American, 'but would that be a Scotch accent? Only, I got folks up there in Scotch-Land – a liddle place called Edin-Burrow. Where you from, if you don't mind me askin'?'

The elastic band in Felix's mind had fully unwound – he couldn't even remember where Scotch-Land was, let alone the names of any likely-sounding towns. 'Och, that would be, err... Killiecrankie,' he replied, eventually. 'It's a bonny wee fishing village away up there in the Trossachs.'

'Uh-huh. Sounds beautiful.'

'Aye, so 'tis! I think I can say, without fear of contradiction, that there's nae better place to go a-huntin' the haggis, or a-spurtling your spurtle.'

'Swell!' exclaimed Isiah. 'So, tell me, what brings a guy like you all the way down to somewhere like Freckers-Hall? What's your line of business?'

'A wee bit of buying and selling, just now. Like, err... like the Footsie, y'ken? I'd heard about this important annooncement and thought I'd better toddle along to see what's what. Would you no' be able to help me out, there, gentlemen?'

The two men exchanged glances.

'Just you watch this space!' exclaimed the American. 'I'd say the good folk of Freckers-Hall are in line for a significant uptick in their monetary wellbeing, anytime about now.' He paused to check his watch. 'Now, if you'd excuse me, gentlemen, I need to go take a rain check before Mayor Troy's speech.'

'Dinnae bother yersel', pal,' said Felix, brightly. 'I was ootside a few minutes ago. A fine evening, so 'tis – not a cloud in sight.'

Isiah gave his companion a baffled look, nodded courteously to Felix, then headed off in the direction of the toilets.

After checking they were alone, Rupert edged his chair in closer. 'The thing is Patrick,' he began in a low voice, 'you could be just the kind of chap one's looking for. I happen to have some assets coming my way, which I'm keen to trade. Only worth fifty grand or so, ATM, but I know a little about what's going on here. Quid pro quo, as it were - you scratch my back, etcetera. Can't really talk now but… here, take this.'

Felix scanned the business card he'd been given.

Rupert J Fudgeley–Smythe RICS
F.S. Construction Design and Project Management

Distracted by Keira, who was waving frantically at him from just behind Rupert's shoulder, Felix realised it was time to move on. 'Fandabidozey! No problemo there, Rupie. I'd be pleased to help y'out so I would.

Now, that's my wee wifey stood away back there, so I really should be makin' tracks.'

''Lutely!' chimed Rupert. 'Would you happen to have a card yourself, Patrick?'

'Och aye!' Felix delved into his trouser pocket, handing over the card he found there – the one that until just a couple of hours earlier had been attached to his new underpants, complete with the picture of the six-packed male model, in manly pose. 'See yiz then, Rupie – I'll be in touch, by the way.' He scurried off, chasing after Keira.

Rupert Fudgeley-Smythe took one look at Felix's card and stuffed it into his jacket pocket, hoping no one had been watching.

A roar went up and the audience jumped to their feet, some even standing on their chairs. There was a commotion at the back of the ballroom and a spotlight swung around to track the rotund figure of Troy Wiseley as he slalomed his way through the cabaret tables, slowing only for the occasional high-five and to kiss any number of women who caught his eye.

He looked as ridiculous as ever, his white dinner suit sprinkled with a dusting of glitter that sparkled in the spotlight's beam. By the time he'd reached the front, he'd ditched the jacket, revealing a garish pair of union jack braces, and undone his bow tie, which he draped casually around the collar of his now, open-necked shirt.

Springing onto the stage, he strode purposefully towards the lectern. 'My lords, ladies and gentlemen! Good folk of Frecklesall! Thank you, *merci*, *grazie*, *gracias*.' He pressed his hands together, in a prayer-like gesture. 'Your continuing support is a gift I cherish most deeply. Now, for those of you who don't know me, my name is Mayor Troy Wiseley MBA, and like it says on the tin, I'm the democratically elected mayor of Frecklesall-on-Sea. But let's park the formalities for a moment, why don't we? You can just call me, The Boss!'

Leaning against the wall at the side of the room, Felix could hardly hear himself think over the cheers and laughter as Wiseley ran through the introduction to his speech – the same one that had fallen so flat at Frecklesall High a few days earlier.

'Let's get out of here,' muttered Keira. 'I'm gonna barf if I have to listen to that rubbish again.' She hauled Felix out through a nearby emergency exit, into a deserted service corridor. Slumping to the floor by an ancient, cone-shaped fire extinguisher, she began prising off her giant platform shoes.

Felix was almost bursting with excitement. 'I can't believe it, Keira – hoots! I can speak Scottish, y'ken.'

'I heard you talking to that guy back there,' she said coolly. 'Just be thankful he'd had even more to drink than you, or you'd have been rumbled, straight off.'

'Oh.' He had been feeling a bit odd. He counted up – one… two glasses of wine and that beer. 'Maybe you'd better tell me what you've got first,' he mumbled, trying to hide his embarrassment.

'Well, only what we already know,' she replied. 'Wiseley's got this big announcement coming up, and it turns out that the Bulldog guy is his younger brother, Roy. Troy and Roy – what a joke! And the Scotch eggs are off – a couple of punters have puked already, although that's probably the booze. How about you?'

Felix tried to keep things low-key. 'Just bits and pieces, really. The guy I was talking to back there is

Rupert Fudgeley-Smythe. He's mates with that American – Isiah Wolfe, I think his name is. They're the ones I listened in on when I was hiding from Spuggie outside the lido – y'know, Elvis and Wills.'

For once there was no put-down – she just sat there, looking stunned.

'Anyway, the American as much as admitted that something really big is coming up,' he continued. 'Then the Fudgeley-Smythe guy tried to blag fifty grand off me.' He laughed. 'Like that was gonna happen! Turns out he's some kind of project manager, specialising in construction work. He even gave me his card.'

They sat in the corridor for another twenty minutes, taking it in turns to press an ear up against the door to find out where Wiseley had got to. Eventually, the sound of applause filtered through and after Keira had crammed her feet into her platform shoes once more, they headed back into the function room, finding a couple of spare seats on a table at the side,

The place was still in darkness, save for the spotlight trained exclusively on the mayor.

'So, I bet you're wondering what the heck this is all about.' said Wiseley. 'Why are those guys from the international media camped out on the balcony up there, together with the very lovely Miss Marjorie Spangles?' He paused to allow the wolf-whistles to subside. 'Well, my friends, when I was last out State-side, I cut a deal. Nothing new there – cutting deals on your behalf is very much my job. But I've gotta say, this one was just that *little bit* more special than usual.' He glanced at his watch. 'Y'know, I think it's about time we reached out to the gentleman who made this particular dream come true.'

He walked to the side of the stage and suddenly, the giant screen behind him clicked onto a picture which brought gasps of amazement from the audience. A palatial, three-storey, Spanish-style hacienda, surrounded by exotic palm trees, shimmered in the haze of the afternoon sunshine. The shot panned across an extravagant display of colourful blooms, bounding a perfectly manicured lawn. A large outdoor pool swam into focus, fronted by a pair of generously upholstered recliners, one of which was occupied by a stunning, bikini-clad girl.

'Phhwoaar!' An old boy sitting opposite could barely contain himself. 'Wouldn't mind a night out wi' 'er!'

'*Dirty old man,*' muttered Keira, just loud enough for him to hear. She smiled sweetly as he scowled back at her.

At that moment, an elderly cowboy wearing a white Stetson, shuffled, bandy-legged, into frame. Picking up a tall glass of something cool, he raised it to the camera. 'Here's to y'all, good folks of Ferck-Les-Hall!'

He looked like a kindly granddad – thick grey eyebrows hooding watery blue eyes, the pearl buttons on his blue denim shirt straining to contain a bulging waistline. 'Dee-lighted to make your acquaintance and welcome y'all to my humble home, here in Bug's Tussle, Texas,' he began. 'The name's Herbert T Smilerski the Third, but my friends call me Herb Tea Three!' Chuckling to himself, he gestured to the girl in the bikini. 'And this here's my lovely daughter, Herbina. Ain't she purdy as a picture? Say howdy to the good folks from Lanky-Sheer, Herbina.'

Sweeping the long blond hair from her face, Herbina looked up from the recliner, her brilliant-white cosmetic dentistry dazzling in the Texan sun.

'Now recently I enjoyed the company of a good friend of mine, and someone y'all know and love most dearly – Mayor Troy Wiseley, MBA,' the old man continued. 'We got to breakin' bread out on the porch, back yonder, and he was tellin' me about Lanky-Sheer an' how y'all been havin' slim pickin's over recent times. And that got me a-thinkin' about what I could do to give you folks a helpin' hand. Y'see, twenty-five years ago, I was very much like your good selves – a lost soul: drinkin', womanisin', gamblin'. Near 'nuff threw away every darn thing I had.'

Felix glanced up from his notepad to look around the room. The Lancastrian Suite had seen plenty of drinkin' and womanisin' that night. He couldn't swear to the gamblin', but the bingo was on later – did that count?

The camera zoomed in on Herb's face as he continued in more sombre tones. 'Back then, I'd gotten myself a one-way ticket to oblivion, and Satan himself was a-drivin' the bus. Then, one night when I was lying in a ditch, high on liquor and without a dime to my name, I saw the light and it was goood! Deputy Sherriff's torch as it turned out. Got myself arrested for vagrancy and ended up servin' six months in the county penitentiary.' He raised his eyes, skywards. 'Praise the Lord for He doth move in mysterious ways!

'I'm pleased to say that that's when I discovered my good friend, our Lord and Saviour, Jesus. He came to visit me, one night in that prison cell, and He told me to go forth and bear witness, so that others may not stray from the One True Path. Next thing I know, I'm an international best-seller.' He waved a copy of *Herb T Smilerski's How to Smile Your Way to your First Million!* at the camera. 'Available in all good bookshops now, folks – be sure to go get yourself a copy!'

At this point in proceedings, Herbina offered a welcome distraction by unravelling herself from her recliner. Standing about six inches taller than her father, she kissed him on the cheek and sashayed away, to the accompaniment of raucous whistles from a sizeable portion of the Frecklesall audience.

'You take care, li'l missy!' Herb shouted after her, before turning back to the camera. 'Folks, I'm gonna cut to the chase for y'all, now. Y'see, it just so happens that my company – the Smiler Corporation – have invested in a franchise, over there in Yoorp, which you may well have some familiarity with.' He fished a crumpled piece of paper from his pocket and read carefully. '"*Lay Toor dee Fraynce*"– y'all heard of that? Have to say, it meant diddly to me! Some kind of by-sickle race, apparently.

'Now, you may be a-wondrin' what the heck *Lay Toor* has gotten to do with Lanky-Sheer, and good ol' Ferck-Les-Hall in particular. Well – truth is…' Cupping his mouth with a hand, he offered a comic aside. 'Give those *Monsewers* and *Madamoysels* enough cash money and they'll take that thing just about any darn where. I even thought of bringin' it across to Texas for a few days, but they told me *Lay Toor* would be about as welcome as a skunk at a lawn party round these parts!' He chuckled at his joke. 'So, there you have it folks: the big date is Thursday July ten – about a month from now – because that's when *Lay Toor* will be a-rollin' into Ferck-Les-Hall, courtesy of me and your friends here at the Smiler Corporation. We'll be there alongside you to enjoy the fun, so make sure you're good an' ready for us, y'hear?' And with that, he doffed his hat and was gone.

Back in Frecklesall, the disco burst into life, playing *Ain't No Stopping Us Now,* as hundreds of balloons cascaded down from the nets strung between the ballroom's heavy Victorian chandeliers. A few were smacked, half-heartedly, between the tables but as the music faded, an eerie silence took hold.

And then the muttering began.

'Tour de France? A load of old tripe if you ask me.'

'Most of them Frenchies speak perfect English y'know – they just won't.'

'I went to that Paris a few years back. Couldn't get a decent brew for love nor money.'

Felix glanced across to Keira, who, along with so many others, was struggling to understand what it all meant. 'This is mega,' he said quietly. 'I saw the Italian version on the telly round at Naz's the other day.'

But Felix was in a minority of one.

Wiseley stomped back to the lectern, barely able to hide his frustration. On his signal, an army of waiters trotted out from behind the bar, trays stacked with wine bottles, a handful swiftly deposited on each table to cries of, 'By the 'eck, Troy, lad – that's more like it!'.

'Just a small token of appreciation for your continuing support,' the mayor said, his face cracking into a grim smile. 'And I have to say, your backing is absolutely *mission critical* at this point in our journey. Ladies and gentlemen, if ever there was a no-brainer, this is it. *Le Tour* is one of *the* greatest sporting events in the world. Tens of millions will be watching the drama unfold on our very own roads. Surely you can appreciate what that will mean for Frecklesall?'

Felix looked around the room, sensing a slight thaw as the wine, now glugging noisily down throats, was beginning to have the desired effect.

'That's grand, Troy,' someone piped up, 'but what's in it for us, other than a load of poncey French cyclists clogging up our roads? If you're after a bit of publicity, get someone off the telly – Corrie or Emmerdale – not a load of fancy-Dans with shaved legs and bulging shorts.'

Wiseley banged his fist on the lectern. 'Very good, Nobby, and it's precisely that kind of short-sighted outlook which explains why you're still hiring out deckchairs down on the sea front at a fiver a day.'

Nobby Sprout was withering under the onslaught.

The mayor stepped back from the lectern, puffing his chest out as he addressed the room. 'It's not just the sporting spectacle, nor even that your children and grandchildren will be celebrating this day in years to come. No, indeed! There's money in this – for all of us.'

The deckchair man was first to rise to the bait. ''Ow much, Troy? 'Ow much brass?'

You could have heard a pin drop.

'We'll have a half a million people heading here on the big day,' replied Wiseley. 'They'll want somewhere to stay, something to eat and drink. Who knows, Nobby, they might even want to park their backsides on one of your deckchairs for the afternoon. It's nothing short of a licence to print money!'

'Yeah, but 'Ow much?'

The mayor smiled – he had them now. 'Last time the race came to the UK it generated over twenty million in additional revenue for each of the host towns. I'm guessing it's nearer thirty by now. Is that enough?'

His final words were lost in the roar that engulfed the room. Balloons bounced, corks popped and the DJ played *Ain't No Stopping Us Now* once more, only this time everyone joined in, dancing on the tables and falling over chairs as well-wishers rushed forward to shake the hand of the town's saviour.

7

Wiseley observed the riotous scenes with smug satisfaction. 'Folks, I'm going to hand over now to some very special guests who will road-map the next stage of our journey. So, give it up, please, for Tour de France Race Director, Patrice Perpignan, and leader of Team ChocolatBanane and national champion of Italy, Modesto Scaglioni!'

Felix turned to Keira. 'Isn't that the guy we saw round the back?'

Walking onto the stage, the Frenchman and the Italian were joined by an attractive young woman in a tailored yellow skirt and crisp white blouse. Slim and elegant, she was somewhere in her mid-twenties, the rich copper-red of her pixie cut complementing a gorgeous, heart-shaped face. The stunning brown eyes and the perfect bow of her beautiful red lips were more than enough to set the wolf-whistlers off again.

The trio seemed uncertain of the reception they might receive but needn't have worried – the prospect of a happy pay day was more than enough to unleash 'Tour Fever' amongst the drunken rabble.

Patrice Perpignan stepped up to the microphone. 'It is an honour to bring our race here, to Lancashire,' he began, in perfect English, 'a region which has such a proud and distinguished history in the sport of cycling.'

'Gerron wi' it, mate. We're missing t'disco!' someone heckled.

'Be last 'uns soon, lad!'

'*D'accord*,' Patrice replied. 'I will not delay your enjoyment of the evening for any longer than is absolutely necessary.' He gestured to the young woman standing by his side. 'It is my great pleasure to introduce Ms Giselle Lacroix. She will be staying with you here in Frecklesall, over the next few weeks, making sure all is ready for *le Tour*. And of course, on my left we have the great Modesto Scaglioni. I believe you have some important news for the many keen *tifosi* in the audience this evening, Modesto?'

The Italian's voice was rich and deep, and he spoke with a thick accent. '*Si, naturalmente*, Patrice. Theese year we 'ave a new rider category which we are calling, *Le Domestique du Jour* – the Domestic of the Day. On July ten we will invite the best *ciclisti* in Freckersowl to ride with my team, on *le Tour* itself! *Benissimo*! I am so pleased that it is Team ChocolatBanane, what 'ave been chosen for your beautiful town. With these-a strong support, we must be winning the race, *si*?'

There was further uproar as a middle-aged woman, who'd been rummaging about under her table, dashed up to the stage and threw a substantial pair of knickers at the startled cyclist.

'Let's get out of here,' said Keira, slipping from her chair and heading for the service corridor. Following on a few seconds later, Felix was shocked to find her leaning against the wall, wriggling into a pair of black jeans beneath her long evening dress, the platform shoes already dumped untidily beside her rucksack.

'What are you doing?' he asked, rubbing his eyes. It was partly the glare of the strip lighting and partly his brain, which had developed a distinct fuzziness and the beginnings of a headache.

'We need to get moving,' she replied. Jumping to her feet, she tore off her dress extension and stuffed the original mini into the top of her jeans. Moments later she'd rammed her feet into her trainers, pulled a black polo-neck over her head and tied her hair back with an elastic-band.

Felix's heart sank. He wanted this story so badly – wanted to hang out with Keira – but even in his befuddled state, he knew it was time to call a halt. 'Actually, I think we've probably got enough to go on, already, Keira. We could've landed ourselves in some real hot water just now, but…' He paused, taken aback by the effect his words were having on his companion.

'Are you really up for this, Felix?' she said, fixing him with a hard stare. ''Cos if you're not, if you don't think you can see it through, 'fess up now and I'll sort it myself.'

'No, no! We're in this together. It's just that… well, I've got a bit of a headache coming on.'

'Headache? Hangover, more like!'

'Yeah, whatever,' he replied nonchalantly, although alarm bells were ringing. He'd never had a hangover before. How long did they last? Should he go to the doctor?

Now dressed entirely in black, her fancy outfit stuffed into the rucksack, Keira marched off up the corridor. 'The way I see it,' she said, 'if this bike race is the biggest thing since sliced bread, why would that Herbal Tea guy bring it all the way over here, to a dump like Frecklesall? He's, like, the richest man in the world, isn't he? I'm telling you, Felix – this is about money. It's like my dad always used to say – "There's no such thing as a free lunch".'

Felix, who considered himself a bit of an expert on free lunches, decided against arguing the point. 'Right, err… What happens now?'

'They're are all getting off on each other, back in the ballroom, so I reckon this is as good a time as any to pay Wiseley's office a visit.'

'Are you sure? I mean—' Seeing that look again he slammed into reverse. 'Bring it on! Let's do this thing! So, err… where would that be, then?'

'Dunno,' she replied, heading for the narrow stairwell at the end of the corridor, her reluctant companion, tagging along behind. 'Not on the ground floor – the ballroom is pretty much all there is down here.'

'Actually, I think I might have been there once…' Felix hesitated as he dredged through his befuddled memory. 'It was with the Cubs, a few years back. We came on this trip and got to visit the mayor's parlour. Do you think that's the same thing?'

Keira shrugged. 'Could be.'

'It had this really nice view, out over the sea, so it must be up on the top floor at the front, somewhere. I got to wear the mayor's Napoleon hat – his chain as well. Then they gave us lemonade and biscuits, and these special colouring crayons…'

But Keira wasn't listening. She'd reached the top of the stairs and was gesturing to him to stay put while she checked around the corner. Moments later she stepped back to brief him.

'Listen up,' she said, quietly. 'If we want to get to the top floor, we'll have to break cover, which could be a bit tricky. Take a look for yourself, but be careful.'

Felix dropped to his hands and knees. Crawling forward, he peered gingerly around the corner into a gloomy lobby area. It formed the entrance to the first-floor balcony, where, less than ten metres away, the barrel-backed mayor of Frecklesall-on-Sea was midway through a TV interview with Marje Spangles. An untidy scrum of hacks had gathered around the camera crew, voice recorders thrust forward in the hope of a half-decent sound bite. And hovering menacingly, just behind them, was Roy the Bulldog Man.

They knew where they needed to go, but that meant traversing a no-man's land, in full sight of the European media pack and Troy Wiseley's psycho sibling.

'It'll be fine,' said Keira. 'Give me a few seconds, then you follow.'

She made it look easy. Crawling, commando-style, she used the darkness of her clothing and the distraction of the TV cameras to sneak across the gap, undetected. Disappearing into the shadows on the far side of the lobby, she turned and beckoned him to follow.

Felix peered around the corner once more.

The interview was beginning to wind up. He had to get over to Keira before it finished – it was his only chance. But what if they spotted him? He tried to move but it was as if his whole body had been paralysed. He could hear his heart hammering away in his chest, feel the sweat trickling down his back. And then the shakes started. Over on the far side, Keira was all but begging him to join her, but it was no use – the whole thing was an impossibility.

Suddenly, Bulldog Man was squinting over the heads of the reporters, like he'd spotted something that shouldn't be there. Shunting the protesting journalists aside he began his inexorable journey towards the former editor of the *Frecklesall Pen*, who was now whimpering, flat out on the floor, doing his best to melt into invisibility on the grubby carpet.

And then something rather odd happened.

Glancing up, Felix saw – or thought he saw – an odd-shaped object whizzing high overhead, right at the top of his field of vision. No one else seemed to notice as it arced above the media pack, narrowly missing Roy's shaven head before disappearing over the balcony railing.

Moments later, the sounds of shattering beer glasses, women screaming and a gruff shout of, 'You've gone too far this time, Chuckie, lad – outside, now!', confirmed the outbreak of World War III in the ballroom, below.

The Wiseley/Marje love-in came to an abrupt halt, the mayor barking instructions to his brother who had already hurtled past Felix's quivering form and was now thundering down the stairs.

'*Move it, Felix – quick,*' hissed Keira.

Before he knew it, he was careering across the gap, belting past his partner in crime and charging off up the corridor. Stealth and cunning had gone out of the window – headless chicken was now the name of the game. Up staircase after staircase and still he was running, bouncing off the walls, arms and legs flapping wildly. Keira gave chase, eventually gaining just enough ground to clip the back of a trailing foot.

Her co-conspirator was sent sprawling to the floor.

She whacked him across the back of the head as he sat up. 'You idiot! What the hell are you playing at?'

'Thought… I'd had it… back there…' he panted. 'Sorry… What happened? I thought I saw something.'

She slumped down beside him. 'I never liked those shoes Do that again and the other one'll be aimed at you!'

They sat together in the gloom of the emergency lighting, trying to catch their breath. The place was deserted, which was just as well given the barnstorming nature of their arrival.

'So, Akela, if this is the top floor, where's the mayor's office, then?' asked Keira, not really expecting a reply.

'Actually,' said Felix as he examined the carpet burns on the palms of his hands, 'I think we're sat outside it, right now.' He pointed over her shoulder at the brass plaque attached to the door she was leaning against:

Mayor's Parlour – Strictly Private

*

It had been a funny kind of day, he thought, as he stooped down to give Keira a leg-up. When he'd woken that morning, he'd had no idea it would end with him breaking into the mayor's private office dressed as 003½, having had too much to drink, been chased by a man who looked like a dog and groped by a woman at least five times his age – not to mention being party to an international incident sparked by a low-flying platform shoe. If this was the cutting-edge of investigative journalism, he was definitely going to have to re-think his career plan.

'Hold it there,' said Keira, straining to pull herself up.

'Get a move on!' Felix grimaced as one of her trainers caught him a glancing blow to the side of the head. 'This is killing me!'

'Stop your moaning, willyer?' She was peering through the tiny window, set just above the door frame. 'It's hinged at the top. There's no lock and I can move it, see?'

Following a creak of rusted hinges, the weight lifted from his shoulders and he staggered across the corridor, windmilling his arms to try to get the circulation going. Keira had managed to lever the window open and had wriggled her way in. Only her top half was now visible as she began lowering herself, feet-first, into the office.

'It's not too much of a drop,' she said, glancing down into the room. 'Wait there and I'll get the door for you.'

Felix had one last go. 'Are you sure about this, Keira? I mean, if you can't open it, you'll be stuck in there.'

'Nah, be reet,' she replied brightly.

And then she was gone, signalling her arrival in the forbidden territory with a dull thud. Felix heard her rattling the lock from inside. It seemed to take an age but eventually the door swung open.

Grabbing her rucksack, he dived in.

Entering the mayor's parlour, Felix's eyes had to adjust to the surreal glow of two giant lava-lamps – lime green bubbles rising and falling in a restful orange syrup. They'd landed in a large, square room, containing a couple of old leather settees, set either side of a low-level table. Lurking menacingly against the far wall was an ancient oak dresser which housed a head and shoulders mannequin. The mayoral chain of office had been slung around its neck and the infamous Napoleon hat was resting on its head. The mayoral mace was also on prominent display, its metre-long shaft topped with a polished brass orb and crown.

It was a corner room with a high ceiling and half a dozen, full-height sash windows, framed by thick velvet curtains – some of which had been drawn shut. A couple of the windows had been left open to welcome the cooling effects of the late evening breeze. Felix had been right – it was a very pleasant outlook across the rooftops to the twinkling lights of the gas platforms on the distant horizon, but this was hardly the time to admire the view.

They crept through an ornate archway leading into a smaller side-office, which was kitted out for twenty-first century communications. There were a couple of laptops sitting on a huge desk, a smart-looking mobile phone, charging in its holster, and a sumptuous leather swivel-chair.

Keira clicked on an angle-poise lamp, directing the beam down onto the desk so it gave out just enough light for them to see what they were doing. 'We're looking for anything linked to the lido,' she said. 'You check the filing cabinets, I'll have a go at these.'

She sat in the big chair and switched on the first computer, leaving Felix to start on the nearest cabinet. He opened the top drawer, revealing file after file, all neatly labelled up – street cleaning, dog wardens, waste recycling, road safety – you name it, it was there. It was no wonder Wiseley wanted to shake things up, he thought – it looked really dull.

Keira wasn't having much luck, either. Abandoning the first laptop, she'd reached across to the second computer. Meanwhile, Felix had discovered a signed copy of *Herb T Smilerski's How to Smile Your Way to your First Million!* in the mayoral bookcase. He put on his cheesiest grin and struck a pose next to the cover.

'Stop messing, you id—' the words died on her lips as she clocked the yellow Post-It note stuck to the desk. 'Hey, look at this – "TroyBoy5". That's got to be it, hasn't it?'

Looking over her shoulder, Felix spotted a second 'TroyBoy' sticker, with the numbers one to four crossed out. 'Yeah,' he replied, laughing, 'total no-brainer!'

Moments later, the screen flickered into life. Scrolling down the long list of folders, Keira ignored the dozens of Tour de France files, settling instead for an email that had been sent on the second of June, under the subject heading: 'FreckPen1'.

Felix read aloud from the monitor. '"To: ParadigmShift-optics.com; From: His Worshipfulness the Mayor of…"'

'Get on with it, Felix – we haven't got all night.'

'Oh. Right then. "Hi Tarquin, Max exposure through usual back-channels, please. Given forthcoming announcements, considerable media interest anticipated – domestic and international. Source: non-attributable, ANONYMOUS. Kind regards. Mayor Troy, MBA".'

Keira clicked on the attachment and a headline popped up. It was one Felix knew all too well:

Slaidforth's Blue Pennant Party Pooper!

'Oh my God, it was Wiseley!' he shrieked. 'He leaked Naz's story on purpose. It's no wonder the press were all over it. He's had his media agency send it out to every newspaper in the country, and half of Europe by the looks of it!'

Keira sighed. 'He's into spin, isn't he? All politicians are. He must have thought it would warm things up for his big announcement.'

Felix clenched his fists. 'I'll kill him!'

'Yeah, whatever… Hang on a minute.' She pointed at one of the files listed on the screen. 'This one looks interesting – he was checking it out, just before he came down this evening.' She clicked onto a folder named 'Blue Sky Vision – Renaissance Masterplan 3'.

It was a massive file and it took a minute or so for the image to materialise on the screen, but when it did, they were both stunned into silence. The picture was a perfect, computer-generated view of Frecklesall, as if shot from a drone. The school, the high street and the town hall looked so realistic, Felix half-expected to see the donkeys trudging along the beach on their morning shift.

And then things began to change.

A red line appeared, snaking its way silently along the southern end of the Prom, around the town moor and the lido, before moving swiftly up to the Paddock, where it cut a swathe through the field where the donkeys grazed.

'This is it,' said Keira.

Moments later, the buildings inside the line began to melt away. And then the surrounding roads burst into life – new junctions, a dual carriageway and a gigantic roundabout, all materialising right in front of their eyes. They sat there, mouths hanging open, as the outline of a new structure emerged in the space where the southern end of the town had once stood. A massive series of ugly, single-storey blocks melded together to form a giant, H-shaped building, which squatted across half the site. A huge car park morphed into view next to the Prom, to fill what was left. It had a petrol station, hundreds of parking bays and even a scattering of brightly coloured cars.

'They can't do this,' muttered Felix. 'Most of Frecklesall's been buried under that thing.'

Keira turned to him, a look of concern on her face. 'Shhh… I think I heard something.'

They froze, hardly daring to draw breath. And then they both caught the sounds of voices in the corridor outside.

'What do we do now?' croaked Felix.

Keira clutched her rucksack to her chest. 'Find somewhere to hide. I'm sending this file.'

But Felix had already disappeared.

She clicked the lamp off and was still tapping away on the keyboard as the key rattled in the lock. There were peals of drunken laughter and then, slowly, agonisingly, the door began to open.

Felix was hopeless at hide-and-seek. When Flo and her friends bullied him into joining their games at home, he was usually the first to be found. Lacking imagination, he always ended up behind the curtains in the dining room. And here he was again – crammed in behind some curtains, hoping his feet didn't stick out too much.

Coming! *Ready or not*!

They were in the main room now, just a couple of metres from where he was standing.

'Troy, you're so masterful!'

Felix instantly recognised the dulcet tones of Marje Spangles.

'Come over here, sexy lady. Come to Uncle Troy!' roared Wiseley.

There was a squeal, followed by a rustling of fabric and a sound which Felix could only describe as someone slurping a forkful of spaghetti. Peeking through the gap in the curtains, he winced at what he saw.

'Steady on Tiger!' Marje shrieked as she ran around the settee, Wiseley playfully giving chase.

Moments later they were entwined in a tangle of flailing arms, ruffled hair and slobbering lips.

Marje broke off to take in air. 'Oh Troy,' she gasped, 'you're my big hunk of alpha-male beefcake - my gorgeous disruptor in chief. You're wasted on this dump and you know it!'

There was a pause for more spaghetti slurping.

'It's a total no-brainer, isn't it?' panted Wiseley. 'This place is the pits – and the people? Losers, every single one of 'em! It's just a stepping stone for me, Marje. As soon as my legacy is secure, I'll be off. Westminster beckons!'

Shunting her onto the furthest settee, he dived on board, to the loud Poingg! of breaking springs.

Felix's mind was in turmoil. The door didn't look too far away – maybe he could make it? But it had taken Keira a few seconds to spring the lock when they'd broken in, and there was no way he'd have that much time. Anyway, he couldn't abandon her – sink or swim, they were in this together.

But where was she?

The answer appeared suddenly, stopping the torrent of lust, dead in its tracks.

'What the bloody hell was that?' Wiseley's shout echoed around the room as he struggled to get up from the settee.

Amidst the commotion, Felix spotted a blurred shape, dashing for the door. The mayor was trying to disentangle himself from Marje's clutches, but somehow, she'd become enmeshed in his braces. The sound of twanging elastic, snapping into the substantial flab of the mayoral gut, was followed by a loud howl.

'Oww!'

Keira was rattling the door knob as Wiseley lunged towards her. She darted beyond his reach and he lost his footing, the whole room shuddering as he crashed to the floor. But his dramatics had blocked the only route out.

'You've had it now!' he screamed. 'You're not going anywhere!'

In the next instant she'd reached into the depths of her rucksack. Suddenly, the room was filled with a series of blinding flashes, illuminating a grotesque sequence of snapshots: the mayor, red-faced, clutching at his stomach as he tried to stop his trousers dropping to his ankles; the celebrity roving reporter, blubbering away on the sofa, looking like she'd gone ten rounds with a Turkish wrestler.

The eye-scrunching strobe-effect gave Keira the few seconds she needed to deal with the lock. Hauling the door open, she yelled, 'Do one, lad – NOW!', before sprinting off up the corridor.

Wiseley turned as if to give chase, but immediately thought better of it. Stomping back into the room he switched on the main lights. 'You!' he yelled at Marje. 'Get on that phone now – triple zero. Tell them there's been a burglar or a terrorist, or something – it doesn't matter. Whatever happens, tell them they've *got* to get hold of that camera!'

Marje wasn't listening. Desperately trying to tidy herself up, she was straightening out her skirt, disentangling her hair and rooting around in her handbag for a compact mirror.

'Just bloody do it, woman!' barked Wiseley. 'This is an emergency!'

'Don't you talk to me like that, you horrible little man!' she replied indignantly. 'I can't have civilians seeing me like this, I have a *brand* to protect.'

'You idiot! If we don't get hold of those pictures, it'll be all over the tabloids in the morning – my career, my marriage, all ruined! Now, lock the door, I've got some unfinished business to sort out.'

He picked up the mace from the dresser and stomped off across the room, waving it around like a medieval broadsword.

Marje scurried over to the telephone. 'Oh my God Troy, what are you doing?'

Ignoring her protests, he marched through to the side-office and set about jabbing the mace under the desk and chairs. 'Ha! When that *scum* made her getaway, she shouted to an accomplice. He's in here somewhere and when I get hold of him, he'll wish he'd never been born.'

Stomping back into the main room, he heaved the mace above his head, then slammed it into the curtains covering the window immediately next to where Felix was hiding. The curtains, complete with the pole they were hanging from, came crashing to the floor.

Marje had, at last, got an answer at the other end of the phone. 'Security…? There's been an intruder in the mayor's parlour… Yes… A girl – short, dark hair, wearing black… You've got to stop her! But it's worse than that – much worse. It's the mayor. I think he's gone mad. Send someone, quickly!'

Her words were drowned out by the clatter of a portrait of Mayor William Eckerslike (1876-1879), sent flying off the wall by another wayward swing.

'Come out and face me, man-to-man! Come on you little…' Breathless from the exertion, Wiseley was now standing directly in front of Felix's window. He squared up to the full-length burgundy drape, like a Tudor executioner on a performance bonus.

Trembling on the other side of the curtain, Felix crouched down, desperately trying to shield the back of his head with his forearms as he waited for the blow to land.

And then someone was hammering on the door.

'Troy! It's me – Roy!'

'Thank God!' shrieked Marje. 'He's flipped! You've got to stop him before he hurts someone!'

'Troy – Speak to me, man!' pleaded Roy.

'Bugger off, Roy!' yelled his brother. 'No one messes with Mayor Troy Wiseley MBA and gets away with it. Focus on finding that girl and her bloody camera!'

Staring hopelessly into the abyss, Felix heard a primal grunt and a final Swish! as the business end of Frecklesall Town Council's ceremonial mace sliced through the air towards him.

If you were to look up from the street at a three or four-storey building, you'd probably think it wasn't such a big deal. Twenty or thirty metres doesn't sound so high, does it? Not when you compare it with something seriously tall, like the Empire State Building, or Preston bus station car park, for example.

Now, imagine yourself teetering on the precipice of a narrow sandstone sill, four particularly tall stories up. One hand is scrabbling across the smooth stonework in a desperate search for something – anything – that might offer you some stability, while the other is pressed back against the window pane in a futile bid to fend off the imminent impact of five kilograms of ornamental Victorian brass-work, being wielded by a lunatic who wants to kill you.

Don't feel quite so cocky now, do we?

Felix had used the distraction of the rescue party to do the only thing he could – to clamber out of the window. When this kind of thing happens in the movies, there's always a conveniently placed ledge or a nearby gargoyle which the hero can hang on to. The former editor of the *Pen* was disappointed to discover that these crucial design features were decidedly lacking on the third-floor exterior of Frecklesall town hall, which had been built in 1895, to a tight budget.

He had to concentrate, on not looking down, on not slipping. If he could just keep his footing, maybe there was a chance…

The last thing he remembered was the crash of shattering glass and the unreal beauty of a million glistening shards, star-bursting all around him. In the next instant, his foothold had gone, his flailing limbs connecting with nothing more than the warm night breeze.

For a moment, he was floating on air, silhouetted against the moonlight, frozen in time and space.

But it was only for a moment.

8

They say that just before you die, your life flashes before you – the joy, the sorrow, the good, the bad and the ugly, all served up in a monumental highlights show, as you pass from this world into… well, who knows? But the possibilities of an afterlife were far from Felix's mind as he plunged earthwards like an absent-minded sky diver who'd forgotten to strap on his parachute. No – all he could think of were the words of his dad, who'd told him many years earlier, having watched a documentary about people who'd had miraculous escapes after falling from incredibly high buildings, 'It's not the drop that kills you, Son, it's the sudden stop at the end.'

'Ooff!'

The wind slammed from his lungs as he crashed into the horizontal arm of the lamppost. Desperate hands scrabbled for purchase, the underside of his chin grating against the unyielding metal section. Hanging by his fingertips now, his legs writhed around for a brief moment, before dangling uselessly.

He screamed again – a cry for help this time. What he needed was someone with a really, really long ladder – someone who could be there in, say, the next twenty seconds, because that's roughly how long he thought he might be able to cling on for.

'Help! I can't hold on much longer!'

He could see Marje at the window, looking distraught, but before she could do anything to help, she'd been hauled away. And then another face made an unwelcome appearance.

Wiseley's chubby chops wobbled as he leaned out through the shattered pane. 'There you are you little…' he yelled. 'Not laughing quite so much now, are we?'

'He's going to fall, Troy. DO SOMETHING!' shrieked Marje.

Frecklesall's first citizen ducked back inside, reappearing moments later with a demented look in his eye. 'Want some help, toe-rag?' he screamed. 'Read this!' He hurled a hefty, hardback copy of *How to Win Friends and Influence People* at Felix, narrowly missing his head. 'Didn't like that one, eh? Try this for size!' Another weighty volume, *The Seven Habits of Highly Effective People*, caught his hapless target square in the midriff.

Felix heard the sounds of splintering wood and shouting voices in the room above, but whatever was going on up there, it was too late. He felt a fleeting moment of relief as his fingers slipped and gravity took hold a second time.

If you were to catch the last bus from Slaidforth Sands to Frecklesall, on a weekend after the pubs have shut, you'd find yourself shoehorned into a parallel universe of drunken revelry. There are songs, rows, moments of knee-trembling passion and passengers falling about like skittles as the double-decker lumbers along on its twenty miles per hour white-knuckle ride. Truth be told, for those venturing out to the pubs and clubs of Slaidforth on a Friday or Saturday night, the last bus home is usually the highlight of the evening's entertainment.

Its return to the Slaidforth Depot could not be more of a contrast. After decanting its inebriated cargo at the Frecklesall terminus, the number 39 does a swift U-turn and speeds back, completely empty, from whence it came. This particular evening was no exception. After waving a courteous good-riddance to the drunken rabble, the driver was looking forward to nothing more than his bed – it had been a long day. Yawning, he switched on his radio, checked in the rear-view mirror and realised, to his horror, that he'd missed one.

A dishevelled, middle-aged man was staggering towards him along the aisle, bouncing off the seats on either side. 'Sorry, pal – I fell asleep upstairs an' missed me stop. Can I gerroff now?' He started banging on the side door.

The driver groaned – this was just what he needed. 'Wait yer 'urry, lad – I'll drop you at the next one.'

A minute later, the bus squealed to a halt and as the side door opened, the drunk fell out onto the pavement in front of the town hall steps.

'Ta mate, yerra lovely fella!' The slurred expression of gratitude echoed up the deserted street.

Landing with a Thud! onto the roof of the double-decker, Felix struggled to his feet. It took a few seconds for his addled brain to comprehend what had just happened, but his elation didn't last long. The bus lurched forward, toppling him onto his back and sending him sliding towards the curved precipice. He only just managed to grip onto a small air vent protruding from the panelling, the momentum sending his body spinning sideways, his legs dangling helplessly over the edge.

'Stop the bus! Help! I want to get off!'

Radio on full-blast, the driver was blissfully unaware of the drama unfolding up above, but a gang of hooded youths had caught the tail-end of the action and were roaring in admiration.

'Whahey! Ride that sucker!'

Felix screamed still louder, but no one was listening. The bus picked up speed and he found himself spread-eagled across its roof, clinging on for all he was worth. It was about survival now, about hanging on and waiting for the next stop. But that came and went, as did the second and third – all flashing by without a soul in sight. Surely someone needed to get the last bus back to Slaidforth? Surely someone would stick out an arm and save him?

They were steaming along the main road when a detour through the village of Grotley, caught him by surprise. Clawing his way back to the centre of the roof he dared to glance up, and almost wished he hadn't. The rapidly approaching railway bridge was a solid, brick-built affair, arched, with a 'Warning! Low Headroom: 4.5m' sign at the top.

There was no way they were getting under that in one piece!

Thoughts of jumping for it flashed through his mind but in the end, all he could do was hang on and pray. Twenty metres from impact, the bus lurched into the centre of the road. Screaming in terror, Felix buried his head in the metal panelling and braced himself for the imminent crunch of steel against masonry.

But it never came.

The deafening rattle of the old diesel engine boomed around the archway and in the next instant, they were out on the other side and chugging along the open road, once more.

And so it continued over the next fifteen minutes, like the most terrifying roller-coaster ride imaginable. The bus roared past stop after stop, Felix ducking to avoid skirmishes with low-hanging tree branches and lampposts, while clinging on to his precious air vent for dear life. After trundling through the outskirts of Slaidforth, the double-decker made a sharp right into the depot, before manoeuvring into a parking spot inside the rusting corrugated iron shed, amidst a cloud of choking black exhaust fumes.

Nursing aches and pains in muscles he never knew he had, Felix worked his way across the tops of two adjacent buses to reach a metal ladder, slung from the steel rafters. He climbed down as best he could but slipped on the last few rungs, landing in a heap on the concrete floor, just as the driver and the depot supervisor were walking past.

'Bloody hell, it's that weirdo off The Cure!' shrieked the driver, taken aback by Felix's appearance. 'You can't stay 'ere lad, we're locking up for the night.'

Felix grabbed a nearby handrail for support. 'I'm really sorry. I… I stopped off for a few drinks in town and things got a bit out of hand. What time's the next bus back to Frecklesall?'

'Next bus?' The driver was laughing now. 'By the 'eck! We get 'em every weekend, don't we, Reg? Next bus? That'll be around quarter-past-seven in the morning. And before you ask – no, you can't kip 'ere, we're locking up.'

'Oh. Y'see, I really need to get home. My mu… I mean, my wife will be worried sick.'

'Tough,' replied the supervisor. 'Come on pal, just do one, willyer?'

Felix suddenly felt incredibly weary. 'OK… Sorry. Can I use your toilet first, though, please?'

'I suppose so, but make it quick – we've got homes to go to, even if you haven't.'

Felix staggered off to the washroom. Shaping up in front of the tiny, stained sink, he glanced up at the mirror. What a state! His blazer and shirt were covered in grime, as was his face, which was otherwise a ghostly shade of white. The mascara moustache had run, the black tram lines either side of his mouth giving him a sinister, Goth-like appearance. Then there was the hair. While most of it was still cemented down, three or four tufts poked out at a range of unnatural angles. Dousing his head in water for the third time, his ablutions were interrupted by a loud hammering on the door.

'What you doing in there, lad – laying the Atlantic Cable? Gerra move on!'

It was one o'clock in the morning and he was stumbling home along the main road, his mind doing somersaults. He was in massive trouble: Marje Spangles, the Turd, the suspension from school? All of that paled into insignificance compared to this latest calamity. Breaking and entering the mayor's parlour! He could almost see his photo-fit image on *Crimewatch UK* and was so caught up in the inevitability of his next TV appearance, he barely noticed the police car as it eased up alongside. The back door swung open and he crawled in, too tired to argue.

'Frecklesall is it, sir?' asked one of the policemen. 'Where can we drop you off?'

Blimey, they were offering him a lift! But there was no way he could be delivered home in a police car. Even if his mum and dad were asleep, one of the neighbours was bound to spot him, and then it would be game over.

'Oh… err, if you could drop me at the bottom of Winthrop Avenue that would be great, thanks,' he replied.

As they set off, the police radio burst into life and a deep, vaguely familiar voice buzzed out through the dashboard-mounted speaker. 'Come in, foxtrot-tango-delta-one-niner? Report your position please. Over.'

'This is foxtrot-tango-delta-one-niner,' the officer in the front passenger seat replied. 'PC Fox speaking. Proceeding north on the main road, about four miles out of town. What's up? Over.'

'It's that missing juvenile we logged earlier. Any sign? Over.'

'Bloody hell, Sarge! Give us a chance, will you? You only asked us ten minutes ago. Over.'

They all heard the sergeant's sigh. 'Listen Vinnie – his mum's been on again, bending my ear. She's doing my head in. Just keep an eye out for him, will you? And less of the lip. Over and out.'

The two policemen looked at each other and burst into laughter.

'Always the same, isn't it?' said the driver. 'Some lightweight overdoes it on the pop and we're the ones left to clear up the mess.'

PC Fox shouted back to their passenger, who was struggling to keep his eyes open. 'Winthrop's up Scundale Chase way, isn't it? Only, you might know him – the missing lad that is. Have a look at this mugshot, see if it rings any bells.' He held his phone up over his shoulder.

Felix glanced at the tiny screen. 'Bloody hell!' he shrieked, before remembering who he was with.

'So, you recognise him, then, do you?'

'Well… kind of,' Felix replied, wincing. 'That's, err… that's actually a picture of me.'

Moments later, the blue light was flashing, the siren blaring and Felix was pushed back into his seat by the force of the patrol car's acceleration.

His eyes had been welded shut, his brain shrivelled to the size of a small tin of baked beans which was clunking around inside his skull, while his body had turned into one massive ache. He was eventually dragged from his torment by the sound of the bedroom door opening and the rattle of a tray being placed on his bedside table. It was Flo, and she'd brought him some breakfast.

'Come on, Felix – you're going to have to face the music sooner or later,' she announced, brightly.

Ungluing his head from the pillow, he heaved himself up onto an elbow. 'Thanks, Flo – you're a star.' It felt like his tongue had swollen to twice its normal size, not to mention the fur coat it must have grown during the night.

His sister sniffed the air and grimaced. 'You need to open some windows and get in the shower, before Mum and Dad get home.'

'Right…' He reached for his watch, but the effort was too much. 'What's the time?'

'Nearly mid-day.'

'What? I should have been down at Doreen's an hour ago. Why didn't you wake me?'

'Well, Mum said you needed to sleep it off, so she phoned Aunty Doreen and you got to have a lie-in.'

He glanced around the bedroom. 'Where is everyone? Mum's working, but Dad's off today and Fred's never up before mid-afternoon on a Sunday.'

'Well, Mum's on her shift down at the Spar,' replied Flo, 'but Freddie and Dad are out on a bike ride.'

Felix couldn't believe his ears. Freddie had a bike – largely unused – and as far as he knew, his dad didn't even know how to ride one. Park that for a moment, because the idea of the two of them doing anything together was totally beyond belief.

'No - it's for real!' shrieked Flo, excitedly. 'It's been all over the TV and the radio. The Tour de France – the world's biggest bike race – it's coming to Frecklesall!'

Of course it was. Felix winced as his memory of the night before lurched back into focus. 'Oh… yeah, I heard about that.'

'But how could you? You've been asleep all morning. We only found out at breakfast time from Radio Lancashire.'

'Umm… Freddie must have mentioned it when he got up. Anyway, it doesn't explain why he'd go out on a bike ride with Dad – that's just ridiculous.'

'Well, you didn't hear it all then, did you?' His sister folded her arms across her chest. 'They've organised a competition for local cyclists – it's for anyone who's a member of Frecklesall cycling club – boys only, of course.' She pulled a face. 'There's going to be a special race – *Le Grand Prix de Frecklesall*. It's like a local qualifier. Whoever wins, gets to go on a ten-day training camp in the south of France with one of the top pro cycling teams. And after that they get to ride in the Tour itself, when it comes here on July the tenth!'

Wow! He'd missed that bit.

'Hang on a minute,' he said. 'Frecklesall Cyclonics folded years ago. Didn't they used to meet up at the Labour Club, before it got torched?'

'Kind of. Their club house burnt down, which means they don't actually have proper meetings any more, but there are still plenty of members around. You did that cycling road safety test at school in year six, didn't you?'

Felix groaned at the memory.

'Freddie did it – even Dad did, way back when,' she continued. 'I'm going to be doing it next year, Mum says. If you pass, you get a badge and a certificate…' She paused while Felix stifled a yawn. '*And* you get lifetime membership of the Frecklesall Cyclonics! It's to encourage you to keep on cycling when you grow up. That's why Dad and Freddie are out on a ride this morning, along with everyone else. They're all in the Cyclonics and they all want a shot at being the *Domestique du Jour*, when the Tour de France comes to town!'

The rattle of the back door opening prevented Felix from making things any worse.

'Someone's here – you'd better get moving,' said his sister as she scampered out of the bedroom.

His dad had been home a good fifteen minutes but Felix found him, still slumped in a chair in the kitchen, red-faced, the sweat dripping from his chin into a rapidly growing pool on the floor.

'Morning!' Felix greeted him cheerily. 'Good ride?'

His dad looked up, a haunted expression on his face. 'Bloody awful, actually. I borrowed your bike – I've left it round the back.' He shook his head, ruefully. 'I tell you, Son, that thing needs some fettlin'. The brakes are rubbing – slowed me down something terrible – and now I've got this pain.' He pointed at his groin and winced.

Felix laughed. 'Face it, Dad, you're not getting any younger, are you?' The words splurged from his lips before he could stop them. 'Oh, sorry. What I meant to say was… I, err… Actually, I need to be off – I'm late for Doreen as it is.' He reached for the door but his dad hauled him back.

'You're not going anywhere, lad – not until we've had a chat about what you got up to last night.' His finger was jabbing now. 'Your mother was worried sick, and you're bloody lucky you didn't have to spend the night in a police cell. Oh, and where's the change from that fifteen quid I gave you?'

9

As rollockings go, it could have been a lot worse. There was a load of stuff about his mum thinking he was dead, about wasting police time and what the neighbours would be saying, but it all seemed a rather odd – almost as if, by the end, his dad was pleased that he'd been up to no good. And with a girl as well!

'Don't tell your mother, but it's been a bit of a relief, actually.'

Felix looked at him, incredulously. 'What d'you mean?'

His dad smiled. 'Meeting your friend, Keira. Nice lass, I thought.'

'And?'

'And nothing – it's just that, well, your mum and I thought you might be not so interested in girls.'

So that was it!

'I don't believe this – it's Fred, isn't it?' spluttered Felix. 'And you were stupid enough to believe him!'

'Steady on, Son, that's a bit strong… Well, err… to be fair, he did happen to mention you might be leaning that way, and we never like to pry, so—'

'I wondered why you two were acting so weirdly last night. This is ridiculous! And anyway, what if I actually was gay – would that be such a problem for you?'

'Of course not.' His dad offered up a knowing wink and patted him on the shoulder. 'At least we've cleared that one up, eh?'

'I'm really pleased for you!' shouted Felix, as he headed outside to pick up his bike. 'I wouldn't want to cause you any embarrassment. Maybe you'd rather I ended up like our Fred? He's a great role model, isn't he?'

Felix chuckled to himself as he coasted down the hill into town. How stupid was his dad? Still, it had got him out of the doghouse, for the time being at least. Pedalling along the Prom, past the town hall, he saw a workman leaning from the platform of a huge cherry-picker as he manoeuvred a fresh pane of glass into the window of Wiseley's office. Head down, he accelerated away towards the far end of the beach.

Doreen seemed highly amused by his late arrival. 'What you been up to, lad?' she asked. 'Out 'til all hours with a young lady? Fetched home in a police car? Anyone would think you were trying to outdo your big brother.'

'No, no… it wasn't like that. I'd rather not talk about it, if you don't mind.'

She laughed. 'Fine by me. I could tell you a few stories from when I were a lass that would make your hair stand on end.'

He was dying to let her know what had happened, but it was all too risky. Anyway, if what they'd seen on Wiseley's computer was to be believed, she'd be finding out soon enough.

'Would you mind if I made a quick call?' he asked.

'Who am I to stand in the way of true love?' Winking mischievously, she waved him away.

He found a sheltered spot at the top of the slipway and selected Keira's number on the speed-dial. There was no answer, so he tried her landline.

The call was eventually picked up by her mum. 'Keira? No idea where she's got to. Listen, if you see her, tell her to come home, will you? I'm worried I might forget what she looks like.'

His heart sank – she hadn't made it! She was probably being interrogated in some windowless cell in the basement of the police station, and when she cracked... well, it didn't bear thinking about. It had all started as an adventure, a bit of a laugh, but now it had gone too far.

Then he heard a familiar voice.

'Hey! Haythornthwaite – you big soft lad. I thought I might find you here.'

He almost fell to his knees in relief.

Sitting at a corner table in the Full Monty, the grubby café overlooking the Prom, Felix was onto his second mug of tea by the time he'd got to the end of his story.

'Total nightmare,' muttered Keira, from under her dark curly fringe, the glamour of the evening before already a distant memory. 'Did anyone else see what went on?'

'I don't think so,' he replied. 'There were these lads hanging around on the street but they just thought it was a laugh – like I'd got on top of that bus on purpose.'

'Idiots.'

'Yeah.' He looked around to check that no one else was listening. 'So what do we do now? If we blow the whistle, Wiseley's going to come after us, isn't he?'

'Nah - think about it. You were wearing that stupid disguise and he didn't get a proper look at me. He won't know it was us.'

'Maybe…' Felix sighed. 'And after all that, we didn't even get any evidence.'

'That's not quite true. While you were playing hide-and-seek with Troy and Marje, I managed to fire off a couple of emails.'

'Really? That's brilliant!'

'Calm down, will you?' She smiled sweetly at the café's disreputable owner, Wally Knockles, who was eyeing them suspiciously from behind the counter. 'I got the one Wiseley sent to that PR firm about the *Pen* story, and then I had a go at that Frecklesall Renaissance file. It was mega – it'll be a miracle if it gets through.'

'Where did you send them?'

'The *Pen* address, at school,' she replied, casually.

'What?' Felix's chocolate biscuit disappeared into the depths of his mug. 'Bloody hell, Keira, why did you do that? I might as well go and hand myself in at the police station, right now!'

She looked at him, dismissively. 'Wiseley's the chair of the board of governors, isn't he? There'll be loads of email traffic between him and the school – he'll never spot it. Anyway, I deleted them from his 'Sent Items' folder after they'd cleared. We were never there, OK?'

'We were never there.' Felix repeated her words as if trying to convince himself. 'It was nothing to do with us. But we're going to get him, aren't we?'

She laughed 'Yeah. We're *definitely* doing that.'

They paid up and headed outside. It was a sunny day and the two of them walked along the Prom together, dodging wayward skaters and a travelling conga of pensioners sporting tartan 'Jimmy' Tam O'Shanters and Rasta wigs. Felix would have been happy to hang out with Keira for the rest of the afternoon, but it wasn't an option – Doreen would kill him unless he went back. He was about to say his goodbyes when he spotted a familiar gaggle, swaggering in their direction. It was Spugley and his mates – Ricky Sowerbutts, who was sporting a spectacular black eye, Charlie Stoat, and three year ten girls. Felix gulped nervously – it was a busy afternoon, surely Spugley wasn't going to cause trouble out in the open like this?

They were a good fifteen metres apart now and the thought of making a run for it crossed his mind. But Keira was going nowhere.

'*Might as well give 'em something to talk about, eh?*' she whispered, slipping an arm around his waist and pulling him closer as they walked along.

It was Ricky who opened his big mouth first. 'Hey look, Spug – Beyonce and Jay-Z!'

The girls sniggered and Felix braced himself for the worst, but then a funny thing happened.

'Shut yer gob, Butty, lad,' growled Spugley. 'You're gettin' on me wick.'

'But… but Sean,' pleaded Ricky. 'He owes you – big time! I thought…'

Spugley drew deeply on his cigarette, before slapping him across the back of the head.

'Oww!'

'Oreet,' Spuggie grunted, nodding to Keira as he walked by. His friends gawped at each other in disbelief, leaving Ricky fuming in silence.

'Oreet, Sean,' Keira replied, as if saying hello to Frecklesall's number one head-the-ball was an everyday occurrence.

The best Felix could manage was a strangled squeak.

The afternoon shift on the beach had lasted a lifetime and when Naz came down to join Doreen and Felix at the end of the day, he almost had to carry his friend up to the Paddock. Half an hour later, the three of them were on deckchairs in the front garden, with some much-needed orange squash. Felix was a wreck, the excesses of the previous night having well and truly caught up with him. All he wanted to do was go home and crawl into bed but instead, he found himself listening to Naz, droning on about the big announcement.

'And this *Domestique du Jour* thing… I'd give my right arm to have a go at that.'

Felix stifled a yawn. 'I don't want to sound stupid, Naz, but what is a *domestique*? Is it, like, someone who does the tidying up – maybe a bit of ironing?'

Naz laughed. 'No way! A big race like the Tour is a team event, see? Each team has eight riders and they all have their own specialisms. So, you've got your sprinters – the guys who give it full-gas over the last few hundred metres on the flat stages, and your climbers who are good on the hills, for when they're up in the mountains. Sometimes they have a stage where they race individually against the clock. That's where the time-trial specialists come in. Then you've got your team leaders – like Modesto Scaglioni and Heinz Krankel. They're the all-rounders who go for the big prize: the General Classification – the GC, they call it. The overall leader of the race is given a yellow jersey – the *maillot jaune* – at the end of each stage. That's what the GC winner gets after three weeks in the saddle, when the whole thing wraps up in Paris.'

Landing a paltry yellow jersey after three weeks of pulling your tripe out on a bike sounded like scant reward to Felix, but he stuck to his task. 'OK Naz, I get it, but what's with these *domestique* lads?'

'Oh, right… Well, they're the work-horses who support their team mates, out on the road. So, if one of them needs food or water, it's the *domestique's* job to get it. They might have to act as a pacemaker for their leader, or protect him if things get rough. Sometimes they even have to give up their bike for him, if he's involved in a crash, or has a puncture.'

Felix couldn't see Freddie doing that for anyone, and was about to say as much when he was distracted by the sound of squealing brakes, coming from just beyond the front gate. A mountain bike had been dropped onto its side and his brother was staggering, bow-legged, up the path towards them.

'Blimey! What have you been up to?' asked Felix, shocked by Freddie's dishevelled appearance.

His brother flopped lifelessly into a deckchair. Before anyone could stop him, he'd picked up the jug of squash from the table and downed it in one.

Doreen shook her head in disbelief. 'I heard you went out for a ride with your dad this morning, Freddie. Florence says he's in a right state. What have you done to him?'

'We thought we'd give this Tour gig a shot,' he replied, still catching his breath. 'The old fella couldn't hack it, so I dropped him and did about fifty-five this morning. I refuelled over Longridge way and got down as far as Chorley, before heading back.'

His great-aunt looked impressed. 'That sounds like one heck of a long ride.'

'Got the stats here, look.' He pulled out a cycle-computer from his back pocket and dropped it onto the table. 'According to this gizmo, that's one hundred miles all in, at twenty-six miles an hour, give or take. Whaddya know? Our Flo told me the average on the Tour last year was just over twenty-seven. Hey – maybe this isn't going to be such a stretch after all.'

Felix guffawed. 'You're having a laugh, Fred! That's just their *average* speed. They go much faster than that, y'know, especially on the flat stages. The race is over three weeks and covers three and a half thousand kilometres – Naz was telling us about it, before.'

'But I only need to keep up with them for one day, don't I?' his brother replied. 'I'm not bustin' a gut riding up them Himalayas, or wherever else it is they go. *And* I've got home advantage. Everyone will be cheering me on – especially the really fit girls!'

Naz picked up the cycle computer, his brow furrowing as he examined the readout. 'It is a long way down to Chorley and back, Freddie, especially as you've not been doing any training. But it's not a hundred miles.'

'Hey, get your specs on, lad!' snapped Freddie. 'The stats are the stats.'

'I can see what it says,' said Naz, 'but what it's showing you is *kilometres*, not miles – see?' He double-clicked a button at the back of the device. 'Look – your average speed converts to just on sixteen miles an hour.'

Freddie's face fell. 'Bummer! I thought I'd cracked it.'

Felix roared with laughter. 'You plonker, Fred – you've got no chance!'

117

Freddie shaped up to give his younger brother a clout but was stopped in his tracks by a stern look from Doreen. Meanwhile, Naz had wandered over to check out the bike. He grunted as he lifted it up.

'Just as I thought,' he said. 'This thing weighs a ton. The specification is rubbish – cheap steel frame, full suspension, and these tyres look like they've come off a tractor. It's like trying to ride the Grand National on an old cart horse. The road bikes they use in the Tour are aerodynamic, lightweight, super-fast... and really, really expensive.'

Freddie was beginning to lose it. 'Hey, the guy who sold it me said those wheels are top-end. And you can get up the side of a house with them gears.'

Naz shrugged. 'Look on the bright side, Freddie – sixteen miles an hour is pretty useful on something like this. With a bit of training and a half-decent road bike, who knows what you'd be capable of?'

'Right on, Naz, my friend!' Freddie suddenly sounded a lot perkier. 'Wake up and smell the *fromage* you Frenchies – this dude is shaving-down, lubing-up, and getting ready to rumble!'

Felix laughed. 'Dream on, Fred. How d'you think you're going to get hold of one of those lightweight road bikes in time? They cost thousands and the Grand Prix is only two weeks off.'

Naz headed home while Freddie wobbled off to his appointment with the contents of the fridge at Scundale Chase, leaving Doreen and Felix to discuss Freddie's average speed, and the unbelievable notion that he just might have some kind of remote shot at competing in the Tour de France.

'So, he knows his stuff, your pal Naz, does he?' asked Doreen, in a matter-of-fact kind of way.

'Yeah, he follows all the big races. He's really excited at the news.'

'Well, if it's a road bike Freddie's after, I might be able to help him out.'

Five minutes later they stumbled into the dank interior of the Paddock's semi-derelict outbuilding. Set in the far corner of the field, with its crumbling brickwork, rotting timber windows and sagging slate roof, Felix had never thought there could be anything of value in such a rundown wreck of a place. Doreen eventually found the light switch and as the bulb fizzed and flickered into life, he realised he couldn't have been more wrong.

They were in the midst of a grimy old workshop, crammed full of ancient bicycle parts.

'Where did you get this stuff?' Felix asked, his eyes blinking as they adjusted to the gloomy lighting.

Ignoring the question, his great-aunt gestured towards a lumpy, waxed tarpaulin, next to one of the work benches. After clearing away a few old planks, she managed to peel it back. Felix gasped as a handful of vintage road bikes were revealed, stacked together in various states of deconstruction. Battered and ancient as they were, it was obvious these were serious machines, built for speed.

Felix picked up the nearest frame. 'This one's light.'

Doreen pointed at the last bike, hidden away at the back. 'That was always Billy's favourite. You should give it a go.'

Felix began moving the other bikes aside. 'This must have been really good gear, back in the day. Where did you get it from?'

She let out a sigh. 'That's for another time… Now, do you think your brother could use any of this lot?'

Felix lifted out the last bike and tried spinning the wheels to check whether they ran true. He pulled the sleeve of his sweatshirt over the palm of his hand, wiping away the grime from the crossbar. A rich, dark-red colour emerged, and with it, some white lettering which spelt out a vaguely familiar name.

Hill Special

*

There was no way he could ride the bike home – the tyres were disintegrating with each turn of the wheels, the leather saddle had rotted and was green with mould, while the brake and gear cables were long gone. It had looked good in the gloom of the outbuilding but in the cold light of day, it was just a tired, rusting old heap.

He was wheeling it along the footpath when something flashed by on the road, so close, it made him jump. Falling over the antique machine, he sat up and yelled abuse after the speeding cyclist.

The rider executed a sharp U-turn and began coasting back towards him. Felix had seen all sorts out on two wheels that day – all shapes and sizes in any number of make-do outfits – but this guy had the gear, from the electric-blue Lycra skinsuit to the aerodynamic, full-face helmet. Then there was the bike – matching colour of course – slick and ultra-light, with top-notch equipment. Felix looked down at the museum piece he was pushing home. Who was Naz kidding? Freddie had no chance.

'Did you say something, boy?' The rider's voice was muffled by his helmet.

Felix did his best to make light of the situation. 'Sorry mate, you startled me. Nice bike, though – must have cost a few quid.'

'You see, Haythornthwaite, I thought I heard you disrespecting me, back there. And I won't be taking any lip off the likes of you, obviously.'

He knew that voice. The fancy headgear came off and his worst fears were confirmed.

'Where you heading with that pile of junk?' sneered Gareth Llewellyn-Evans, eyes staring madly as he adjusted the multi-coloured bandana he was wearing beneath his helmet. 'You know you're not old enough to be in the race, don't you?'

'It's for my brother, Freddie,' replied Felix. 'I thought we might be able to do it up for him.'

'Ha! Freddie Haythornthwaite? I remember him – a no-mark, just like you. Don't think for one minute that pile of scrap is going to help him. Feast your eyes on this lot.' He gestured towards his bike. 'Twelve grand's worth of state-of-the-art, flown in from Italy yesterday. And best of all, this beauty has a professional sportsman riding her – a proven winner.'

Felix looked confused. 'Oh, right. And who would that be, then?'

'Don't you get smart with me, boy! And while we're on the subject, be sure to pass this message on to your brother: I'm going to win this race, obviously, and God help anyone who even *thinks* they can take me on.'

Donning his high-tech helmet, the PE teacher clicked his dazzling white cycling shoes into the designer Italian pedals and sprinted off up the road.

10

Breakfast at 21 Scundale Chase – a potential flashpoint of near Preston North End v Blackpool proportion. With the whole family shuffling into the kitchen, in varying degrees of crumpled nightwear, this particular Tuesday morning was no exception.

Felix was seething. 'Don't tell me you've troughed it all, Fred? Dad, he's done it again – there's no bread left!'

His dad was engrossed in the *Frecklesall Journal*, having taken the morning off work to check out the Hill Special, which he'd foolishly promised his eldest he'd get into a rideable state. 'Freddie's in training,' he grunted, without lifting his head from the paper. 'The lad needs to eat.'

'But Dad, he's eaten *everything*.'

'Quit your moanin', doofus,' drawled Freddie. 'It's fuel in the machine, innit?'

'That's enough!' snapped their mum, momentarily distracted from the huge pot bubbling away on the hob. 'I've made plenty of spaghetti Bolognese for everyone.'

Felix poured himself a glass of orange juice and sat down opposite his father.

'Bloody hell,' his dad grumbled. 'Seventeen pages of this stupid bike race. You'd think there was nowt else going on around here. Look at this lot: Manley Torso, Team SpamFritter Deluxe; Modesto Scaglioni, Team

Chocolate Banana; Denmark's Bent Smorgasbord…? Where the hell do they find these guys, and who even heard of Chocolate Bananas?'

'Very observant,' said his wife. 'I suppose you'll be making snidey comments like that when your son wins the Frecklesall Grand Prix and gets to be Modesto Scaglioni's team-mate.' She glanced over his shoulder to check out the Italian's photograph in the paper. 'Ooh, he looks proper fit, doesn't he?'

'Yeah! That's my team you're dissing,' added Freddie. 'You're just jealous 'cos you're out of the race.'

'Hmmph! You wouldn't be cycling quite so fast if you had my hernia,' said his dad. He flicked on through the *Journal's* pages stopping abruptly, just before the used car adverts. 'Unbelievable! Just Un-Be-Flippin'-Lieveable!'

His wife sighed. 'What is it now, Brian?'

'Have you seen this? Look!' He waved the newspaper at his sons. 'You can stick all this stupid Tour de France nonsense – this is what's really going on in our town.'

It may have been on page eighteen, but there was no missing the screaming headline:

YobWatch!
Bus-Surf Terror Hits Frecklesall
Mayor Offers £1000 Reward: 'ASBO this Yob Now!'

Felix wrestled the paper from his dad's grasp and there, beneath the headline, was a grainy black and white shot taken from the north end of the Prom, looking back towards the town hall. It was night time, the street lamps providing just enough of a glow to illuminate the double-decker as it lumbered up the road, complete with the slim, silhouetted figure, seemingly dancing on its roof.

'You big soft lad - no one can tell it was you.' Keira laid into him as they huddled around a screen in the school IT suite, later that morning.

'Yeah, but they're sending the footage off to the FBI, over in the States, for revolutionary digital enhancement pioneered in the fight against organised crime.' The *Frecklesall Journal's* words were indelibly imprinted on Felix's mind.

'Look, the Tour de France is coming to town. No one cares about any of this stuff – apart from your dad, of course.'

'That's easy for you to say.'

Ignoring him, she continued scrolling through the *Pen's* email account. 'Hang on – this is it.' There was an agonising pause while the computer whirred and churned away.

'Oh no!' Felix shrieked as an auto-message popped onto the screen.

Your system does not have the software compatibility to run this program

'That Frecklesall Renaissance file was huge,' said Keira. 'I should have known there's no way the school's server could cope with something so big.'

'And after everything I went through,' Felix muttered. 'I wish I'd never bothered.'

'Hey, if it'd been down to you, we wouldn't even have made it past the bus stop!' Undeterred, she opened the second email despatched from Wiseley's office that fateful evening, only this time, she was the one with her head in her hands.

Felix was livid. 'Bloody hell, Keira – you sent the wrong one! It was supposed to be Wiseley's Blue Pennant email. This is something else, altogether! I've no chance of clearing my name, now, have I?'

She slumped forward across the desk, groaning. 'I'm so sorry, Felix, it was mental in there. I tried my best.'

The email, dated thirtieth of May, was from an outfit they'd never heard of before – Crannage, Saighton and Wolfe, corporate attorneys based in Dallas, Texas – although the name of the sender was all too familiar.

Dear Mayor Troy, Reference International Transaction Number 0881. Confirmation of remuneration details duly contained in scanned attachment.

Have a nice day!

Isiah J Wolfe

Isiah J. Wolfe
Lead Partner – Corporate Interactions (Global)

Keira tried to open the PDF attachment and suddenly, things got a whole lot worse:

Virus Slamdown!

System Security Message: This file is from an unknown source and has been blocked. Please refer to your System Administrator for access.

The door to the IT suite swung open and the slim figure of Miss Sidhu – 'Sid', as she was more commonly known – the school's head of IT, breezed into the room. 'Hi you two. Anything I can help you with?'

'There is, actually,' Felix began. 'It's about this email—'

Keira stopped him in his tracks. 'No thanks, Miss Sidhu. We were just checking the *Pen's* in-box. Turns out most of the stuff we've been sent over the past few days is junk.'

'Really?' The IT teacher sounded surprised. 'You shouldn't be getting any of that now. We've just introduced this new Virus Slamdown! software. All medium to high-risk emails and attachments are intercepted – that's anything from an unrecognised source. The recipient gets a pop-up referring them to the system administrator. That's me, by the way! I have a special password allowing me to access anything that's been blocked.'

'In that case, would you mind—' Felix narrowly suppressed a squeal as he sustained a painful kick to his shins.

'After I've printed out a hard copy,' Sid continued, 'I pass it across to Dr Brown, who has the final say on whether it should be released. We really can't be too careful these days. Why do you ask, Felix – have you found something you want me to take a look at?'

'No, nothing at all.' Keira jumped in, stabbing the 'Delete' button with a finger. 'You were just interested in how it all works, weren't you Felix? But thanks so much, Miss Sidhu, we'll be sure to let you know if we need any help.'

'Super!' said the teacher as she headed out of the room.

Keira turned on him the moment the door had closed. 'What planet are you on, you idiot! If Arsey sees any of this stuff, we're dead in the water. Is that what you want?'

'No, of course not,'

'Well, wake up, then. Start thinking things through, for once. You can't carry on like this.'

She stomped out of the IT suite, leaving Felix alone, the dark clouds of depression looming large.

'Yes indeed, Mrs Brown and I were honoured to be guests at the Mayor's Ball on Saturday night, and what a glamorous and glittering occasion it turned out to be,' Arsey enthused, at the end of assembly. 'The very cream of Frecklesall society were there, resplendent in their finery. And I'm sure you'll all be aware of the big announcement, delivered via a live satellite link, all the way from the United States of America!'

'*Glamorous and glittering*?' Felix whispered to Bernie, who was slouching in the chair next to him. '*Drunk and disorderly, more like.*'

'Yeah, right. Like you'd know, wouldn't you?' replied his friend.

'Naturally, there's been an amazing level of interest in our own qualifying race, *Le Grand Prix de Frecklesall*,' the head continued. 'As a consequence of which, I have an important announcement to share with you all this morning.' He paused to smile benevolently at his audience. 'Following due deliberation, the governors and I have decided that our school should "step up to the plate", as it were, by sponsoring a competitor in the event. And I'm absolutely thrilled to confirm that after an exhaustive selection process, we have decided that Frecklesall High's favoured rider is to be none other than our very own Head of PE, Mr Gareth Llewellyn-Evans!'

There were groans all round as Gazza strutted onto the stage in his shorts and blue, muscle-fit T-shirt, the bandana still firmly tied into place.

'Thank you, Dr Brown!' he began, almost tearfully. 'Boys and girls, I stand before you this morning, a humble lad from the tiny Welsh village of Pant-y-Girdle, way up there in the valleys. I may not be the cleverest among us here today…' The head teacher nodded in agreement. '… but I do know this much,' Gazza continued. 'On the tenth of July I'm going to be riding my heart out with Team Chocolate Banana, in the greatest bike race on the planet. And I'll be doing it just for you!' He beat his fist against chest. 'Know this much – Mr Gareth Llewellyn-Evans will *not* be letting you down!'

Arsey broke the stunned silence. 'Indeed, Mr Llewellyn-Evans, our thoughts and prayers are with you... Oh, and by the way.' He turned to his incredulous audience. 'PE and games sessions are cancelled until further notice, to give our champion-in-waiting and his team, the chance to prepare properly for *le Grand Prix*.'

That Tuesday's lunchtime meeting was proving as riveting as ever.

'We'll be leading with a profile of Mr Llewellyn-Evans,' Basil announced. 'I'll pull that together, but I'll need your race reports on the big day. Felix, Sean – be sure to get out and recce the route in advance. Same goes for you, Keira – suss out the best places for some action shots, please.'

'Really?' moaned Bernie. 'I mean, no one's going to want to read about this. It's just a massive waste of time.'

The teacher turned on him. 'This is a huge story Bernard – a great opportunity for all of us to do some proper reporting for once. If you don't want to be a part of it, you can leave now, but believe me, you won't be coming back. And that applies to everyone here – apart from you, Sean, of course.'

Spugley slumped forward, groaning, but no one moved from their seats.

The meeting dribbled along to the two o'clock bell and as Felix made his usual bid to be first out the door, Spugley, whose surly non-cooperation was an equally familiar feature of their meetings, lifted his head from the table.

'Anyone see that Bus-Surf thing in the *Journal* this week?' he grunted. 'That ASBO boy is the business!'

'OK Sean,' said Basil. 'I can't agree with you on that particular point, but why not check out the story? It'll be excellent for you to get involved in some first-hand research, and who knows – you might even end up with the £1000 reward. I'm told the mayor is funding it from his own pocket.'

Felix glanced across the table and saw Spugley wink at him, a ghoulish smile spreading across his face.

As the days crawled by it was clear that Wiseley had been right about one thing, at least: Frecklesall-on-Sea was getting its act together.

Contracting gangs descended on the town, labouring day and night on a monumental facelift. Steaming black tarmac with brilliant white markings replaced the previously pock-marked road surface, scabby plots of open space were tidied up, while hanging baskets with brightly-coloured blooms appeared outside even the drabbest of houses. Wolf-whistling packs of decorators set about painting everything that didn't move, and even a few things that did, including a group of pensioners who tarried too long on one of the benches out on the town moor.

To cap it all, the Big Lamp roundabout – the town's decrepit gateway – underwent its own makeover. The rubbish was cleared and the waist-high weeds dug out; replaced with well-watered turf and a garish array of brightly-coloured bedding plants. The Big Lamp itself was patched up, courtesy of a bucket-load of filler and a liberal coating of black gloss. A small crowd gathered to cheer the demolition of the decrepit 'Welcome' sign from the 1950s.

Frecklesall was firmly in the grip of Tour Fever, but that wasn't quite how Felix was seeing it. Trapped in his own world of paranoia, he jumped at each ring of the doorbell, turning into a gibbering wreck every time he heard a police siren. And to make matters worse, he knew it was only a matter of time before he landed a terminal encounter with his nemesis – Sean Spugley.

Lounging on his bed after tea that Thursday evening, he was reflecting on how things had changed at home. These days, Freddie was either out on his bike, stuffing food into his face, or asleep. Somehow, his feckless big brother had transformed himself from brainless poser into wannabe pro cyclist, and no one could quite work out why. Felix had been around him long enough to know that there had to be a reason… and it was bound to be something really stupid.

Checking beneath Freddie's bed, he was shocked to discover that his brother had made the greatest sacrifice

of all. His comprehensive library of porno mags had disappeared and been replaced by the likes of *ProCycling*, *Cycling Weekly* and… *Celebrity Top Goss.*
Hmmm.

He fished the gossip magazine from the undergrowth for a closer look. It seemed like an odd choice. Reading about the latest D-list celebrity's boob-job or the tragic death of her pet goldfish, would not normally have been on Freddie's radar. Leafing on past the diet page – 'I gave birth two weeks ago and now I'm a size six!' – Felix eventually found what he was looking for:

Beautiful Heiress to the Smilerski Billions tells Top Goss about her hopes for *L'Amour* at *Le Tour*!

The six-page spread was accompanied by a plethora of airbrushed photographs of the impossibly gorgeous Herbina, languishing beside the Bug's Tussle pool. Felix read on:

Since her breakup with multi-millionaire TV mogul, Benny Santamaria, Herbina Smilerski, heiress to the Smilerski billions, has become a real home-bird, spending as much time as possible with her octogenarian father – business tycoon, Herbert T Smilerski III. We caught up with her at the family's stunning home in the beautiful Texan town of Bug's Tussle:

Top Goss: Herbina, we were all so shocked to hear about your surprise split with multi-millionaire TV mogul, Benny Santamaria. How are you feeling right now?

Herbina Smilerski: Benny hurt me real bad – he was my soulmate and losing him has broken me in so many ways. But my therapist tells me I'm ready to move on now – to real commitment. So, I'll be making a guest star appearance on *Celebrity Love Lagoon*, next week, and immediately after that, I'm heading over to Europe to check out something they're calling the Tour de France. Apparently, it's some kind of cycler race? I'm so excited to be going! Those cycler guys have such lovely legs and some of them are pretty cute. Who knows, I might even get to bring one of them home with me!'

TG: You're famed for your natural beauty, Herbina. Given your jet-set lifestyle, just how do you manage to keep in such great shape?

HS: My new exercise programme *Get Legs Like Herbina Smilerski (or your money back!)* is available in download or DVD format, next month...

Felix groaned – surely Freddie wasn't that stupid?

He was still chuckling about it when he heard the familiar house-shaking thuds of his big brother, loping up the stairs. Grabbing a copy of *ProCycling* from under the bed, he did his best to look engrossed.

'*Ciao!*' Freddie greeted him as he burst into the room. 'Good to see you doing some background reading, at last.'

Felix glanced up from the magazine and did a double-take. His brother's hair had changed, his long greasy locks now streaked with blond highlights and fluffed up into a loose perm. He looked like an extra from *Charlie's Angels*.

'New hairstyle, Fred?' he asked innocently.

'You know what they say – if you wanna impress, go get some finesse!'

'So, who's next in line? It wouldn't by any chance be…' Felix picked up the copy of *Celebrity Top Goss* from the floor and wafted the centre-page spread at him.

'Guilty as charged!' exclaimed Freddie, grinning broadly. 'The moment I saw her I knew she was The One. It's written in the stars!'

'Congratulations,' said Felix, trying to stop himself from laughing out loud. 'She's a stunner, Fred, and I'm sure she's a really nice person as well. But… how on earth is someone like you going to get to meet someone like Herbina Smilerski?'

'That's very much a work in progress at this particular moment in time, Bro. If you've read that article, you'll know she's in the market for a top *Euro-Cyclismo*. Better still, sources tell me she's going to be presenting the trophy to the stage winner, right here in Frecklesall!'

Felix looked puzzled. 'Sorry, you lost me there.'

Freddie rolled his eyes. 'Hey - work it out, Stephen Hawking. All I gotta do is win myself a couple of bike races, and it's game on!'

Felix was left almost speechless. 'Listen Fred, I don't want to sound pessimistic but—'

'Hey, Captain Glass-Half-Empty – two things I gotta say to you: *uno*… who dares wins… and two-o, err… Well, quit raining on my parade, willyer?'

'Nah, you're pulling my leg!' Bernie laughed as he, Naz, Keira and Felix, trudged back from school the next day.

'That's why he's training so hard,' said Felix. 'It's not just winning the Grand Prix – he's got to do it all over again on the Tour, against the best professionals in the world. And after he's pulled *that* off, he's counting on Herbina falling for him, up on the podium, when she presents him with the stage trophy.'

'He's bright, that brother of yours,' said Bernie, drily. 'The problem is, we still need him to win – or at least, to make sure that idiot Llewellyn-Evans doesn't. Can you imagine what a nightmare it would be if he got to ride in the big race?'

'I don't even want to think about it,' Naz added. gloomily.

'I was talking to Derek Sidebottom from year eight,' said Keira. 'His dad runs the bookies in town. He reckons most of the teachers have been in, putting serious money on Gazza to win. Even Arsey's had a flutter.'

'It's no wonder they're letting him train in school time,' said Bernie, grunting as he jumped up to try to dislodge a Smiler Corporation sign from half-way up a recently painted lamppost. 'I bloody hate all this Smiler Corporation stuff – "We Planted This", "We Painted That", "Making Frecklesall a Dog Turd Free Zone"! It's really starting to get on me nerves. What do they do, anyway? How do they make their money?'

'Flo's into all this big business, share trading stuff,' said Felix. 'She's going to so some digging for me.' He'd casually asked his sister to check out Herb's company on the Internet, a few days before, telling her it was for an end of term school project.

'Maybe Freddie's not so daft, after all,' squeaked Bernie, shinning up the lamppost to attack the sign from above. 'That Herbina's a top bird. If only I was a few years older…'

They were still laughing when the black stretch limo drew up alongside, the rear window whirring open to reveal a chubby, all too familiar face.

Bernie dropped to the ground, dislodging his glasses in the process.

Frecklesall's first citizen eyed up their school uniforms with disdain. 'I've already got the police out, hunting down the ASBO boy, so if you know what's good for you, you two.' He pointed at Bernie and Naz. 'Get yourselves away home, now!'

Felix sensed the contents of his lower intestine gurgling ominously. What if Wiseley was on to them? What if he knew? It wasn't worth hanging around to find out. He grabbed Keira by the arm, and—

'Ooff!'

A massive bear-paw locked onto his shoulder and suddenly he was being hauled towards the car. He could see Roy's bullet-headed figure in the drivers' seat – so who was the new heavy? Keira was struggling to break free but it was no use. A rear door swung open and the whole limo tilted to one side as their giant captor climbed in behind them.

Wiseley sat facing them and as the car pulled away from the kerb, he leaned back into the plush upholstery, a smug look on his face. 'Mr Haythornthwaite and Miss Makinson, I presume? Such a pleasure to meet you properly, at last.'

'Look, we're really sorry about the sign back there,' said Felix. 'We'll pay for any damage.'

The mayor sighed. 'Oh, no, no, no! I'm afraid it's rather more complicated than that, and *much* more serious.' He leant forward. 'I believe you've already met my associate, Mr Pike?'

135

The giant sitting next to him fixed them with a bone-chilling stare. He was huge – so tall he had to bend his neck just to fit into the back seat, and broad with it too. His massive frame had been squeezed into a light-blue suit which strained at the seams, half-mast trousers revealing a flash of white sock. Sitting on top of his gigantically proportioned shoulders was an almost comically small head, his tiny-featured face and babyish complexion crowned with precisely-parted blond hair – like his mum had combed it for him before he'd left home that morning.

The mayor gestured towards the man-mountain. 'Randy handles some of the Smiler Corporation's more sensitive security issues—'

'*Randy?*' Keira snorted, loudly. '*Randy Pike*? Are you serious?'

'Deadly serious,' replied Wiseley. 'I'd advise you to remember that, given there's a very good chance your future wellbeing will depend upon it.' He smiled, insincerely. 'As I was saying – *Randy* is one of Mr Smilerski's most loyal lieutenants. He was telling me earlier about how he's turned his life around – from his early days on Chicago's South Side, running an extortion racket for the mob, to a senior job as Mr Smilerski's personal "fixer". It's quite an inspiring story, actually. I was genuinely surprised to hear how many transferable skills there are between the two roles.'

Felix's skin crept at the mayor's tone, but Keira seemed oblivious to the threat.

'Dunno what you're on about,' she said, coolly.

The mayor sighed. 'Allow me to spell it out for you, then. Both myself and Miss Spangles are busy people at the top of our respective professions. We simply will not tolerate people spying on our private business dealings.'

That's a laugh, thought Felix, who knew exactly the kind of 'private business' the two of them had been getting up to.

'There's a law against kidnapping in this country, Randy,' said Keira. 'Didn't they teach you that at clown school?'

The American lunged forward, but Wiseley stopped him with a wave of his hand.

'Oh, don't you worry,' said the mayor. 'I've briefed the police and they're pretty much up to speed on what's happened. I haven't quite given them the *full* story yet, but that's easily rectified. As their boss, they always seem rather keen to hear what I've got to say.'

Randy let out a high-pitched, snickering laugh.

Wiseley sat back, stroking his chin, thoughtfully. 'The real question is how much more you'd like me to share with them? I had hoped this little trip would give us the chance to clear things up, amicably, but if not? Well, it's back to the station to discuss the long list of charges you'll be facing – breaking and entering, criminal damage, underage drinking…'

'Rubbish! Where's your proof?' said Keira.

'Ah – the evidence… It turns out my friends in the constabulary had that, all along!' Chuckling, he reached into his jacket pocket and pulled out the two *Frecklesall Pen* press cards they'd handed to Sergeant Pluck when they'd blagged their way into the ball.

'Those cards were stolen from us last week, weren't they, Felix?' said Keira.

It was a pathetic line, but he did his best to back her up. 'Yeah, stolen – we were nowhere near the town hall last Saturday night.'

He saw Keira wince.

'Who said anything about the town hall… and last Saturday night?' said Wiseley, smirking. 'So, let's cut the stupid games, why don't we? Have either of you talked to anyone about what you *thought* you might have seen in my office last weekend?'

Seeing Randy shift menacingly in his seat, they both shook their heads.

'Progress at last!' exclaimed the mayor. 'Now, in reality, I could have you both sent down for a long, long time, after everything you've been up to. I'm particularly disappointed in *you*.' He waved a podgy finger in Felix's direction. 'I put my neck on the block to get you reinstated at school, and this is the thanks I get?' He reached across to ruffle Felix's hair. 'Hey, don't look so concerned, Haythornthwaite, I'll get over it – especially now I won't have to cough up for that one-thousand-pound reward.'

Felix's brow furrowed. 'What are you on about?'

'You know exactly what I'm "on about", ASBO Boy!'

It felt as if someone had punched him in the stomach. 'But… but I had to jump on top of that bus. I had no choice. You were trying to kill me!'

'Reasonable self-defence, that's what the lawyers call it – particularly given the serious sexual assault you'd perpetrated on my poor, elderly mother, just an hour earlier.'

'You what?'

'She's seventy-four, and she's still traumatised by what you did to her. Just be grateful it's me you're talking to. My brother, Roy, has always been much more *robust* in dealing with this kind of thing.'

A low growl came from the front of the limousine.

'But… I didn't do it…' pleaded Felix. 'I mean, she tried to snog me. It was dis—'

Wiseley grabbed him by the lapels. 'You filthy, lying pervert. If you know what's good for you, you'll shut up and listen to what I have to say.'

One glance at Randy was enough to persuade them both that it was time to shut up and listen to what the mayor had to say.

'My YobWatch! campaign is unequivocal on this point,' the mayor continued. 'Zero tolerance for scumbags like you – one strike and you're out! That's why people voted Troy Wiseley MBA at the last election. But if my audience with Nelson Mandela taught me one thing, it is simply this…' An insincere expression struggled onto his face. '… The essence of greatness is knowing when to exercise forgiveness.'

Keira laughed. 'That's a good one.'

'Show some respect, girl! What I'm saying is, there's a possibility I *might* be persuaded to turn a blind eye to your delinquent behaviour, and put it down to, say… adolescent tomfoolery.'

Felix saw a glimmer of light at the end of a very long tunnel, and for once it wasn't attached to the front of a train, speeding towards him.

'But only on two conditions,' Wiseley continued. 'Number one: you don't tell anyone what you *thought* you may have seen in my office last Saturday evening – perception and reality are two very different things. And number two: you provide me with *all* copies of the photographs you took that night, as well as the memory card they're stored on. Images like that could easily be misinterpreted, which would be in no one's interest.' He produced a couple of sheets of paper and a pen. 'Here –

my legal team have drafted a confidentiality agreement for you to sign.'

Felix had forgotten about the shots Keira had taken as she'd made her escape, but thank God she had. A simple trade – hand over the evidence of Troy and Marje's extra-curricular hanky-panky, and all the bad stuff disappears!

Wiseley leant forward, expectantly. 'So, what's it to be? Shall we resolve this here and now, like adults, or would you prefer to spend the night in a police cell?'

There was an agonising pause. Every sinew of Felix's body was screaming out to give the mayor the answer he was looking for, but Keira jumped in first.

'Dunno really,' she replied. 'I mean, we can sign your stupid papers if you want, but who's to say you won't grass us up anyway?'

Felix couldn't believe it – what was she playing at?

'Roy!' barked the mayor. 'Police station, at the double!'

The car screeched through a U-turn and accelerated back towards the town centre.

'OK, OK – we'll do it,' muttered Keira.

Randy watched on as they signed the documents, and a short while later the limousine drew up to the same spot they'd been picked up from, fifteen minutes earlier.

'Before the Grand Prix, next Sunday,' said the mayor. 'I want all the pictures and the memory card by then. And you'd better keep your mouths shut, or you won't know what's hit you.' He grabbed Felix by the arm as he was clambering past him towards the door. 'To be clear, Haythornthwaite – you so much as go near my mother again and Roy will kill you.'

The car pulled away and they found a bench to sit on while Felix tried to calm down. 'Bloody hell! I've never been so scared in my life. That Randy guy – have you ever seen anyone that size? I thought we were dead.'

'Wiseley may be an arse, but he's not completely stupid,' said Keira. 'He's got us over a barrel and he knows it.'

'But we've got something he wants, haven't we? The tabloids would pay a fortune for those pictures. We hand them over and it all goes away. Simple!'

'Not quite,' she mumbled.

'Don't worry – I'll buy you a new memory card, it's the least I can do.'

'You don't understand, Felix.' Her eyes were downcast now. 'I had my compact camera with me that night. The memory card was full. I just used the flash as a distraction, so I could get to the door.'

The pavement was rippling in front of his eyes – it couldn't be happening, he could clear this up. 'But I saw you,' he said. 'You took loads of shots. I remember thinking—'

'Read my lips,' she replied, glumly. 'There are no pictures. They don't exist.'

11

A crowd of girls had gathered in the school gym, giggling as they waited for the main event. 'Check out the competition,' Naz had suggested, and Felix had eventually agreed, hoping it might help take his mind off things. But being around bicycles – even Gazza's static exercise machine – was just making him feel worse.

Felix had to shout over the din of chattering voices to make himself heard. 'I don't think I'll hang around, Naz. There's no point, really.'

'Cheer up, mate,' pleaded his friend. 'You've had a right cob on you, these past few days. Maybe this'll perk you up a bit.' A sudden hush fell across the audience. 'Ay up – looks like the show's about to start.'

It was too late to leave now – he'd just have to get through it as best as he could.

The double doors banged open and in marched Ricky Sowerbutts, the bruising around his right eye now fading from livid purple to a sickly yellow tinge. He was struggling, with a huge ghetto-blaster wedged under one arm and Gazza's full-face cycling helmet under the other.

'What's that prat doing here?' asked Felix.

'His old man's chipped in on the sponsorship deal,' replied Naz. 'So he's been roped him in to help out with Gazza's training programme.'

142

Marching up to the exercise bike, Ricky switched on the sound system and the gym was filled with a brassy fanfare, which morphed swiftly into a pumping 1970s rock beat.

'Theme from *Rocky* – total classic,' Naz said in a low voice. 'Sylvester Stallone plays Rocky Balboa, no-hope boxer, drink problem, the works. He goes on to be the world heavyweight champion.'

Gazza's muscular figure was framed in the doorway. Wearing his tracksuit and an eye-dazzling pair of fluorescent trainers, the ever-present bandana wrapped around his head, he jogged into the gym, shadow boxing in time to the music. Arriving at the exercise bike, he unzipped his top to reveal a tight-fitting Frecklesall High T-shirt.

'He's always got that stupid tea towel on his head, these days,' remarked Felix. 'He looks a right knob.'

The girls clustered around, taking selfies on their phones as Gazza finished off his warm-up routine with some extravagant stretches.

'Nice to see so many of my fans here today,' he announced. 'Just four days to go and I'm bang on schedule – hitting all the numbers. There's nothing out there that comes close to my output. The Grand Prix is in the bag – bring on the Tour!'

There were giggles all round.

'*Big-headed plank*,' whispered Felix.

Gazza suddenly froze, and then he was pointing furiously at them. 'You boys! What the hell are you doing here?'

'We just thought we'd come along to watch your session, sir,' Naz replied, innocently.

'Sowerbutts, get here now!'

Ricky ran to the PE teacher's side and was promptly clipped around the ear.

'Oww!'

'I told you, didn't I? Security is key. If Haythornthwaite's brother gets his hands on my programme, the whole game plan will be compromised. Get them out of here, now!'

Ricky span around, his face red with fury, but he was too late – Felix and Naz had already made a sharp exit.

'Gazza chucked you out?' Freddie shook his head in disbelief. 'He always had it on for me. Can you believe it? I mean, what's not to like?'

Felix had been running through the lunchtime incident, back home with Flo and their big brother, who appeared to have changed colour.

'Looking a bit Tango there, Fred – what's gone on?' asked Felix.

'A lot of guys do this before the big races,' he replied. 'I swung by Tangenitalz in Slaidforth for a quick spray-job. I'll pick up the real deal when I'm away with the Chocolate Bananas.'

Felix shook his head in disbelief.

Flo got them back on track. 'So how good is this Gazza, Felix – would you say he's a threat?'

'He reckons it's in the bag,' he replied glumly. 'He's got all the gear and he's a PE teacher, so he's got to know what he's doing with the training and diet and stuff, hasn't he?'

Freddie, begged to differ. 'You guys need to check out the stats. Llewellyn-Evans is an old wheezer – he must be twenty-five, at least – whereas yours truly is a young gun, just hitting his groove. And hey, in the unlikely event of a tie-break scenario, that has-been ain't half as good looking as me!'

Felix groaned – when he thought about it, there probably wasn't that much to choose between his stupid big brother and his obnoxious PE teacher. He couldn't help thinking there must be some other rider out there who was worthy of his support – someone who wasn't such a monumental pain in the backside.

'It's not just about the two of you, though, is it?' said Flo. 'I've seen lots of riders out on the road these past few days. Some of them look pretty useful.'

Freddie laughed. 'As if. What you mean is – no shortage of out-of-shape dads playing Russian roulette with their arteries.'

'I'm just saying… Don't think you're going to have it all your own way. My friend Charlotte told me Pedalo Pete's gone into training.'

Felix was impressed. 'Wow - total legend! He's got calves like Popeye's forearms.'

Freddie stifled a yawn. 'Yeah, right. Pete may be the top guy when it comes to racing the jet skis off Slaidforth beach and so forth, but the Grand Prix is taking place on dry land. And that's where The Fred, will leave him for dead!'

'Then there's Reg Rowbottom,' his sister continued. 'He's my friend Paula's uncle. He may be getting on a bit but he's a proper club rider – out on his bike every weekend. And there'll be others as well.'

'Hey, for all I care, they can put up that Lance Armstrong dude, and pump him full of every drug they can lay their hands on. It don't make no difference. I'm on a mission to fruition, and that mission is a total fox going by the name of Herbina Smilerski! Now – I got hair to wash.' He turned and flounced away.

'Plonker,' muttered Flo as they watched their brother heading up the stairs.

'It must be getting to him,' said Felix. 'He knows he's got no chance, he's just too thick to admit it.'

Flo looked at him, questioningly. 'Are you OK, Felix? You've seemed a bit out of sorts these past few days.'

He sighed. 'I'm fine, really. It's just that… well, I've got loads on at school – end of term projects, that kind of thing. I was planning to catch up at the weekend but Sunday's a wipe-out, now, because of the Grand Prix.'

'So, it's not girlfriend trouble, then? Only Mum and Dad think you must have fallen out with Keira since your date on Saturday night, and that's what's been getting you down.'

'Nah – we're just friends. Anyway, it's Fred they should be worried about. He's the one lining up a Texan wedding!'

Flo laughed. 'Ooh, that reminds me. I've been doing a bit of digging on your Smiler Corporation project. I've sorted a few printouts for you.'

She disappeared off to her bedroom, returning a few minutes later with a sizeable bundle of papers.

Later that evening, Felix was lying on his bed, scanning the mass of paperwork his sister had given him. As he flicked through the corporate guff from the official Smiler Corporation website, the impossibility of trying to pin down how the multinational made their money was becoming ever more apparent. They seemed to be into everything, everywhere, with a myriad of offshoots, and offshoots to those offshoots, raking it in right across the globe. Felix had done some modules at school about globalisation and the power of the multinationals, but why the billionaire owner of one of the biggest in the world would take such a close personal interest in a dump like Frecklesall-on-Sea, was beyond him.

After scribbling a moustache on a photo of Herb T's grinning face, he dumped the official printouts onto the floor. Maybe he'd got it wrong – maybe Smiler Corp really were the kind of outfit that would want to do something nice and help a failing northern seaside town keep its head above water. The corporate blurb he'd seen was crammed with stuff about their charitable work – 'Corporate Social Responsibility' they called it. If the Tour really was as huge a deal as everyone said, bringing it to Frecklesall would be massive publicity for them.

Bored now, he turned his attention to a handful of sheets at the bottom of the pile. They looked different – a different style, a different typeface, and a radically different message from the sanitised gloss of the Smiler Corporation's meaningless 'Mission Statement'. He sat up, jolted from his torpor by the attention-grabbing headline:

Join the Fight Against Globalisation! Stop Smiler Corp Expansionism, Now!

He read on through a jaw-dropping catalogue of corporate greed and exploitation. There were reports of child labour and subsistence wages in the sweatshops of South East Asia, human rights abuses in Central America, record levels of fatalities in the South African mining townships – and that was just the start! Sitting on top of the whole stinking pile, squirreling his profits away in any number of offshore tax havens, was everybody's favourite cowboy – good ol' Herb T

Smilerski III. 'The Beast of Bug's Tussle', they called him.

SayNoToGlobal-Exploitation.com had done a comprehensive hatchet job on Herb and everything he stood for, but it was the feature on the Smiler Corp's rapidly expanding Garganto MonsterMart retail franchise, that particularly grabbed Felix's attention – particularly the aerial shot accompanying the article. The photograph of the sprawling store in Austin, Texas, revealed a sickeningly familiar image. The giant, single-storey H block with its massive car park and petrol station, was an exact replica of the CGI he and Keira had seen on the computer in the mayor's parlour.

So that was the end-game! Frecklesall was heading for 300,000 square feet of Garganto MonsterMart, which would wipe out the few shops and businesses left standing, while crushing the very soul of the place. And all to feed Herb T Smilerski's insatiable appetite for market share, turnover and global domination.

Lying back on his bed, Felix was incandescent with rage, so much so that he completely missed the ring of the landline and the sound of Flo trotting up to his bedroom door.

'Felix, Aunty Doreen's on the phone,' she announced. 'She wants a word with you. And... I think she might be a bit upset.'

After hammering on the Paddock's back door for what seemed like an age, Felix was beginning to wonder whether his great-aunt had had a heart attack. The bolts were eventually drawn back and he followed her through into the lounge.

He knew instantly that things had changed. There had always been something special about Doreen – a kind of energy that flickered away, just beneath the surface. But now, watching the vulnerable, almost frail, old lady hunched up in the corner of the settee, it seemed that spark had been snuffed out.

'What's going on?' he asked.

She reached across to hand him a letter. Felix took a moment to read it through:

Dear Miss Haythornthwaite,

I am writing to formally notify you of the Council's intention to terminate the lease, dated 1st July 1938 (copy attached), on the land you occupy, known as 'The Paddock' (shown edged in red on the attached plan). In accordance with the terms of the aforementioned lease, I hereby serve notice that you must vacate said land, providing clear vacant possession to the Council within six months of the date of this letter.

Yours sincerely

J. Arbuthnott

J. Arbuthnott (Borough Solicitor)

'I don't get it,' he said. 'What does it mean?'

Doreen's voice faltered slightly. 'It means I'm out on my ear round about Christmas time, courtesy of that crook Wiseley and his council cronies.'

'But you own this place. They can't just evict you.'

'Except they can. Your granddad always told me he had the freehold to this place, but it turns out he only ever rented it off the council on this stupid agricultural lease. And now they want it back.'

Felix shook his head in disbelief. 'Surely you must have *some* rights.'

Doreen sighed. 'I've been to the Citizens' Advice this afternoon and they reckon I'm stuffed. They say I should go down the housing department and tell them I'm about to be homeless. That's it – end of... There's nowt more can be done.'

She slumped back in the settee while Felix stood there, awkwardly. He'd always been hopeless at consoling people – useless at saying the right thing or putting a comforting arm around a shoulder. An endless ten seconds crawled by as he shifted from foot to foot, agonising over what to do next.

'Don't just stand there like cheese at fourpence!' snapped Doreen. 'Say something, will you?'

Felix shuffled over and sat down next to her. 'I'm so sorry – this is terrible news. But we've got to be able to work something out, surely?'

'I'm not as green as I'm cabbage looking, lad. This town's always needed me and the donkeys – we're the only attraction left standing these days, apart from the lido, although God alone knows what's going on there. But now that idiot Wiseley's got this stupid bike race coming to town, no one cares about us anymore.'

Felix's mind was in turmoil. All the bad stuff that had happened to him – even the bad stuff he was pretty sure was *about* to happen to him – paled into insignificance compared to this. He'd been sworn to secrecy, but with his great-aunt in the firing line, whatever he'd promised Wiseley or Keira, or anyone else for that matter, counted for nothing, now. He pictured, Troy and Herb T, carving up his home town on the porch at the Bug's Tussle mansion, and knew he could no longer look on in silence.

'The thing is, Doreen,' he began, 'this isn't just about the donkeys. It's something much, much bigger...'

The words began to spill from his lips and suddenly, it felt as if a massive weight had been lifted from his shoulders.

12

Felix stumbled into the kitchen that Sunday morning, having already tripped over the two bulging holdalls dumped in the hallway, in anticipation of Freddie's trip to the Pyrenees. He'd been up most of the night on his laptop, polishing his carefully prepared script, and he was exhausted.

His dad was out in the back garden making some last-minute adjustments to the Hill Special. Yawning, Felix wandered outside to join him.

'Awesome bike,' his dad enthused. 'Proper Lanky build, as well – all the way from Padiham! A bit of rust here and there but that's a great frame – light as a feather! You'd pay a fortune for something like this, these days. I've had to fork out for some new tyres and cables, and I've fettled a few of the spokes, but it should do the job for our Freddie. I'm a bit worried about these cotter pins, though. They lock the cranks onto the bottom bracket.' Wielding a huge hammer, he walloped a rust-encrusted, triple A-sized metal cylinder into the left-side pedal crank. 'It's all a bit old school, which means you just can't get hold of replacements. These ones are a bit worn.'

Felix shrugged. 'So what?'

His dad looked at him like he was stupid. 'So, everything can work loose, can't it? And if you're not careful, the cranks and the pedals fall off. When I was a lad, they sold cotter pins just about everywhere, but no one seems to need them these days. Change isn't always a good thing, y'know.'

Felix's mum came out to join them, leaving Freddie alone in the kitchen, shovelling a family-sized ready meal lasagne into his face. 'Just look at him, Brian.' She gestured back indoors. 'When I think how worried we were… This time tomorrow, he'll be setting off on the adventure of a lifetime!'

'I'm sure you're right, Mum,' Felix lied, 'but I wouldn't want you getting too disappointed if he doesn't make it.'

She put an arm around his shoulder and gave him a hug. 'I know what you're saying, love, but it's going to be fine. I've got this feeling.'

He nodded and smiled. He had a feeling too. A feeling that it was time to fight back.

And it started today.

The Haythornthwaites arrived at Grand Prix HQ, down on the Prom, forty-five minutes before kick-off. Doreen had already given her apologies – the prospect of coining it in with the donkeys being too good an opportunity to miss.

The race route was a twenty-four-mile circuit, starting out on the sea front, snaking through the centre of town, then picking up some of the borough's less decrepit highlights. Heading out east, the riders would tackle a couple of minor climbs in the Pennine foothills, before working their way back to the coast. The return into Frecklesall town centre was via Fishfoot Lane – the narrow cutting next to the council estate – dropping down onto the southern end of the Prom for what the organisers hoped would be a showcase sprint finish. It was the same route they'd be using on the tenth of July, but for *Le Tour* itself, the pros would be doing it four times! To Felix, cycling ninety-six miles was an impossibility, but doing that at an average race speed of close on thirty miles an hour, put those guys in the super-human category.

Felix wandered over to the giant outdoor stage set up for the event. A handful of pouting promo girls and a bunch of dancing chocolate bananas were shifting mountains of sweets in the direction of a crowd of clamouring kids.

'Why not try one?' Felix turned to see Bernie's grinning face, an armful of chocolate bananas clutched to his chest. 'Go on, you know you want to. I've been at 'em all morning.'

He grabbed one from his friend. Peeling back the yellow foil wrapper, he took a bite. Sweet and sickly, the cloying artificial flavouring made him want to heave. 'Yeeuughh!' he groaned, spitting globs of half-chewed chocolate onto the floor.

Bernie roared with laughter. 'Disgusting, aren't they? Nearly puked, myself!'

Naz arrived and after the three of them had caught up, Felix belatedly remembered they had a job to do.

'Hey, you two should be out on the course by now. I'll be needing your updates if I'm going to pull this piece together for Basil.'

'Change of plan,' said Bernie. 'We couldn't let you have all the fun back here on your own, so we've decided to stick around.'

'But you said you'd do it! You know I can't rely on Spugley for anything, other than a pasting.'

'Nah – Sean's a pussycat. If he'd wanted to sort you, he'd have done it by now.'

Felix shook his head, but he knew Bernie had a point. Spugley could have battered him on any number of occasions over the past few days, but for some reason he hadn't even tried. 'It's just a matter of time,' he said, sighing. 'Hey, come on, guys – stop your messing. Get out onto the route before they close the roads.'

Naz pointed up at the massive screen, set between the advertising banners that framed the stage. 'It's not a problem, Felix – we can follow it from here, see? This is like a dress-rehearsal for the race *and* the broadcast tech. They beam the live-feed up from the motorbike cameras to the helicopter, then back down to race HQ. We'll get a much better view if we stay here, watching the action on the big screen.'

'Oh, right…' Felix was momentarily distracted by the sight of someone he recognised, standing to the side of the stage. 'Sorry, lads – I've gotta go. Catch up with you in a bit, OK?'

Dave Heptonstall, editor and chief news reporter for the *Frecklesall Journal*, was lounging against a lamppost, drawing on the soggy stub-end of a roll-up. For a man in his early fifties, he was not wearing particularly well. Years of boozing had left him with an oily, pock-marked complexion, a bulbous nose and small piggy eyes. He looked up, uncertainly, as Felix approached.

'Mr Heptonstall!' Felix greeted him, grabbing his hand and shaking it vigorously.

'Err… Do I know you?'

'Felix Haythornthwaite, Frecklesall High. I'm with the *Pen* – the school newspaper.'

A hint of a smile crept onto the journalist's face. 'Are you the lad who ran that Blue Pennant piece?'

'Oh… yes, that was me.'

Heptonstall laughed. 'Nice one. Look, I'm a bit pushed at the moment. What you after?'

Felix had rehearsed his lines well. 'I'll get straight to the point, Mr Heptonstall, sir,' he began. 'With everyone so excited about the Tour coming to town, I think we've forgotten to ask the question, "Why?". Let's face it, there's no such thing as a free lunch, is there?'

The journalist looked bemused. 'What're you saying?'

'What I'm saying is – who are the Smiler Corporation? What do they do? And why would they want to spend so much of their money in a place like Frecklesall?'

'Aah! Conspiracy theory, is it? Is that what they're teaching you in GCSE Media Studies, these days?' Heptonstall produced another roll-up from the tin in his pocket and lit it up. 'Look lad, you're wasting your time – nowt like that's ever going to happen around here.'

Felix held his nerve. 'D'you see the lido over there? It's closed, isn't it? Wiseley won't say when it's going to re-open, because it's not. And you can wave goodbye to the donkeys after this summer, because they're going as well.'

The journalist snapped to attention. 'Flippin' 'Erry! Doreen's throwing in the towel? I didn't see that one coming.'

Felix moved in for the kill. 'It's not her – she doesn't want to stop – it's the council. They want the land back. The lido, the Paddock, the town moor – put those plots together and you've got a prime site. Something a big outfit like the Smiler Corporation would be very interested in developing. And if they were to build one of their Garganto MonsterMarts around here, you know what that would mean for Frecklesall, don't you?'

'Err… Not really.'

'Look, I'm going to make this easy for you.' Glancing over his shoulder to make sure no one was watching, Felix pulled out a large envelope from inside his jacket and handed it over. 'Check this lot out. My number's in there as well. Call me when you've looked through it, but I need you to promise you'll keep this quiet, for now. There are a lot of powerful people around these parts who'd like to see this story disappear.'

As he walked away, Dave Heptonstall dropped his cigarette to the floor and ripped open the envelope.

The thirty riders, milling around behind the start line, were a motley selection of Frecklesall's finest – some geared up and raring to go, others looking like they were heading out on a leisurely Sunday morning spin. A variety of low-tech bicycles were on display, including the unlikely steed of fifty-five-year-old Bob Bulgy, the 'Fat Fryer' from the burger van on Frecklesall Prom. Wearing a faded orange football shirt, Bob stood out from the crowd on his purple, 1970s-vintage, three-speed Raleigh Chopper – complete with ape-hanger handlebars, gear stick shifter, and classic 'easy rider' saddle.

Beyond the ranks of the also-rans, there were a handful of competitors who looked like they were taking things that bit more seriously, all Lycra shorts and brightly coloured cycling tops – the really keen ones sporting proper cycling shoes. There was Pedalo Pete, his massive calves looking like they'd been stolen from a body builder overdosed on steroids; Reg Rowbottom, defiantly in the over-forty age bracket but standing solidly on gnarled old cyclists' legs; Kevin Fettler, an Accrington Stanley trialist, who'd left Frecklesall High a few years before Freddie, with an awesome reputation for all-round sporting brilliance.

And there were others as well – lean and mean and confident, with wraparound sunglasses and useful-looking bikes.

Freddie was freewheeling the Hill Special over to some of his friends when a ripple of excitement ran through the crowd. Gareth Llewellyn-Evans had arrived and was posing for selfies with some giggling Frecklesall High School girls, the bulges in his electric-blue skin-suit leaving nothing to the imagination.

A whistle sounded and four high-powered police motorbikes roared off to clear the route. Another couple of machines, complete with cameramen riding pillion, purred into position a little further up the road. A helicopter clacked noisily overhead as the competitors began inching their way towards the start line.

Wiseley marched onto the stage. 'Ladies and gentlemen, boys and girls, welcome to *Le Grand Prix de Frecklesall*!' he announced. 'But first, a quick word from our sponsor.'

A man in a chocolate banana outfit bounded up next to him, waving his arms around and shouting at the top of his voice, '*Allez le Tour de France*! *Allez le* ChocolatBanane! *Allez le* Frurck-lay-all!'

Suddenly, the sky was filled with chocolate bananas, drifting down on mini-parachutes into the crowd below.

'It's snowing bananas!' a pensioner next to Felix exclaimed, only to be bowled over by the surge of marauding children, desperate to get their hands on the dodgy French treats.

Banana man waved his arms again, and following a further shout of, '*Allez*! *Allez*! *Encore*!', more boxes of confectionary were emptied from the helicopter, high above. All eyes turned expectantly towards the fluttering shower but moments later, the squeals of delight had turned to screams of horror as waves of killer chocolate bananas, their parachutes detached and useless, rained down onto the crowd. Everyone dived for cover, screaming mothers scooping up their children, fearing for their lives, while others dropped, face-down, onto the muddy grass, shielding their heads as best they could. Meanwhile the chief executive of the ChocolatBanane Corporation was wrestled to the ground before further deadly salvos could be unleashed. His protests were drowned out by the sharp clatter of French sweets hammering onto the stage's wooden boarding.

It was all over in a matter of seconds. Some people in the VIP area had been hit, but the impact on the riders, tightly packed behind the start line, looked much more serious. Any number of them were lying flat-out or sitting up groggily on the tarmac, the worst of the damage sustained by the favourites on the first few rows.

Felix looked out over the chaotic scenes, searching for his brother. Freddie was an idiot, but he didn't want his dreams to end this way, especially if there was a chance he'd make a complete arse of himself in front of a global TV audience in just a few weeks' time.

The paramedics did their best, but it wasn't enough for many of the competitors. The much-fancied Kevin Fettler had paid the price for not wearing his helmet and was now on his way to hospital, while an inconsolable Reg Rowbottom was hunched up on the kerb, clutching a bruised collarbone. Other useful-looking riders began shuffling home, their hopes and dreams shattered by the confectionary cluster-bomb from hell.

The good news was that Freddie had escaped, unscathed. The not-so-good-news was that, so too had Frecklesall High's head of PE, and the teacher smirked as the odds on his victory shortened still further.

A good half an hour later, the mayor waved the red starter's flag and the race got underway, the much-depleted field tootling sedately up the Prom while children clutching armfuls of chocolate bananas ran alongside, yelling abuse at them. Things settled down over the next few minutes, until a flurry of action brought gasps of amazement from the crowd. The larger-than-life figure of Bob Bulgy had sprinted away on his 'easy rider' Chopper, putting a good fifty metres between himself and the rest of the field. This sudden burst of activity seemed to take race commentator, Radio Lancashire's, 'Nifty Nev' Blackrod, by surprise.

'Now then!' His voice crackled from the PA system. 'I wouldn't normally expect a breakaway this early on in proceedings but it looks like we have our first attack of the day. Bob Bulgy, sponsored by the Bulgy Burger Corporation, has laid down the gauntlet and so far, no one seems that interested in picking it up!'

Naz and Bernie had joined Felix, the three of them watching, open-mouthed, as the purple-faced Fat Fryer strained every sinew in a frantic effort to maintain his lead.

'What's he doing? He'll never keep that going!' Felix shouted above the noise of the crowd, who were roaring Bob on to victory, or more likely, an early grave.

Suddenly the cheers gave way to shrieks as the burger man lifted both hands from his ape-hanger handlebars and started trying to pull his shirt up over his head.

'Total madness!' screamed the commentator. 'Bulgy's stripping off. Maybe he's overcooked it and he's too hot? But he can't see where he's going... Can someone tell me what the heck's going on out there?'

Bob slewed blindly across the road, his shirt now pulled taut over his face. Narrowly missing a lamppost, he somehow managed to wobble back into the middle of the highway, giving the cameraman just enough time to focus on the white vest he had on, underneath, which was plastered with the slogan:

Bob's Bulgy Burgers
South Prom Now!

Seconds later, the early pace-setter hit a kerb. Somersaulting over his handlebars, he ended up face-down in a drainage ditch at the side of the road.

Following Bob's dramatic exit, the race began to settle into something loosely resembling a rhythm. The pace looked painfully slow, but despite this, many of the riders seemed to be struggling.

'Something tells me they're not taking it that seriously,' Felix remarked as the pack rolled through the village of Grotley, where a group of tail-enders dumped their bikes on the grass verge before disappearing into the public bar of the Clog and Billycock.

'A few guys stopping for a rehydration break, there. Smart move!' announced Nifty Nev. 'It's vital these lads take on fluid at every opportunity on a warm day like this.'

Every now and again Felix caught a glimpse of Freddie, just off the front and clinging onto Gazza's back wheel. Head down, his face was a picture of concentration.

'The pacemakers are beginning to crank it up now, and it's proving too much for some of the old-timers,' Nifty Nev continued. 'Look – those guys have cracked! This really is turning into a test of endurance.'

It didn't seem that way, as two of the riders waved cheerily at the camera before leaning their bikes against a tree to join a roadside picnic.

Felix turned to Naz, who was engrossed in the action. 'Have you seen Keira? I said I'd meet her here.'

'Maybe she's out on the route, taking pictures,' his friend replied, without shifting his gaze from the giant screen.

Bernie laughed. 'Or maybe she got clouted on the head by a chocolate banana and she's in a coma, waiting for Prince Charming to come to her rescue!'

Felix wasn't listening. He'd spotted the lone figure loping along the footpath towards them, shoulders rolling, the sun glinting from his single diamond earring. Sean Spugley was on the prowl and he needed to make himself scarce. 'Gotta go, lads,' he said, urgently. 'Keep an eye out for Keira, will you? There's something I need to tell her.'

He darted away, weaving through the crowd before slipping behind the ugly, race HQ portacabins…Straight into the waiting, tree-trunk arms of Smiler Corporation henchman, Randy Pike.

13

All it took was a single swipe from a giant, shovel-like paw, the violence of the assault made all the more chilling by the effortlessness of its execution.

'Oww! Come on – no need for that!' squealed Felix. Pinned against the rough grey wall of the cabin, he tried to wriggle free, but it was no use.

The American lifted a clenched fist, ready to strike. 'This is Randy… Affirmative. I have hands on Romeo. *Repeat.* Hands on Romeo. I guess it's payback time, huh?'

It didn't make sense – the giant was speaking in a bizarre, high-pitched voice, into the sleeve of his tight-fitting suit jacket… And then Felix worked it out – he was wearing one of those secret service radio transmitters, the microphone tucked away in the cuff of his sleeve, a near-invisible receiver unit stuffed into his ear.

'And the girl…?' the American continued. 'You have Juliet...? OK, so that's an affirmative.'

'I think there's been a bit of a mix-up, Randy,' Felix ventured, nervously. 'I… I don't know anyone called Romeo, or Juliet, for that matter. Maybe if you put me down, I could help you find who you're looking for?' He scanned the horizon, searching for someone who might come to his aid, but the crowd gathered on the other side of the portacabin, were totally engrossed in the race action.

Randy smiled, a terrifying, bowel-loosening grimace, his brilliant-white veneers glinting in the sunshine. 'A pleasure to hook up with you, Romeo. I've been lookin' forward to seein' you again.'

Wafted with his pepperminty breath, Felix could do little more than squeak. Up close he could see the American's eyes – cold, ice-blue, and without a hint of emotion.

'I'm guessing you have some familiarity with the many fine plays and sonnets penned by that guy, Will I Am Shake-Speare?' asked Randy.

Felix looked puzzled – it wasn't just the oddness of the question, it was the way he said it. Randy's accent was straight out of a gangster movie, but his soprano pitch rendered him less Al Capone, more Bugsy Malone.

'The Bard, man,' the exasperated heavy continued. 'Jeez – you kids have no respect for your culture! Romeo and Juliet – you read that in class?'

Felix nodded - he'd struggled through it in English, the year before.

'So, you know how it turns out, huh? A total crock, whatever which way you shake it down. Kinda sad, them croaking so young. Just kids really – about your age, too. You understand what I'm sayin'?'

'W…what do you w… want?' stuttered Felix.

'Let's cut the crapola, why don't we? You signed the papers, Romeo – you and the lovely Miss Juliet. I was there, so don't even think of bullshittin' me! Today is collection day. Give me the shots and the memory card and you might just walk away from this meeting with your faculties intact. Hold out on me and… well, believe me, that's not a scenario you wanna even contemplate.'

Felix's mind was racing. 'The thing is, they don't actually exist, Randy… I mean, I haven't—'

The American tightened his grip on his throat, lifting him clean off the floor. Felix could hear the rasping sounds as each breath became a super-human effort, the brightness of the day rapidly fading to a gloomy monochrome.

And then, from out of nowhere, he heard a shout.

'Let 'im go, knuckle-'ead! LET 'IM GO!'

In the next instant the *Pen* reporter had been dumped to the ground. Hands reaching up to massage his throat, he was sucking in great lungfuls of air, while Randy careered around, his giant frame dwarfing the smaller figure that had attached itself, limpet-like, to his back. Felix had to scramble aside to avoid a trampling as fists and boots flailed in a whirl of grunting, foul-mouthed combat.

In the end, it was no contest.

Regaining his footing, Randy hurled his adversary over a shoulder and in a flash, was on top, pinning him to the ground.

Propped up against the portacabin and still wheezing noisily, Felix was powerless to help.

'Jeez! You guys need to show due respect.' Randy smiled that awful smile once more as he drew back his fist. But the blow never came. Hand cupped to an ear, he was talking into his sleeve again. 'Juliet, uhh… yeah…? You have what you need? For sure? Cos I'm in the middle of a somewhat productive discussion with the Romeo, here and… OK, that's a wrap!' Jumping to his feet, he brushed down his suit and strolled away, like nothing had happened.

Felix heard the crowd roar, just as Naz, Bernie and Keira came skidding around the corner.

'Bloody hell, Felix!' exclaimed Naz. 'What's gone on, here?'

Keira knelt down and put an arm around his shoulder, while Bernie made a bee-line for the other casualty.

'You OK, mate?' Bernie asked. 'Looking a bit the worse for wear, if you don't mind me saying!'

The dusty figure of Sean Spugley sat up, grinning. 'Nowt I can't handle, Bernie, lad. Hey, did you see the big guy doing a runner, there?'

Felix's heart sank. It was worse than he'd feared. Randy must have killed him, after all, and this was some cruel twist being played out in the afterlife.

A slap across the chops from Keira was enough to bring him to his senses. He really was still alive. He really had been rescued by Sean Spugley.

What was going on?

'Hey, look!' exclaimed Spugley. 'He dropped his ciggies – American ones 'n all. I always fancied giving them Lucky Gaspers a go.' He picked up the unopened packet and slipped it into his pocket.

Naz turned to Felix, his voice full of concern. 'Come on mate, let's get us a brew. You've got some explaining to do.'

They huddled together in the corner of the Full Monty, struggling to comprehend what Felix had just told them.

'That Roy's an animal,' said Keira. 'He wasn't for letting me go. Then when I heard him talking on the radio, it all sounded a bit heavy, so I gave him the memory card. I'm guessing that's when he told Randy to lay off.'

A faint glimmer of hope sparked in Felix's mind. 'Memory card? But you said—'

'How many times, Felix… There *are* no pictures. I just fished out the one I had in my SLR. I told him we hadn't printed anything off it, and the stupid lummox walked away, happy as Larry.'

'So, what *was* on it, then?' Felix asked.

'Oh, all sorts – this stuff I was doing for school, and that rugby thing, with him in his trollies.' She pointed dismissively at Spugley, who let out a low growl. 'A few shots from today, as well.'

'Hey, Thwaitey!' Spuggie exclaimed. 'A minute longer and I'd have pasted 'im. Whaddya say, mate?'

'Spot on there, Sean… err, *mate*,' replied Felix, who was still struggling to get his head around what was happening. 'So, Keira, err… how long before they work out that all they've got is some shots of Sean in his Calvin Klein's, rather than Wiseley and Marje getting it on in the mayor's office?'

She shrugged.

'I can't believe you didn't tell us about this, Felix,' snapped Bernie. 'Unbelievable!'

Felix gave his friend a rueful smile. 'Well, you never took anything I said seriously. And then when things turned heavy, we decided we needed to keep it tight.'

Keira rolled her eyes. 'Yeah, so tight that you end up handing everything we've got to that numpty, Heptonstall. It'll be all over the *Journal* on Tuesday.'

'The more people who know what's going on, the better,' Felix said, defensively. 'They can't do this to Doreen – they can kick me out of school for all I care.'

'Thanks, mate,' said Keira, glumly. 'Nice to know my education and future life chances are being sacrificed for such a worthy cause.'

As the noise of the crowd reached a crescendo, Felix's mood began to turn to gloom. He'd missed the race action and hadn't got a clue how he was going to write his piece for the *Pen* – no pictures, no story, and no chance of getting one now. And to cap it all, he found himself walking alongside Sean Spugley, on the way back to the finish line.

Felix broke the silence. 'Sean, I, err… I just wanted to say thanks for getting stuck in back there. If you hadn't jumped in when you did…'

'No problem, Thwaitey, lad!' said Spuggie. 'I like a bit of a ruck now and then.' He broke off into a bout of shadow boxing.

'Yeah, I kind of noticed that. But I didn't think you'd want to help someone like me. Not after everything that's gone on.'

Spuggie grabbed hold of him, spinning him around so they were facing each other. 'The thing is *Thwaitey*, you were never on my radar, but then you had to go and wind me up, didn't you?'

'It wasn't on purpose,' replied Felix, wishing he hadn't raised the subject. 'It… it just kind of happened.'

'Yeah, right.' Spuggie tore into the cellophane wrapper of Randy's cigarette pack and lit up a Lucky Gasper. 'I've got a reputation to maintain, haven't I? So, obviously, I needed to sort you out. But then I heard you and Keira were an item.'

'Well, actually—'

'And then I'm thinkin', ay up, he can't be all that bad, can he? I mean, respect to Keira – she don't take it off no one. Next thing, I was out with some mates, a few nights back, and I saw you on that bus-surf gig. Totally *awesome*, man!'

'That was you?' Felix asked, incredulously, before remembering who he was talking to. 'Yeah… err, it was kinda crazy, but that's just the way I roll.'

'Well-good!' enthused Spugley. 'How 'bout a bus-surfari sometime? See how far we can get without falling off!'

'Oh, err… Why not? Let's do it!'

'Anyways, when I saw your mate, Randy, having a pop back there, I thought I'd better get stuck in. He won't be messin' with the Spug again, will he?'

'Appreciate it, Sean!' Felix replied, barely able to believe what was happening.

'So, we're cool, Thwaitey lad. Can't say the same for Butty, though. He's got a right downer on you after I lamped 'im that time.' He chuckled at the memory.

'Oh… That could be a bit awkward, actually. Our dads work together. Maybe I should talk to him?'

Spuggy snorted. 'Nah - leave it be. Ricky's all talk an' no trousers. He'd have forgotten about it already if he wasn't lookin' at that shiner, every time he sees his ugly mug in the mirror.'

They heard another roar from the crowd and had to sprint flat-out to catch up with the others.

Nifty Nev's commentary was heading into overdrive. 'Total commitment - these guys are riding on the rivet! Well clear of the field and under the one-kilometre marker, and the man in the box-seat is Pete Pedalo, sponsored by Pete's Water Sports and Aquatics Centre, down there on Slaidforth Beach. Look at the legs on that lad! And tucking in behind, just like a pro, is the home-grown talent – lido lifeguard, Freddie Haythornthwaite.'

The crowd's loyalties were split fairly evenly as the two riders flew down the Fishfoot Lane cutting, and onto the southern end of the Prom. They were really shifting now, Freddie crouching forward onto the low section of his handlebars, all his energy focussed on leg speed; Pedalo Pete, a whirlwind of flapping knees and elbows, driven forward by the brute force of his mighty calves.

'What a race, ladies and gentlemen!' shrieked Nifty Nev. 'These boys are going head-to-head, wheel-to-wheel! At this stage, it's about who wants it more! They're onto the Promenade now… We should be able to see them soon… Five hundred metres left and Pedalo Pete is on the attack! Look at that lad go!'

As Felix turned, trying to get a clearer view of the action on the big screen, he caught a glimpse of Doreen, yelling encouragement from the midst of the crowd on the opposite side of the road.

'Now then - look at this!' Nev was almost apoplectic with the excitement of it all. 'Pete's gone early but the youngster's coming back at him! I can't believe it! He's moving up the gears and he's dropping the hammer!'

'Go on, Freddie! GO ON, SON!'

Felix could hear his dad yelling, and before he knew it, he too was caught up in the excitement of it all, pogoing up and down and shouting for all he was worth. His brother had been caught out by the early attack, but was now clawing his way back onto Pete's wheel. With less than a hundred metres to go, Freddie pulled out wide, and it was as if someone had attached a motor to his back wheel.

'Classic counter-attack by the youngster!' screamed the Radio Lancashire man. 'His pedals are moving as fast as bees' wings! He's trying to nick it on the line...!

Is he going to do it...? He's... he's...My word! What happened there! I can't call it... Photo finish!'

The two riders scorched over the line in an inseparable blur, slumping forward across their handlebars before touching wheels and clattering to the ground. Felix's mum suddenly burst into life, leaping over the safety barrier like an Olympic hurdler, her cries of, 'My baby! My baby!', adding to the deafening roar of the crowd.

Nifty Nev's breathless announcement arrived little more than a minute later. 'What a sprint, ladies and gentlemen, and what a finish! The result is now in! With a lead of only *three centimetres*, the decision goes to... the youngster, that's Frecklesall-on-Sea's Freddie Haythornthwaite! So, well done to him but *chapeau,* as they say in France, to both lads for a fantastic contest!'

It took a while for Felix to push through the throng to join his brother and the rest of the family. His mum was sitting on the pavement, arms around the crumpled figure of her eldest son, whose face was buried in his hands.

'Totally amazing!' Felix shouted over the din. Where did that come from?'

His brother didn't look up. 'Dunno,' he mumbled.

Felix had never heard him sounding so low. 'Cheer up, Fred – you're a winner! You've made it onto the Tour, so you've still got a chance with Herbina!'

The other family members turned as one, looking at him in disbelief.

Nifty Nev interrupted the awkward silence. 'Ladies and gentlemen, we've got a few minutes before the main bunch rolls in, so I've just enough time to confirm the official podium spots. Today's winner – the guy who's booked his seat on the next flight to the Pyrenees, before returning to this very spot in only ten days to compete in the actual Tour de France…' A loud cheer went up. 'In a time of one hour, thirteen minutes and thirty-two seconds… It's the man of the moment, our very own *Domestique du Jour* – sponsored by Frecklesall High School, a Domestic Science Beacon of Excellence College – I give you, Gareth Llewellyn-Evans!'

Felix was gobsmacked. 'But… but I thought…'

Flo turned on him. 'What planet are you on, Felix? Llewellyn-Evans finished five minutes ago. Freddie and Pete were racing for second place.'

He looked across to the cabins by the start line, where the bandana-clad PE teacher was punching the air and hurling sweaty items of cycling kit into the crowd.

Felix slumped down onto the pavement next to his brother, the two of them sitting together in silence until one of the race officials came up to ask Freddie to report to race HQ for compulsory drugs testing. He trudged away, head down, his hopes and dreams in pieces – cold comfort from his mum's words:

'Don't worry, Freddie – there's always next year.'

But there wouldn't be a next year – there couldn't be. The Tour de France wouldn't be visiting Frecklesall-on-Sea again – ever. And as for Freddie's dreams of romance – short of blagging a wildcard entry onto *Celebrity Love Lagoon*, the chances of him getting to meet foxy billionaire heiress, Herbina Smilerski, were now less than zero.

14

'Anyone else I could have coped with – anyone! And they all had money on him, didn't they? They're going to make a fortune out of this.' Felix was in full rant as he and Keira walked in through the school gates the following morning.

'How's Freddie taken it?' she asked.

Felix winced. 'He hardly said a word last night – moped around for a bit, then sloped off to the Pig to drown his sorrows. He staggered in around three this morning – woke me up, of course. I left him stinking in bed, still wearing all his clothes from the night before.'

Monday mornings were usually years seven and eight assembly, but when they saw the masses being cattle-prodded into the hall, it became clear that something odd was going on. They met up with Bernie and Naz as they funnelled in.

'What's this about?' asked Keira.

'Special school assembly,' replied Bernie. 'Gazza's Victory Parade.'

It was most definitely not a good start to the week, thought Felix, as the four of them split up to search for spare seats.

Arsey sprang onto the stage, an uncharacteristic smile cracking his face. 'An historic day for our school, I think you'll agree, boys and girls! But before we wish our head of PE *bonne chance* in his exciting new collaboration with Team ChocolatBanane, I have an important announcement to make. As we all know, the Tour de France will be visiting our home town on July the tenth, which is, of course, the penultimate day of term. Now, I'm sure you'll have been wondering how you can get to see our new sporting superstar riding in the big race. Well, wonder no more! The governors have decided that, given his heroic victory, yesterday, school will close for the summer break, two days early – that is on Wednesday, July the ninth.'

A massive roar went up, some of the teachers joining in from the sidelines with a celebratory jig.

'Boys and girls, please welcome the newest member of Team ChocolatBanane – our very own, Mr Gareth Llewellyn-Evans!'

The school's PA system crackled into life, playing a wonky version of the *Rocky* theme. The hall doors were swung open by the Misses Pomfrett and Catlow, and in came the PE teacher, in full racing regalia – on his bike. Acknowledging the cheers, he wobbled slowly up the aisle, blissfully unaware that the scenes of unbridled joy were the result of an extra couple of days' holiday, rather than his own underwhelming sporting achievement.

Ricky Sowerbutts fielded the bike and helmet as Gazza clambered onto the stage in his racing skinsuit, the multi-coloured bandana tied firmly in place.

'Boys and girls!' he began, 'I haven't got long before my plane leaves, obviously, but I'll be hanging around a bit after assembly for photos, autographs and so forth.'

Murmurs of discontent rumbled around the hall.

'As the great Julius Caesar once said to me, "I came there, I saw 'em, and I kicked all of their sorry arses"!' Eyes bulging, he fist-pumped the air in triumph. Arsey looked mortified but sitting beside him, head boy Bradley Halfbarrel was sniggering so much that a snot-rocket shot from his nose and smeared down the sleeve of his blazer.

'Some of you lot may be wondering how I managed to pull off such a stunning victory,' Gazza continued. 'Being in peak physical condition, like I am, is vital, obviously.' He puffed out his chest. 'But all the top athletes have something else, as well – see?' He paused, tapping the side of his forehead. 'It's something the boffins call PMA – that's Positive Mental Attitude, innit? Those of you what know me, will know this: I'm always positive, I'm always mental, and I've always got an attitude – which is why I'm always a winner!'

Sitting there, amidst the groaning audience, Felix was seething. Who did Gazza think he was kidding?

No one, as it turned out.

Something was going on in the yard outside and within seconds, everyone was gawping through the windows, scrambling for the best view as a patrol car skidded to a halt and three police officers jumped out.

Felix nearly sank to his knees in despair. Wiseley must have gone straight to the police as soon as he'd discovered the memory card was a dud. He looked around for Keira but by the time he'd spotted her, the hall doors had burst open, revealing the familiar figure of Sergeant Pluck, flanked by the constables Steve MacCruiskeen and Vinnie Fox.

Gazza was so full of himself, he hadn't noticed the arrival of the boys in blue, only pausing his moronic monologue when Arsey pointed out the sergeant, who was now up on the stage, standing immediately behind him. With attention focussed on the row that followed, few noticed the two constables as they worked their way along the aisle, checking the ranks of increasingly raucous students, for something… or someone.

Hardly daring to look through the gaps between his fingers, Felix caught a fleeting glimpse of PC MacCruiskeen, who was now just a few metres away. The policeman hesitated, close to where Keira was sitting. He looked along the row, studying the faces… before moving on. Somehow, she'd got away with it! Felix ducked down, frizzing his hair forward in a desperate bid for anonymity. Seconds crawled by like hours, but eventually MacCruiskeen stepped past him to check out the next row.

Phew!

A commotion broke out a little way back – chairs scraping, muttered grumblings. Felix ignored the tap on his shoulder, ducking down to pick up the pen he'd 'accidentally' dropped to the floor. It came again, this time as a hefty thump between his shoulder blades.

'Thwaitey! Wake up, you numpty!'

He twisted around to confront year eleven's Russell Belcher, who simply smiled at him and pointed towards the aisle, where a stony-faced PC MacCruiskeen was beckoning him out of his seat. He did his best to look surprised, shrugging his shoulders as if to say, 'Who? Me?'.

Everyone watched on as Felix made his miserable exit into police custody.

This was getting to be a habit – two rides in a squad car in the space of a few days, blue lights flashing, siren wailing and roads clearing magically as motorists pulled aside to let them zip by. Easing back into his seat, Felix eavesdropped on the exchange with the police control centre, which crackled through on the car's radio.

'This is Frecklesall control. Come in, foxtrot-tango-delta-one-niner. Do you have target? Repeat – do you have target? Over.'

PC MacCruiskeen reached across to pick up the dashboard hand-set. 'This is foxtrot-tango-delta-one-niner. All good here, inspector! The lad's got his keys on him and reckons the target is still in the house. Out on the razz last night, apparently. We've got Ms Lacroix in the car as well. She's coming down to the airport with us to make sure he catches the right flight. Over.'

'Ms Lacroix? Jammy buggers! Right lads, do *not* mess this up. That plane leaves Manchester in two hours, so put your foot down! Over.'

'What about the PE teacher?' asked the constable. 'Has he been booked in yet? Over.'

They all heard the groan. 'Don't talk to me about *him*! It's a riot down here – press all over us like a rash, that bloody school vicar, banging on about "forgiveness". Listen – just do your job, lads, that's all I ask. Over and out.'

The two police officers grinned at each other, while behind them on the back seats, Felix edged his way just that little bit closer to the lovely, Giselle Lacroix, who was nervously checking her watch.

'Don't worry Giselle,' he said, brightly, 'he'll be right where I left him this morning. He's still in his clothes from last night and his bags are already packed. All we need to do is wake him up and get him in the car.'

'Ahh, Felice! It is my career on the line, *oui*?' she replied, her brow furrowing with concern. 'I 'ave 'ad nothing but problems since I arrive 'ere, and now this. *C'est un desastre*! Unless I can find 'im, *vite*, Monsieur

Perpignan will, as you say 'ere in *Angleterre*, 'ave my guts for garters.'

Felix smiled reassuringly and as the police car screeched around the corner into Scundale Chase, she leant across to give him the briefest of kisses on the cheek.

He had to pinch himself to check he wasn't dreaming.

Unceremoniously hoicked out of assembly and frog-marched to the back of the hall, Felix knew the game was up. After all, it was his word against Wiseley's, and who was going to believe a spotty, bus-surfing ASBO Boy, over Frecklesall-on-Sea's democratically elected first citizen? But before he and PC MacCruiskeen had even made it to the main doors, things had kicked off, up on the stage. A few choice words turned into some old-fashioned argy-bargy and moments later, Sergeant Pluck had been dumped onto his backside. In the next instant, Gazza was charging down the aisle with the gusto of a Sumo wrestler hearing the 'last orders' bell at an all-you-can-eat buffet.

If Felix had learnt one thing from his calamitous foray into the world of rugby, it was that when confronted with thirteen stone of marauding wingback, the only sensible course of action is to get out of the way – fast! So, as the constable readied himself for a heroic interception, Felix stepped smartly to one side.

But the PE teacher knew his trade. In spite of the narrowness of the aisle, he executed a near-perfect side-step, sending the police officer diving the wrong way.

There was no time to think – some base instinct clicked on in Felix's brain and as Gazza hurtled past, he stuck out a foot. Caught in mid-stride, the Welshman flew into the air like an electric-blue dolphin at an oceanarium. But instead of catching a fish in his mouth and arcing elegantly back into the water, the PE teacher smacked face-first onto the grubby wooden flooring, to the accompaniment of clattering chairs, tearing Lycra and cheering students. Moments later, two burly PCs were kneeling on his back.

PC MacCruiskeen recited the arresting officer's mantra with more than a hint of satisfaction: 'Gareth Llewellyn-Evans, I am arresting you on suspicion of assaulting a police officer. I'm also detaining you for additional drugs testing, in connection with suspected breaches of the French Sports Code. You do not have to say anything, but it may harm your defence…'

Arsey tried to intervene. 'There's been a terrible mistake, constable! I beg you—'

'Back off, the lot of you, or so help me there'll be more arrests!' yelled Pluck as he stomped down the aisle towards them.

'Look, if you have to nick him, can't you at least wait until we've been down the bookies to collect our winnings?' pleaded 'Rambo' Ramsdale, the school's rather portly head of RE.

'I'll pretend I didn't hear that, reverend!' snapped the sergeant. 'Now, like it or not, we are taking the suspect into custody. Unless any of you fancy sharing a cell with him tonight, you'd be well advised to get out of the way… Oh, and this one here.' He reached across to ruffle Felix's hair. 'Haythornthwaite, isn't it?'

'Err, yes sir – that's me,' replied Felix, nervously.

Pluck turned to the head teacher. 'I'm after borrowing the lad, here, for an hour or two, if that's alright with you, Dr Brown?'

Gazza was handcuffed and led, snivelling, from the hall, his skin-suit ripped to shreds, public decency preserved only by a strategically placed policeman's helmet.

The squad car had been abandoned across Scundale Chase and all eyes were now on Felix as he fumbled with the door keys.

Steve MacCruiskeen checked his watch for the umpteenth time. 'Get a move on, will you? He's got a flight to catch. I don't know why he wouldn't answer when we were round, earlier. Are you sure he's in there?'

'Don't worry,' replied Felix. 'You'll see.'

They burst in through the back door, yelling Freddie's name as they charged up the stairs.

The three of them careered into the bedroom, Giselle and Steve bouncing back onto the landing a millisecond later, their faces contorted in disgust.

'*Sacre Bleu!*' shrieked Giselle. 'That stink! It is worse than the one 'undred year old Camembert. *C'est incroyable!*'

Felix, whose sense of smell had long-since been dulled by a lifetime of bedroom sharing with his big brother, was slapping his snoring sibling around the head. 'Wake up, Fred – you've got a plane to catch!'

Freddie surfaced from his slumbers like a monster rising from the depths of a very dark lagoon. 'Wassamarrer… Gerroffmewillyer.'

Wincing at the rank foulness of his brother's breath, Felix held a hand up to shield his nose. 'You need to get up. The police are taking you to the airport.'

'What you on about? Leave me alone, willyer?' Groaning loudly, Freddie buried his head back into the pillow.

'This is for real, Fred! Gazza just got arrested at school. He bombed-out on the doping test, which means you won the Grand Prix and you're off to the Pyrenees with the Chocolate Bananas. You're riding the Tour!'

Freddie was dragged downstairs and bundled into the back of the patrol car, his bags dumped in the boot. Felix felt a pang of concern as he watched PC Fox execute a screeching three-point-turn at the end of the close. Poor Giselle, he thought – she was going to have to sit next to that dog-breathed slob, all the way to Manchester Airport.

As they drove past, the beautiful Frenchwoman leaned out through the car window. 'Felice, I am so grateful for your *assistance!*' she shouted. 'If I can do anything for you, you must say, *oui?*'

'*Bon voyage*, Giselle. *Adieu!*' he replied with a flourish.

She smiled and blew him a kiss.

I'm in there! he thought.

Wandering back inside he could scarcely believe his luck – ten days with a bedroom to himself and the rest of the morning skiving off school! Things were definitely on the up, which meant now was as good a time as any to check in with his recent acquaintance at the *Frecklesall Journal*.

That evening, a bottle of Asti Spumante was cracked open with the Haythornthwaites' celebratory tea, following a phone call from the gravel-voiced, still-hungover Freddie to say he'd arrived in the Pyrenees and everything was 'cool'. They gathered around to watch the early evening news and afterwards, on *It's Grand Up North!*, they cheered the footage of Gazza being led in through the back door of Frecklesall police station, his face concealed by a large brown paper bag, shoved over his head.

The PE teacher paused to harangue a nearby journalist. 'I didn't do it, see. Gareth Llewellyn-Evans is innocent - I'm no drugs cheat!'

'So how do you explain the extraordinary levels of testosterone found in your urine sample?' asked the journalist.

Gazza pulled the bag off his head. Red-faced, eyes staring madly, the veins in his neck pulsed disturbingly. 'I dunno about that, do I?' he began. 'But I bin thinking about it, obviously. Testosterone's a man thing, innit?' He thumped his chest. 'I'm all man, me – one hundred and ten percent Welsh beef. So, all what's happening here is, I'm being punished for my manliness. There's a word for that y'know – discrim-*man*-ation, and I for one, won't stand for it!'

The teacher was dragged away protesting his innocence, and the image cut back to a second reporter who was standing outside Frecklesall High School.

'Breaking news! Llewellyn-Evans' solicitors have just issued the following statement.' The reporter read from his phone. '"Our client, Gareth Llewellyn-Evans, has never knowingly taken performance-enhancing drugs and is entirely innocent of all charges. However, we have just learnt that an Albanian hair restoration product, Baldy-B-Gone, recently purchased by our client via the Internet, could well be the cause of the excessive levels of testosterone found in his sample."'

A picture of Freddie, sprinting along the Prom on the Hill Special, flashed onto the TV screen. 'Regardless of any appeal that Llewellyn-Evans' solicitors may lodge,' the reporter continued, 'the UCI – cycling's governing body – has just confirmed that the disgraced PE teacher's *Domestique du Jour* slot has been awarded to the runner-up of Sunday's qualifying race. Which means Frecklesall-based lifeguard, Freddie Haythornthwaite, is set to re-write the record books. At seventeen-years-old he'll be the youngest ever competitor in the history of the Tour de France.'

After the weather forecast, Felix's mum and dad set off for the sports club to continue the celebrations, leaving him mooching around in the lounge and his sister, plugged into the Internet on a half-hour pass before bedtime.

'I still don't think we should tell Mum and Dad about this Herbina thing,' said Flo, earnestly. 'I mean, Freddie's got no chance in that race, so…'

Her brother was staring into space, his mind wandering to more pressing matters.

As ever, Flo was quick to notice. 'What is it now, Felix? Are you still mithering about that story you've been working on – the one about the lido and the Paddock being sold off to make way for that new supermarket?'

'What? How do you know about that?' he spluttered.

'Don't blame me – you shouldn't be leaving your laptop switched on all over the house if it's so secret squirrel, should you?'

He thought it through for a moment. Getting mad with Flo was pointless – after all, he'd given everything he had to Dave Heptonstall, on the basis that once the

Journal put it out there, the people of Frecklesall would rise up in revolt.

Not that that had got him very far.

'Sorry Flo. What did you make of it, then?'

'Well, it's an interesting take,' she replied. 'I mean, it kind of adds up, but the evidence is all a bit… circumstantial.'

Felix nodded. 'That's just what Dave Heptonstall told me when I called him this morning.'

'What? You showed it to *him*?'

'Yeah – everything we've got. People round here need to know about this, and I thought he was our best bet.'

His sister looked horrified. 'I've been thinking it through and I've had an idea that might help, but... the *Journal*? I mean – that's just ridiculous.'

'What else was I supposed to do?' Felix replied defensively. 'Anyway, he's told me he's not running the story, so it doesn't matter.'

'Except it does matter,' said Flo. 'Dave Heptonstall is just the monkey – it's the organ grinder you need to be worried about.'

He looked at her, blankly.

Who knew? The *Frecklesall Journal* (circulation 4,562) – part of the Metro Media Northern stable, in turn, a subsidiary of Metro Media UK. Their parent company? Global News (Europe Ltd), an offshoot of WIN (Worldwide International News) Ltd. And who owns the majority stake in WIN? You guessed it – Smiler Corporation International (Texas)!

Funny things, multi-nationals, funny things… There they sit, astride the capitalist food chain, the apex predators of the business world – devouring the opposition and siphoning profit out of local economies to enrich faceless shareholders and billionaire owners. Owners like Herb T Smilerski, for who a fifty-million-dollar investment in a dump like Frecklesall-on-Sea is peanuts, compared to the money he'll be raking in when the Smiler Corporation's first UK Garganto MonsterMart is up and running.

'Got to look on the bright side, I suppose,' muttered Keira, as the *Pen's* editorial team trudged away from school, the following afternoon. 'At least Arsey doesn't know what we've been up to, yet. I reckon we can count on Wiseley keeping his mouth shut, for the time being at least. The last thing he needs right now is to have his name plastered across the tabloids in a sex-scandal. I've got to say, though, handing the story to the Smiler Corporation is probably the dumbest thing you could have done, Felix.'

Felix groaned. 'How was I to know? I was just trying to get it out there, wasn't I? Flo's right about one thing, though – we need more evidence if we're going to stand this story up.'

'We haven't got anything else, though, have we?' said Naz, gloomily.

'There's that email on the *Pen* account,' said Bernie. 'The one from those American lawyers with the attachment you couldn't open. That Wolfie guy seems to know what's going on. It's a long-shot but there might be there we could use.'

Keira rolled her eyes. 'Keep up, lad! The only way we can get into that is through Sid, which is as good as telling Arsey what we've been up to. Anyway, it's gone now – I deleted it.'

Naz's face registered a flash of concern, but before Felix could ask him what was up, Bernie had chipped in again.

'That just leaves our secret weapon, then, doesn't it?'

Felix looked at him, incredulously. 'Secret weapon?'

'Och aye, see you. Patrick Thistle's the man for the wee jobbie, the noo!'

Felix winced at Bernie's terrible accent. 'You've got no chance, mate. I had a lucky escape last time. I only got away with it because everyone was drunk.'

'That's not quite how you told it to me, is it?'

'Come on Keira, back me up here,' pleaded Felix.

'I dunno…' Keira blew her cheeks out. 'I mean, let's face it – Patrick Thistle's all we've got left. That Fudgeley-Smythe guy seemed to take quite a shine to you. Couldn't you could just call him up?'

'Yeah! Come on, Thwaitey lad,' grunted Spuggie. 'I'll keep an eye on you. Any sign of trouble and, wham!' He slammed his fist into a nearby lamppost. 'Sorted!'

Arriving back home, Felix was in the kitchen fixing himself a Marmite butty when he heard voices coming from the lounge. Wondering who it was, he headed into the hallway and pressed an ear up against the door.

'…I know, they're always a worry, Mrs H. You think as they get older, things will be easier, but the teenage years can be such a trial.' It was a man's voice – the source difficult to identify through the door and the inconvenient hum of the fridge.

'We've known for a while that our Freddie was struggling to find his way, but...' His mum was putting on her posh telephone voice.

Who on earth was she talking to?

'You must be so proud of him,' said the man. 'And rightly so – he's become an excellent ambassador for Frecklesall. But younger brothers can so easily go under the radar. You don't realise the mischief they're caught up in until it's too late.'

'I... I don't think so. I mean, Felix is a good boy. He's never given us cause—'

'Happened in my own family, Mrs H – or can I call you *Christine*? And you know as well as I do, there are so many troubling things going on in our broken society at the moment. Check out the *Journal*, any week of the year – vandalism, muggings, burglary – it's a total no-brainer!'

Wiseley! What the hell was he doing in there? Felix froze as he caught the next chilling snippet.

'This bus-surf craze, for example. I simply will not rest until the ASBO Boy has been brought to justice. That's why I've launched my YobWatch! campaign. A lad about your Felix's age, they're saying. Of course, we'll know more when we get the enhanced CCTV footage back from the FBI.'

Felix threw himself against the door, stumbling into the room and nearly tripping over the coffee table, which was groaning under the weight of Sunday-best crockery, laden with biscuits and cakes.

'Felix!' his mum greeted him. 'Look who's popped in to offer his congratulations to our Freddie'

Wiseley was sitting back in the easy chair, clutching a teacup and saucer, the high waistband of his trousers straining against his belly.

'Troy was just telling me how he managed to get you reinstated at school, after that awful *incident* on Slaidforth beach,' said his mum. She turned back to the mayor. 'None of it was his fault, Troy, but even so, Brian and I are incredibly grateful for your help in sorting it all out.'

'It was nothing Christine,' he replied. 'Mayor Troy Wiseley MBA is the kind of guy who will always go the extra mile if it means giving one of our youngsters a second chance in life.'

Felix fought a desperate urge to pick up the teapot and smash it over his head.

His mum smiled. 'Another cup of tea, Mr Mayor? Ooh – who'd have thought I'd be saying that, and in my own living room, as well?'

'You're an angel, Christine,' oozed Wiseley. 'And while you're doing that, maybe I could have a little face-time with the lad, here? I'm always keen to reach out to the local youth – find out what's *going down* on the street.'

The mayor grabbed Felix by the arm, the moment his mum had headed out to the kitchen. 'I got a call this morning – from Texas,' he hissed. 'Smiler Corp know all about your stupid games.'

'Oh yeah?' Felix tried to sound cocky – it didn't work.

'They want your head on a plate, boy, and why should I care?'

Felix guessed it had something to do with a celebrity roving reporter and some compromising photographs (that didn't actually exist) but he kept these thoughts to himself.

'They told me to let Randy off the leash,' Wiseley continued. 'Luckily for you, I'd prefer to avoid casualties – for the time being at least – so listen up. You and your gang, you back off. No more of that Save the Lido crap. And you hand over all of those photographs and the memory card by this Saturday – otherwise…' He leant back into the chair, smiling. 'Otherwise, Randy will be making you an offer – an offer you can't refuse.'

Felix's mum popped her head around the door. 'Everything all right in here? Would anyone like some more Madeira?'

Wiseley was charm personified. 'Very kind of you, Christine, but I've just had a call from the office. I'm so sorry, but I'm going to have to dash.'

'Oh dear. Well, it was really nice to meet you, Your Worshipfulness. Call again soon, won't you? And don't worry, I'll be sure to pass on your best wishes to our Freddie, the next time he rings. Are you going to say goodbye, Felix?'

Felix sat there, motionless, as Wiseley levered himself up out of the chair.

'My, what were you talking to him about, Troy?' Felix's mum chuckled. 'He looks like he's seen a ghost!'

Wiseley glanced back as he was making for the door. 'I bet he's dying to tell you, Christine, just dying.'

Felix studied the keypad on his mobile, even practicing a few well-worn phrases in front of the mirror – wincing at how pathetic he sounded. It was a suicide mission but any doubts he'd harboured had just been blown away by the pompous buffoon who'd strutted into their house, eating their best biscuits and schmoozing his mum. And his threat – 'An offer you can't refuse' – what the hell was that all about, then? He was about to punch in Rupert

Fudgeley-Smythe's number when his phone rang. He clicked on the call.

'Naz! How you doing, mate?'

'Not so good actually, Felix,' replied his friend. 'My uncle died today and we've all got to go to London for the funeral on Friday. We're back on Sunday.'

'Oh… Sorry to hear that. Thanks for letting me know.' He probably should have been more sympathetic, but he was desperate to tell him what had just happened. 'You're not gonna believe this, mate, but we had a visit today from—'

'Felix, there's something important I need to say.' Naz interrupted him. 'It's just that, well… I was checking out the *Pen's* account in the school IT suite, the other day, and I came across that email from those American lawyers – the one Keira forwarded from the mayor's office.'

'But she deleted it. She told us, didn't she?'

'Not quite. She moved it into the "Trash" but she never deleted it from there.'

She's good, but she's not that good, thought Felix.

'You know how I get on really well with Miss Sidhu?' Naz continued, sounding decidedly glum. 'I'm so sorry, mate – I thought if I showed her the email, I could get her to—'

'Oh no!' Felix had his head in his hands. 'Tell me you didn't, Naz – *please.*'

His friend sighed. 'I feel awful about it. The whole thing's been a nightmare. She used that administrator password she's got and opened the attachment, there and then. I tried to have a look over her shoulder, but I couldn't see anything. I did everything I could to persuade her to let me have it, but she wouldn't budge…'

15

He was flying, crouched forward over the handlebars, wind whistling through his hair, the tarmac a blur beneath his wheels. He could see himself as if from the helicopter high above, the lone rider on the successful breakaway. Under the one-kilometre red kite, now – the crowd cheering him on to a glorious solo victory. Felix was using the Hill Special while Freddie was away and it was brilliant, just built for speed. Of course, he always felt like this heading into town – slogging up the hill on his way home was another matter, altogether.

'Don't worry about it,' said Doreen, after he told her what had happened. 'That idiot Heptonstall's always been a waste of space. We're moving to Plan B.'

'Plan B?' Felix asked, uncertainly.

'If the *Journal* won't print the story, we'll put it out there ourselves. I've some friends who'll do the photocopying – I just need you and your pals to lend a hand with distribution on Saturday morning.'

'Oh… right.'

Doreen put an arm around his shoulder and gave him a hug. 'You've come down here on the Hill Special, haven't you? You'd better look after that bike, y'know – it means a lot to me. It brought a tear to my eye seeing Freddie sprint for the line on it, last Sunday.' She paused, adding in almost a whisper. 'He'd have made Billy proud.'

She made the comment so quietly, Felix wasn't even sure he was supposed to have heard it. A few weeks back, he'd have waved it on its way, unquestioned, but now he knew his great-aunt well enough to know that she wanted to talk.

'This Billy – it was his bike, wasn't it?' he asked.

She nodded.

'Was he that young guy in your photo album?'

'Aye, that were Billy, alright. He was the top rider in the north of England back in '64 – probably the best in the whole country, I reckon.'

'And the girl he was with? She was beautiful. What happened to her?'

'Ah, the girl…' Doreen sighed as she headed across to the walk-in cupboard, returning a few seconds later with an armful of old photo albums. 'You're talking to her right now.'

It was past eleven by the time they'd finished, and that was only because Felix's mum had phoned, asking where he'd got to.

'I have to go now, Doreen,' he said. 'Mum's going to kill me when I get home.'

She stood up and gave him a hug. 'Thanks, lad. I haven't looked through this lot in years. It was nice to do it with you.'

'Yeah, I enjoyed it as well.' He stifled a yawn. 'I'd better be off, though.'

'Right. I'll see you and your mates on the beach – Saturday, at eleven o'clock, sharp.'

As he struggled back up the hill, legs burning, he thought of Doreen and her memories, all bound up in a handful of dusty photo albums. There was no way he was going to get old. No way!

It was the last week of term and Felix clung to the forlorn hope that if he could just make it to the break without things blowing up, there was chance that everything would be alright.

Who was he kidding?

The printout from those American lawyers was sitting there in Arsey's in-tray, ticking away like a time bomb.

Nice one, Naz!

Despite his own personal traumas, life at home had slipped into something of a new routine. Freddie phoned every evening and his calls quickly became the highlight of the day. It was a funny thing – the Haythornthwaites had started off hardly even knowing what the Tour was, and now they were all completely hooked. Freddie told them he was having a great time – long training rides in the cool mountain air, a crash course in race tactics and rub-downs every evening from a gorgeous French masseuse. 'Getting into the zone', he'd said, when he phoned that Thursday evening, just a week away from the Tour's visit to Frecklesall, and the day the rest of the ChocolatBanane riders were setting off to the Belgian city of Liege, to prepare for the traditional race curtain-raiser – Saturday's Prologue time-trial.

It all sounded a bit too good to be true, which of course, it was. Only Felix knew the real story.

Freddie had called him a couple of times, desperate for someone to talk to.

'The thing is, the guys have got a major downer on me,' he'd said, close to tears. 'They're saying if I lose it in the middle of the pack or in a bunch sprint, I could wipe them out as well. And the training runs are a nightmare. They only let me go out with the junior squad and I still can't keep up. I mentioned Herbina to them and they all think it's a joke – they've been taking the Mick ever since. I tell you, Bro, the whole thing's doing my head in.'

'Positive Mental Attitude, Fred – just focus on the racing,' Felix had replied, his tongue firmly in his cheek. 'You'll have the last laugh when you're collecting that trophy off Herbina, up on the podium. You know what happens then, don't you? Beautiful billionaire heiress congratulates youngest ever stage winner with the traditional kiss? That's your big chance! Just make sure you've brushed your teeth, beforehand. Anyway, everyone's talking about you back here – especially the girls.'

It was all rubbish of course, but if that's what he had to do to guarantee his brother's appointment with global public humiliation, it was a small price to pay.

Toe-curling embarrassment didn't come close to describing Felix's feelings as he sat at the kitchen table, round at Keira's house, being poked, polished and preened by the lovely Nicole, trainee beautician at Slaidforth Sands' top beauty salon – Phwoar!!. Keira's older sister had eagerly accepted the task of transforming his appearance for the evening's deception, keen to hone her makeover skills. It was all a bit awkward, but at least his topless, skinny-ribbed discomfort was a distraction from the nightmare that lay ahead.

Keira sat in the corner, smirking as her big sister provided a running commentary on the deficiencies in Felix's grooming regime, over the clack of an alarmingly large pair of scissors.

'Look at this hair, Keira – it's completely out of condition. We've got all sorts of treatments down the salon that could help you, Felix. I can let you have a voucher, if you'd like?'

'That's really kind of you, Nicole,' he replied. 'But all I'm after is getting through this evening without being recognised.'

'Sure, yeah. So have you been anywhere nice on your holidays?'

Keira ducked out of the room, reappearing a short while later with an armful of men's clothes, raided from her dad's wardrobe. 'The hair's looking good Nic – almost human, but that bum-fluff moustache is a give-away. Is there owt you can do with it?'

'Not a problem,' her sister replied, rummaging about in one of her many bags. 'I popped into House of Hairpieces at lunchtime and told them I was going to a fancy dress as Freddie Mercury. They gave me this.' She pulled out what looked like a dead hamster. Before Felix could register a protest, she'd glued it firmly to his top lip. 'Ta-daa!'

Keira roared with laughter.

'Thanks,' said Felix, wrinkling his nose to try to counter the tickling sensation. 'You're really boosting my confidence, here.'

Nicole span him around to face the mirror on the table. It took a second for his eyes to focus, or maybe it was the shock of seeing the startled stranger who was gawping back at him.

'Bloody hell!' he exclaimed. 'That's amazing!'

The last time he'd ventured out in disguise it had been an unmitigated disaster, but now the transformation was jaw-dropping. The face in the mirror was smiling at him, only it was doing it in a handsome, sophisticated kind of way. Underneath, it was still him of course, but the frizz had gone, replaced with a sharp, smart cut. His pallid complexion had been transformed to deliver a healthy glow, and then there was the moustache! It wasn't just that he'd been loaned the best part of twelve years – he looked alright. In fact, if he ever made it to the ripe old age of twenty-six, he reckoned he'd be laughing!

'Reet then,' said Keira. 'Kit off, lad – I've got some gear for you to try on.'

Half an hour later, Felix stumbled into the public bar at The Pig and Whistle, resplendent in an oversized brown suit jacket, half-mast trousers and a matching tie. He'd been in lots of pubs before, but these had been family-friendly barns with children's play areas and chicken nuggets and chips on tap. The Pig was different – an old-fashioned, real ale boozer, with a dart board and a pool table. It was gloomy and grubby, and it smelt of spilt beer.

His feet stuck to the vinyl flooring as he squinted through the fug to check out the smattering of unhealthy-looking punters, hunched over the Formica-topped tables, nursing pints of murky brown ale. And there at the bar, standing out like a sore thumb in his chinos and open-necked shirt, a cream sweater draped across his shoulders, was Rupert Fudgeley-Smythe.

Felix walked over to greet him. 'Rupie! How yiz doin', pal!'

Rupert seemed taken aback. 'Patrick – is that you? Gosh. I didn't recognise you for a moment. You look… different.'

'Och aye, well no monkey suits tonight, Rupie, eh?'

'Absolutely! Drink?'

The barman eyed them warily.

Felix hadn't really thought this through. 'Err… a beer for me, please, pal.'

'What kind?' the barman asked, arms folded impatiently across his chest. 'Bottled, draught, lager, mild? We've got five kinds of bitter.' He wafted a hand over a range of hand-pumps with a sarcastic flourish.

Felix pointed uncertainly at the nearest one.

'Old Todger's,' said the barman. 'Would that be a half?'

'No thanks,' replied Felix. 'I'll have a whole, by the way.'

The barman rolled his eyes. '*Pint* of Todger's and a large gin and tonic, coming right up.'

As they carried their drinks over to a corner table, Felix fumbled around inside his jacket pocket, switching on the voice recorder on his mobile. The plan was simple – work the conversation around until it got interesting, record whatever Rupert had to say, then get the heck out of there.

They sat down and Felix took a couple of gulps from his glass. Yeeuughh! It was disgusting. He only just managed to stop himself from spitting it out.

'All good, Patrick?' asked Rupert, glancing over his shoulder to check out some new arrivals at the bar.

'Fine, so it is. And how's tricks with you, my friend? A wee chookie told me your Smiler Corp pals are planning a development project, doon there at the lido. I wouldnae mind a wee snifter from that particular single malt, if you get my meaning.'

Rupert looked petrified. 'Gosh – keep it down will you? That's all strictly Chatham House ATM. How the devil did you find out?'

'Och, just keepin' my nose to the groond.'

'Here's the thing, Patrick,' said Rupert, in a low voice. 'I happen to have a few shares coming my way – worth a bit as we speak, but worth a heck of a lot more in a few weeks' time. Trouble is, I'm in need of liquidity, right now.'

Felix got to his feet. 'Another drink then, Rupie? No problemo!'

'No. Liquidity. Cash. I need to get my hands on some money – PDQ.'

Felix cringed at his mistake. 'Och aye - well that's very much my business, so it is. So, why don't you tell me about these shares, an' how come they're going to be worth so much, all of a sudden?'

Rupert leant in so close, he was all but whispering in Felix's ear. 'Smiler Corp are working up the launch of a new retail franchise, here in the UK. I've a fifty K stock option coming my way – well, that's the starting price. The Texans are delaying the flotation until after the announcement next week. When they hit the market, it's all going to take off.'

Felix had been leaning forward in an effort to pick everything up on his phone. 'Fandabidozey! So, what's with this big announcement, then?' He took another slurp from his glass and wiped his moustache, which was now saturated with beer. There was a technique to this, but he obviously hadn't got the hang of it yet.

'Next Thursday, the day of the race,' replied Rupert. 'Old Herb is jetting in from Texas to sign the land contracts with the council. Your intel is spot on, Patrick – it's the lido, that field with the grubby bungalow, and the scabby common, yah? The deal completes as soon as the race is done and dusted – which is when they go to market. You'll know how these things work – all that publicity from the sponsorship will generate considerable top-end profile. It's absolute cat-nip to the investors. As soon as they hear that the site of the UK's first ever Smiler Garganto MonsterMart is already in the bag, those share prices are only going one way.'

'Totally no-brainer,' chimed Felix, stroking his chin, thoughtfully, although underneath he wanted to jump up and scream. But Rupert had been speaking so quietly, he was worried his phone might not have picked it all up. 'By the way, Rupie, I didnae quite catch that last bit, just now. Would you say again, a wee bit louder this time?'

Rupert eyed him, suspiciously. 'Look Patrick, this is all in the strictest, of course. Forty K and the shares are yours. They'll be worth twice that in a week.'

'Felix Haythornthwaite!' a slurred voice shouted from across the bar. ''Ow do, lad? By 'eck tha's shot up fast!'

Felix froze. The old man staggering towards them, decidedly the worse for wear, was Jimmy Pilkington, who used to work with his dad down at the used caravan lot.

He grabbed his beer glass and held it up to his face in a feeble attempt to hide his identity. 'Sorry pal, I dinna ken who y'are. A wee private business conflab going on here, if you don't mind.'

'Felix Haythornthwaite?' said Rupert, squinting through the gloom at his drinking partner. 'That name sounds awfully familiar.'

'Thass reet!' said Jimmy, playfully cuffing Felix around the back of his head. 'Brian and Christine's lad. He used to come down to Mart's wi' his dad of a Saturday, when he were a nipper. Bit of a TV personality on the side, 'n all. You must've seen 'im on telly a few weeks back, wi' that Marje Spangles lass. Tickled me, that one!'

A look of horror spread across Rupert's face.

Putting his glass down, Felix wiped his mouth with the back of his hand. 'I'm offa' sorry, pal, you've got the wrong guy. I'm no' Felix Haythornthwaite. Like I said before, Rupie, the name's Partick... I mean, *Patrick*—'

'OhMyGoodness!' Rupert was pointing at something dark and hairy, which was swimming around in the pool of beer, spilt on the table. 'What on earth is that?'

It was the moustache.

'Och! I'm, err... I'm just away to the wee boys' room,' blurted Felix. 'Back in two shakes.'

He grabbed the beer-sodden article and fled. Skirting around the side of the bar he thought of making a dash for the exit, but was immediately glad he hadn't. For there, completely blocking his way out, was the solid, barrelled shape of Roy 'Bulldog' Wiseley.

He paused, frozen in terror.

Roy marched over and grabbed Rupert by the lapels, hauling him up out of his seat. After a furious exchange, he shoved him aside and in the next instant, was thundering across the bar, sending tables and chairs flying in all directions.

Felix dived for the nearest door.

He'd never been in a ladies toilet before and somewhat alarmed to find himself in one now.

200

Surprising really, he thought, as he hurtled towards the cubicles at the far end of the room – much the same décor as the gents, but different machines on the wall… and nowhere near as smelly.

'Ladies!' He acknowledged the startled expressions of the two old dears who were adjusting their make up in front of the mirrors. 'Sorry, but I've got a nutter chasing after me. I'd get out the way if I were you!'

He darted into the first of the cubicles and was still fumbling with the lock when a loud Bang! heralded the main toilet door being booted open.

'Where'd he go?' Roy's booming voice sent shivers down his spine.

The first woman jumped to his defence. 'Can't you read, you idiot? This is the *ladies* toilet – you've no business 'ere!'

'And don't think for one moment you can get your *thingy* out and start waving it around,' her friend added. 'Make one move in that direction and I'll scream blue murder!'

Balancing on the toilet seat, Felix was sweating like a pig in a butcher's shop. He could see the small window in the wall, high above the cistern, but it was blocked off by heavy-duty security bars, bolted from the outside. Even if he did manage to get up there, he'd never be able to squeeze through that gap.

'Clear off, you old bats!' shouted Roy.

Felix heard the sound of clumping footsteps, followed by something akin to a bomb blast, as Roy's shoulder slammed against the cubicle door.

'Come out, Haythornthwaite!' he roared. 'Get out here right now or I'll rip this off with my bare hands!'

With one foot on the toilet seat, the other on the cistern, Felix made a grab for the window. But everything was on the move. Wobbling precariously under his weight, the toilet pan and the cistern began to come away from the wall, jets of water spraying out in all directions from fractured joints in the plastic pipework.

He paused for a moment, confounded by the hopelessness of his situation, until the almighty Crash! of Roy's boot slamming into the cubicle door, sent the adrenalin coursing through his veins once more.

With the toilet roll holder providing the most parlous of footholds, he managed to scramble his way up the wall. Balancing precariously now, his other foot wedged against the opposite partition, he was able to reach up and pull the window open. The security bars were just that little bit further apart than he'd first thought, and he made a grab for them.

Hanging there, he caught a tantalising glimpse of the glass-strewn car park, outside – a drop of only four feet or so. And then he was grunting with the effort as he hauled himself up, just high enough to shove his head between the bars.

But he was going nowhere – his shoulders were well and truly stuck.

More shouts and screams were followed by the sound of the cubicle door clattering off its hinges, and Roy's triumphant cry of, 'Hah! Gotcha!'.

Suddenly, strong hands were reaching towards him from outside, gripping him under the armpits. Someone else was there as well, straining to widen the gap. Slowly, agonizingly, he was on the move – squeezing out between the bars into the cool evening air.

Maybe just maybe…

The harsh roughness of the rusty ironwork scraped across his ribs and down his back as he was twisted onto his side. Somehow, painful as it was, it seemed to be working!

But Roy was not giving up without a fight. He'd grabbed hold of Felix's ankles and a bizarre tug of war contest ensued – with the wannabe journalist acting as the rope. Shrieking in pain, he was pulled and stretched, first this way, and then that.

'Spug, you've got to do something!' He heard the desperation in Keira's voice as the tide began to turn and he felt himself being dragged, inch-by-inch, back inside.

Wriggling for all he was worth, he felt the grip on his right ankle loosen, momentarily, and with one final effort, he managed to heave the leg free.

He never saw where the mid-air scissor-kick landed, but there was no mistaking the force of its connection. A loud howl was followed swiftly by the Crump! Of a heavyweight collapsing to the floor.

Felix popped out from between the bars, like a Champagne cork at a Bullingdon club social – landing on top of Spuggie and Keira and sending them tumbling to the ground. He struggled back to his feet, and then he was hobbling along after his friends as they sprinted off across the car park.

16

It was a dull Saturday morning and the solid blanket of grey cloud had brought with it the inevitable Irish Sea drizzle. The day-trippers had fled the beach by lunchtime but it was business as usual for the locals going about their weekly shop, utterly unperturbed by the revelation that the heart of their town was about to be sold to an American multi-national and turned into a giant supermarket.

The four of them huddled together, sheltering behind the donkeys.

'I can't believe it,' muttered Keira. 'Half of them wouldn't even take the flyer off me, let alone read it. They're just not interested.'

'I got a load of abuse,' grumbled Bernie. 'People kept telling me to sod off.'

Felix laughed. 'Nothing new there, then.'

'Hey, shut it, *Herr Kutt*!' It was Bernie's fifteenth hair-related gag that morning and Felix wanted to kill him.

Keira jumped to his defence. 'Yeah, well I think it suits him, actually.'

Bernie nearly gagged on the Mars Bar he was guzzling.

'Anyway,' Keira continued, 'I think what you did last night was pretty amazing, Felix.'

'Didn't get us anywhere though, did it?' he replied, gloomily. He'd risked his life for a series of unintelligible grunts, anything worthwhile drowned out by the deafening rustle of material from the inside of his jacket pocket.

'Come on, you lot, we can't give up now,' said Doreen. 'Even if only a handful of people pick up on the message it'll have been worthwhile…' Her voice trailed away as she spotted something up on the Prom. In the next instant she'd grabbed her walking stick and was striding off up the beach. 'Stay here with the donkeys,' she barked. 'I can't be doing with this any longer!'

Felix had heard that tone before and knew exactly what it meant. 'Keep an eye on them for me!' he shouted back to Keira and Bernie as he gave chase.

He caught up with his great-aunt on the slipway and they worked their way towards a cluster of people sheltering from the rain, next to one of the Bulgy Burger stands. It was only as Felix got closer that he realised what everyone was so interested in.

Wiseley!

The publicity-hungry mayor was in the middle of yet another media interview, this time with an earnest reporter from the BBC, who seemed to be lapping up every word.

'So, what next for Mayor Troy Wiseley, *Lancashire Life's* Man of the Year? An OBE, or a knighthood, perhaps?' asked the reporter, thrusting a microphone into his face.

'Well Karl, those who know the mayor of Frecklesall-on-Sea will tell you this,' he replied. 'It's not the many awards and accolades Troy Wiseley MBA deservedly receives that make him throw his legs out of bed every morning. No. It's the challenge, going forward-wise, and the hard yards on the road ahead that give him all the motivation he needs – and then some!'

'Absolutely!' the reporter enthused. 'We've already talked about the spectacle that is *Le Tour* – but what do you think its visit will really mean for a place like Frecklesall-on-Sea?'

'Well, Karl, I have a dream. This is just the beginning of Frecklesall's journey – vibrant, energised, not so much a holiday resort, more a lifestyle statement. A Happening Place for Happ—'

'That's it – I've had enough of this rubbish!'

Everyone turned to see who was doing the heckling.

'Dream? More like a nightmare, if you ask me!' yelled Doreen. 'I know exactly why you've brought that bike race over here, you moron. You've sold us down the river. The donkeys, the lido, the town moor, they'll all be gone – bulldozed to make way for a monster supermarket. That's why those Yanks are paying millions to bring that stupid race over here and I'm not going to stand by and—'

She was cut off in her prime by two burly security guards who began dragging her away from the camera.

'Absolute nonsense!' Wiseley shouted above the fracas. 'Madam, it's people like you who keep this town shackled to its past. No one cares about you or your flea-ridden donkeys – part of the problem, *not* part of the solution.'

Wrenching herself free, Doreen swung her walking-stick at him, its knobbly handle swishing through the air.

The mayor fell to his knees yelping, 'Help! Police! Assault!'

More blows rained down before the old lady was bundled into the back of a patrol car and whisked away, tyres screeching, blue lights flashing.

They packed everything up as best they could and headed for the Paddock, deciding it was best to get off the beach as quickly as possible – no easy task when you're herding five donkeys with only two speeds: dead slow and stop.

'Bloody hell, Felix, what on earth were you playing at?' His dad's words were still ringing in his ears, twenty minutes after the phone call. 'Stay there at the Paddock – I'm going to the police station to try to sort this mess out!'

Felix sighed. Of course, the whole thing was his fault. If only he'd realised that once you hit seventy you were past the age of criminal responsibility.

By seven o'clock that evening, he was still flapping around outside, making sure the donkeys were settled for the night and everything was in order. Having done all the jobs he could think of, he retreated to the settee in Doreen's lounge, squeezing himself in beside Bernie and Keira as they watched the titles roll on the first of the daily Tour de France highlights shows.

Spuggie had caught up with them a short while earlier and was still getting over his disappointment at missing the fun. 'Hey, she likes to mix it, your aunt, don't she?'

'Total nightmare,' replied Felix. 'According to my dad, they're keeping her in custody, overnight. I've got to stay here and make sure everything's sorted.'

'Nice one,' grunted Spuggie. 'You get the beers in, I'll nip home for me air rifle–'

'Shut it, you two,' snapped Keira. 'It's about to start.'

A hush descended as the wrinkled, suntanned face of legendary Tour de France race commentator, Greg Sprocket, appeared on the screen. 'Welcome to the beautiful Belgian city of Liege at the start of the greatest bike race in the world – the Tour de France!' he began. 'Last year's contest was mired in controversy, with many of the favourites pulling out the day before the race began, under a cloud of doping allegations.'

Bernie laughed. 'Bloody hell, they're all at it! Just like our Gazza.'

'Race Director Patrice Perpignan must have thought he'd seen it all, but now a fresh row has emerged from the high mountain training camps of the Alps and the Pyrenees,' Sprocket continued. 'This time it's about the new *Domestique du Jour* rider category, which introduces amateur riders to the event for the first time in the modern era. It's feared this dispute could overshadow the Tour's visit to England and the most northerly stage in this year's race – scheduled for next Thursday, in our very own Frecklesall-on-Sea, up there in Lancashire. I'm joined now by six-time Tour de France rider, Darren Ackhurst. Darren, what's your take on this breaking story?'

The picture cut to the chunky, potato-faced pundit, who was standing in front of the start line in Liege, wearing a blue polo shirt and clutching an over-sized microphone.

'Thanks, Greg. Frankly, the Tour organisers have got this completely wrong,' Darren began, earnestly. 'I appreciate they're trying to restore the true spirit of cycling, and I'd be the first to agree that something needs to be done to improve the image of the sport I love so much, but allowing amateurs to ride this race is literally an accident waiting to happen. These guys go head-to-head in bunch sprints at speeds approaching fifty miles an hour – one mistake and half the field comes down. We're talking a massive threat to rider safety, here, and the teams are deeply unhappy about it. Back to you, Greg.'

'Well said, Darren! You can be sure this one will run and run. Naturally, we'll be covering all the developments in our daily highlights show, but in the meantime, there was a race starting out on the streets of Liege today. So, let's role the action from this afternoon's Prologue time-trial.'

'Is that your phone ringing, Felix?' asked Bernie.

'Good timing as ever,' he grumbled. 'It'll be my old man wanting to have another moan.'

He walked out to the kitchen, but by the time he'd got there, he'd missed the call. He waited a minute to check on his messages and when he did, he nearly had a meltdown.

'Been trying to get hold of you, Felix,' the voicemail began. 'Lithen, I heard what happened on the beach with your aunt – beathtly luck and all that.'

He didn't recognise the voice at first - downbeat, mumbling, and masked by what sounded like a heavy cold. But then it clicked. There was only one person he'd ever spoken to in his entire life who used the word 'beastly', and that was Rupert Fudgeley-Smythe.

'Awfully thorry about the voithe,' lisped Rupert. 'I'm a tad bunged up at the moment – bit under the weather, TBH.'

Understatement of the year! thought Felix. Rupert sounded like he was speaking to him through a snorkel, from the bottom of a vat of custard.

'Look, I get it, yah?' the message continued. 'I underthtand what you're trying to do to and I have conthiderable thympathy with your campaign. Herb T and co. are not nithe people – not nithe at all! They don't care about Frecklethall – they're into grabbing whatever they can, then clearing orff. What you're doing is awethome, but I've read your article and can't help thinking you need a tad more meat on the bone. I can help you there, Felix – I can get you into the lido and you can thee for yourthelf what they've been up to! Meet me tonight, at the main gate – eleven-thirty. Come alone. Thorry – need to go now.'

The distant chimes of the town hall clock wafted through the cool night air as Felix waited, shivering in the shadows. The old lido building stood behind him, the borrowed glow from the street lamps on Marine Drive emphasising the decayed, worn-out feel of the place.

The footpath to the main entrance was bound by the same laurel bushes that had rescued him from Spuggie and his mates, all those weeks before. Back then, they'd been a lifesaver, but now, eerie shadows lent the scene a sinister atmosphere, like in a horror film where you know something bad is about to happen to the hero.

'Hey! Wake up, you numpty!' Bernie's shrill tones pierced the silence, the foliage rustling as he broke cover.

'Keep down, you idiot,' Felix hissed as his friend sauntered along the path to join him. 'Fudgeley-Smythe should have been here by now. He's not coming, is he?'

Bernie shrugged. 'You're spot on, for once, mate. No worries, though – Spug's got a plan.'

There was no time to reflect on the improbability of this statement as the man himself emerged from the other side of the bushes and swaggered, bold as brass, up to the lido gates.

Felix was mortified. 'Sean! Get down. Someone might see us!'

'Nah! 'Sorright, Thwaitey lad. No bugger 'ere, is there?'

He sprinted forward and launched a flying kick at the main door, sending a sonic boom reverberating out into the night air.

Felix dived for cover. 'Sean… No… Please! We'll get cau—'

Too late. The earth shook again and a nearby 'Strictly No Smoking' sign clattered to the ground.

'Hold it!' snapped Keira, who had jumped from her hiding place and was running towards them.

'Whassup, Keira? What's your problem?' grunted Spuggie.

'You are, stupid!' she growled, checking the flaking paintwork which was now decorated with two size twelve boot prints. After examining the large iron latch on the gate, she clicked it up... and pulled. The rusted hinges groaned as it swung open towards her. 'Tricky things, doors, aren't they? Sometimes you have to *push* but there are other times when you have to *pull*. It all takes a bit of working out.'

The three lads peered past her into the inky blackness.

'Not frightened, are we?' she asked, pulling a pencil-torch from her rucksack and slipping inside.

They'd stumbled into what seemed like a giant black hole. Bunching up behind Keira and her torch, they'd only managed a few paces before Spuggie tripped, dragging a protesting Bernie down on top of him.

'Owww! Gerroff me, willyer!'

'Shut *up*!' hissed Keira, shining the torch to help them untangle themselves. 'Hey, look at that!' Directing the beam, a metre further along, she illuminated a perfectly formed circular hole, about twenty centimetres across. There was a sizeable pile of earth just beside it.

'Bloody stupid place to do some digging!' Spuggie's voice echoed around the deserted buildings.

It felt like there was an endless black void all around them, and the thought of what might be lurking out there drew Felix ever more tightly into the huddle. Their eyes were beginning to adjust to a dim night-vision, but even so, they stumbled and tripped as they inched their way forward. Every four or five metres, they had to steer around another pile of debris and yet another neat, circular hole.

Keira pulled out her camera, the flash providing the briefest snapshot of the wreckage that had once been Frecklesall's pride and joy. The beautiful sweep of the sun deck, where recliners had lined up to make the most of those all-too-brief breaks in the cloud, was now pockmarked with an ugly gridiron of rubble.

'Looks like they've got a mole problem!' Bernie joked. 'What d'you reckon's gone on here, then?'

Felix knew only too well. 'It'll be the site investigations for that new supermarket.'

They groped their way across the terrace, ending up by one of the wooden benches, next to the learner pool.

'Should've brought me trunks!' said Bernie. 'Hey, it's a pity Naz couldn't make it – he'd have loved this.'

'I'd rather be at that funeral than stuck here with you lot,' mumbled Keira.

'Shhh…' Felix called for silence. 'I thought I heard something.'

Bernie looked around, anxiously. 'Like… what?'

Felix strained his ears. 'I don't know. It sounded kind of… metallic.'

'Like a chain being dragged across the ground?'

'I… I'm not sure – why d'you ask?'

Bernie sat down on the bench, beckoning them closer. 'Not many people know the history of this place – I mean the *real* history,' he began. 'Y'see, long before the lido was built, this land was part of the town moor. They say it was just here, on this very spot, that the gallows were sited, back at the end of the eighteenth century. They used to bring the condemned men out on an open cart, all manacled up in chains.'

He grabbed the torch from Keira, using it to illuminate his face to ghostly effect. 'It was the last thing most of 'em heard before the noose was tightened around their necks – the jeers of the crowd and the sounds of those chains dragging up the steps…. And even now, over three hundred years later, they say that when the moon is full, if you listen very carefully, you can still hear them chains: *clink… clink… clink*. Not many people have experienced it over the centuries – at least, not that have lived to tell the tale – but weirdly, and this is the bit that completely freaked me out…' His voice had dropped to a whisper. *'Every last person who's heard them chains – every single one of them poor sods…* IS COMPLETELY STUPID 'COS I JUST MADE THE WHOLE THING UP!'

They jumped up, screaming in unison – even Spuggie, who quickly regained enough composure to grab Bernie by the scruff of his neck. 'Do that again and I'll paste you – I mean it, Devaney.'

Keira rounded on them, angrily. 'Listen up, you idiots – we get to the main pool, we take some shots, then we clear off. Let's get what we came for and get out of this dump. No more messing.'

Everyone nodded in agreement.

'It's just over there,' she said, pointing into the darkness.

'I'm gonna stay back for a bit – put me feet up, 'ave a smoke. Shout me when you're done,' announced Spuggie. Slumping onto the bench he pulled out his packet of Lucky Gaspers.

'But Sean, you saw that No Smoking sign back there—' Felix was hauled away before he could make matters worse. 'What's up with him, then?' he asked Bernie as they followed the glow of Keira's torch.

'Dunno,' he replied. 'Maybe he's not such a tough guy, after all. And how about you? Screamed like a girl!'

They navigated their way down a handful of steps and a few faltering paces later they were teetering on the edge of the main pool. Felix could see the towering outline of the diving platforms to his right, but when he inched forward to peer into the pool itself, he could only make out a vague blackness in the shadows below.

Keira had her camera to hand. 'I'm taking a few shots, guys,' she announced. 'Hang on, everyone.'

The flashlight exploded softly, illuminating the scene in front of them. Felix had stepped back but Bernie was right on the edge of the pool as a second flash flooded the dank pit with light.

'WAAAAAAA!'

Suddenly, he was teetering on the brink, arms windmilling frantically. Diving forwards, Felix made a grab for his friend, only just managing to haul him back to safety. They stumbled sideways, collapsing to the ground by one of the old springboards.

Felix was in shock. 'Bloody hell! What are you doing, you idiot?'

'I… I lost it,' stuttered Bernie. 'It's like it was pulling me in… There's something bad going on here, Felix, I can feel it. I've had enough – I'm heading back to Spuggie.' He stumbled off the way they'd come.

'Screamed like a girl!' Keira jeered after him as he sloped away.

A handful of flashes followed, each one giving a tantalizing glimpse of the ruination below. The once pristine azure of the pool floor had been replaced by a crop of ugly mounds – a giant outbreak of acne covering its entire fifty-yard length. Felix's heart sank – he'd got the killer piece of evidence he'd been looking for, but the lido was a write-off. It would cost millions to sort this mess out and there was no way the council was ever going to stump up that kind of cash. Wiseley moaned about kids breaking a few windows and spraying a bit of graffiti here and there, but this was vandalism on the grandest of scales.

The two of them turned back towards the sound of their friends' hushed conversation, and the tiny red glow from Spuggie's cigarette.

Felix couldn't resist the wind-up. 'Are you sure you've got enough space left on that memory card, Keira? You know what you're like—'

She came to an abrupt halt. 'Shhh… I can hear that noise, now… Over there, by the changing rooms.'

They stopped dead, ears straining.

'Someone's there,' hissed Felix, the panic rising in his voice. 'Blimey, what's that smell?'

'Petrol…' muttered Keira, as the faintest of whiffs gave way to a much stronger pungency. And then she was yelling at the top of her voice. 'Sean, be careful!'

They saw Spuggie jump up from the bench but could only watch, helplessly, as he pinged his still-burning cigarette high into the night air. The glowing red ember arced through the darkness, landing in a flurry of sparks just a metre or so from the entrance to the ladies changing room.

One... two... three... Felix counted off the seconds in his head... *seven... eight... nine...* He turned to Keira. 'Phew! That was a close one—'

WHUUMPFFF!

The changing room exploded into a blinding fireball, flames roaring out through broken windows, snaking into the café block and crackling on through the solarium. Suddenly, the place was lit up like Blackpool illuminations. Felix's eyes blinked in fascination but before he could get his bearings, Keira had grabbed him by the arm and they were off and running. Narrowly avoiding an abandoned drilling rig, they slalomed their way around countless piles of debris, only slowing for a moment when a large pane of glass blew out in front of them, spewing glistening shards across their path.

Bernie and Spuggie were a few metres ahead. Felix saw the pair pause, before charging headlong into the swirling black mass, billowing from the old ticket office.

It looked like madness, but it was their only way out.

Feeling the intensity of the heat, he took a step back, unsure of what to do next.

'Now!' yelled Keira.

Instinct kicked in and they dashed forward, running blindly through what seemed like an endless tunnel of flame. Felix barely noticed the stifling blanket of black smoke and the sharp crackle of scorching timber, as every part of his being focussed on keeping moving and staying upright.

They burst out through the main entrance gate, the spluttering figures of Spuggie and Bernie already sprawled across the footpath, twenty metres further on. Moments later, they'd collapsed in a heap beside them,

Felix retching up gobs of black phlegm between laboured breaths of the cool night air.

He propped himself up and looked back at the lido building, the flames now clearly visible from outside. *Phew*! They'd all made it – Keira, Spuggie, Bernie... and there was one more.

Sergeant Pluck glowered down at them, arms folded across his chest. 'You lot are nicked!' he barked. 'The fire service are on their way, so get yourselves into that police van... And no arguments'

They huddled together, blinking under the harsh strip-lighting, while a stern WPC announced the arrival of their 'Appropriate Adults'. Felix's mum sat down opposite her son, tearful eyes concealed behind a huge pair of sunglasses. All present, if not correct, it was time for the formalities to begin.

'Under normal circumstances,' Pluck announced, 'we'd be booking the lot of you, right now. And that would mean you'd be here all night while we sorted the paperwork.'

'All night?' Bernie's uncle Ronnie gasped. 'Give over, willyer?' He was silenced by a withering glance.

'However, you lot just got lucky,' the sergeant continued. 'The station's all but closed until Thursday and I've neither the time nor the inclination to deal with this mess now. So, I'll be issuing all of you with a caution, and you'll be coming back to see me, the day after the race.'

There were sighs of relief all around.

'But let's get this straight,' he added. 'The mayor has instructed me to stamp out juvenile delinquency as part of his new YobWatch! initiative, which means you lot are in for a bumpy ride. And word to the wise: if you've got any sense, you'll keep your heads down. There are going to be some very angry folk round these parts, when they find out what you've done to our swimming pool.'

'But it wasn't us – it was a set up,' said Felix.

'Name?' snapped Pluck.

'Felix Haythornthwaite… err, sir.'

The sergeant paused, his stern expression cracking for just an instant. 'Blimey, lad, I didn't recognise you with that bosh. You're Doreen's nephew, aren't you?'

Felix's mum started sniffling. She took off her sunglasses to dab her eyes.

'Yes sir,' Felix replied.

'Oh, right then.' Pluck turned to Felix's mum, his tone softening. 'So, you must be Christine? Sorry to have put you through this, love. If I'd realised… I'll get a car to take you home.'

It was only later, in the back of the taxi, that his mum managed to get the words out. 'Felix, it's your Aunty Doreen – she's had a heart attack. She's over at Slaidforth General. Your dad's been with her most of the evening. We tried calling you…'

17

A large, black cloud hovered just above Felix's head as he trudged along Winthrop Avenue the following morning. He'd left the Hill Special at Doreen's the day before and had hoped the walk to the Paddock to pick it up might help clear his mind. Some chance!

Predictably, his dad wasn't interested in the case for the defence. So now he was banned from just about everything – from seeing his friends ('apart from that nice boy Naz, he's far too smart to get mixed up in something like this'); from going anywhere near the lido, and from having anything to do with Doreen's campaign. His laptop and phone had been confiscated, and to cap it all, he'd been lumbered with the donkeys ('they're your responsibility now, assuming you know the meaning of the word!').

Hearing footsteps behind, he turned to discover that his little sister had followed him out of the house.

'What do you want?' he asked, eyeing the plastic folder she was clutching in her hand.

'Ooh! Sorry to bother you, Mr Nowty – it's just that Keira emailed me some photos which I think you'll want to see. There's a note from her as well.'

'Why would she send them to you?'

'I messaged her to let her know you were in the doghouse,' she replied. 'Face it, Felix – how else are you two going to stay in touch?'

'Oh… Thanks. You can clear off now.'

'I'm not going anywhere. Dad told me to keep an eye on you.'

Being minded by his little sister was all he needed – he'd be a laughing stock. He sat down on a nearby garden wall to leaf through the printouts. It was the shots from the night before, and they were dynamite.

'They're just what you need for your article,' said Flo.

'Yeah, but there's nothing I can do about it now, is there? They set the trap and we blundered straight into it.'

'I can help, if you'll let me. I've read everything you've done on this and I've been working up one or two ideas of my own.'

'Sorry Flo, it's way too risky. I nearly got burnt to a crisp last night. I can't have you in the firing line as well.'

'OK, be like that. I'll just tag along, then. It's not as if you're going to have much company over the next few days, is it?'

They'd been at the Paddock for a couple of hours and having completed most of his chores, Felix was sitting in the lounge, slurping from a mug of tea. Flo was in the kitchen, looking through the window at the donkeys, idling away the early afternoon. Heart sinking, he flicked through the printouts Flo had given him, until he found Keira's message:

Hi Felix, You got off lightly last night. We were stuck there for another hour while Pluck laid it on thick. He doesn't want us going anywhere near the lido and says we have to drop the campaign or he'll lock us up until after the Tour.

He's going to tell the school on Monday. No prizes for guessing what's going to happen then.

The shots turned out well for once, but don't even think about using them – we're in enough trouble as it is. I'm grounded, Mum's taken my mobile, but I can still pick stuff up through Nic if you need to get in touch. Flo's got all the contact details.

Hope Doreen's OK.

Keira X

His thoughts were interrupted by a knock on the front door. Flo trotted through and levered it open, past the accumulation of junk mail littering the mat, to greet their visitor.

'How was the funeral, Naz?' Felix asked, pleased to see just about the only person outside his family he was still allowed to talk to.

'Not great, actually... Bloody hell, that's some haircut!' He crouched down to retrieve an envelope from the mess of taxi flyers and takeaway menus squashed up behind the door. 'Hey, this one's for you.'

'Oh... Thanks.' Felix stuffed it in his back pocket without giving it a second thought.

'So, what have I missed? Apart from the makeover, of course.'

Naz and Flo sat next there in stunned silence while Felix brought them up to speed. By the time he'd finished, Naz was incensed.

'You should go to the police. It's attempted murder, that's what it is!'

Felix rolled his eyes. 'Yeah, right. That boat sailed off about half-past-twelve, last night. No one's going to believe a word we say, now, are they?' He sat back, a resigned look on his face. 'I didn't have a clue what Wiseley was on about when he made that stupid threat: "An offer you can't refuse"? I mean, how was I supposed to know?'

'You what?' shrieked Naz.

'Have you heard it before?'

'Oh, *come on,* Felix! Hasn't everyone? It's, like, the most famous line from the greatest film ever made!'

Felix shrugged. 'OK, mate – spit it out, then.'

Naz settled back into the settee. '*The Godfather* – 1972 classic, Francis Ford Coppola directs. It's about this mega mafia boss – the Godfather – played by Marlon Brando. Amazing performance by the way. He won an Oscar for it.'

'Get on with it, will you?'

'Oh… sorry. Anyway, so the Godfather sends some heavies to see this Hollywood film producer at his LA mansion – swimming pool, stables, the works. He wants the producer to put one of his mafia mates in his next blockbuster, but the guy turns him down. So, the heavies say the Godfather will make him an offer he can't refuse. The producer just laughs and tells them to clear off.'

Felix yawned. 'Where's this going, Naz?'

'Next thing, he wakes up in the middle of the night to find his favourite racehorse's head rolled up in the sheets, next to him in bed.'

'Eeuugh! Just as well I don't own a racehorse.'

'No, you don't,' said Flo, who was back in the kitchen, gazing out through the window. 'But you're looking after Aunty Doreen's donkeys until she gets better, and unless I'm mistaken, one of them's missing.'

The impatient toot of the Fiesta's horn signalled their imminent departure to the hospital.

Felix briefed his sister as they headed down the garden path, towards the car. 'Not a word about this to anyone. She'll have just wandered off somewhere – we'll give it a day or two.'

The previous hour had been spent in a frantic but fruitless search. Titch had vanished, without a hint as to whether she'd simply done a runner, or was the victim of a sinister, *Godfather*-inspired kidnapping.

Felix shuddered at the thought.

To make matters even worse, their efforts had revealed one more piece of gut-churning news. The Hill Special, the antique bicycle that had brought a tear to the eye of their battle-hardened great-aunt, had disappeared as well. Felix had left it, unlocked, down the side of the bungalow when he'd come to help with the leafletting, the morning before. And now it had gone. Doreen would be devastated when she found out – it would probably kill her. And this time it really would be all his fault.

A couple of hours later, he was sitting on his own in one of the rain shelters down on the Prom, trying to get his head around how the strong, determined woman he'd struggled to keep up with on the beach, just the day before, could have been so totally transformed in such a short space of time. She'd looked so different, so frail – hollow cheeks and deep-sunk eyes, pale grey skin drawn tightly over her skull, the plastic tubing taped beneath her nose hissing with a constant stream of oxygen. The only upside was that she'd slept all the way through their visit. Waking up to the sight of the Haythornthwaite clan blubbing into their hankies would probably have finished her off, there and then.

They'd driven back from the hospital in silence and Felix was desperate to get out of the house to continue the search. He'd given up after an hour, making his way down to the sea front to agonise over the events of the last few days and wishing that, somehow, he could turn back time.

'Penny for 'em, cock,' an elderly man greeted him cheerily as he Zimmered past. ''Ere lad, I think you've dropped summat out your back pocket.' He pointed to a small brown envelope on the floor by Felix's feet.

'Oh... Thanks.'

He'd forgotten about the envelope Naz had found at the Paddock, earlier that afternoon. It was all a bit odd, now he came to think about it. He never got mail, unless it was his birthday, and anyway, who would have known he was spending time over at Doreen's? He picked the envelope up and ripped it open, pulling out a single sheet of paper.

It was a grainy, photocopied picture of a donkey.

Not just any donkey.

Despite the large, jagged-bladed knife being pressed to her neck by someone just out of frame, Titch looked remarkably unruffled. And in case there was any doubt about what was going on, a helpful message had been spelt out beneath the shot, using letters cut out from some old newspapers and magazines.

Drop the Lido story Haythornthwaite Or the donkey Gets it

*

'Come on, Flo, or you'll miss it!' Felix's mum shouted through to the dining room, where her daughter was ensconced in front of a laptop. She turned to her husband. 'That girl's always on the Internet these days, Brian, have you checked what she's up to?'

He tutted. 'It's nice she's found something she's interested in, Christine – something that doesn't involve burning down a much-loved local landmark building. Not like this idiot!' He lashed out a slippered foot, narrowly missing Felix's leg.

The three of them clustered around the TV to watch their daily dose of Tour action. Saturday's Prologue had been the traditional short-course time-trial, but the first formal stage started today, with the ride from Liege to Charleroi – a spin of a mere two hundred kilometres.

The day before, the riders had gone off individually, racing against the clock, but this time they started together – all one hundred and seventy-six of them. Glory hungry *domestiques* burst to the front, bidding to set up a breakaway, while the main group – the peloton – rolled along in what looked like effortless pursuit. From the air it was as if a giant, multi-coloured amoeba had escaped from some mad scientist's laboratory.

Flowing along the tarmac, it oozed its way around roundabouts, stretching out on the straights and contracting again as the riders and their teams bunched up together, vying for position.

The hour-long show had something for everyone, the race action interspersed with snippets of tactics and mind-boggling cycle technology, as well as highlighting places of historic interest along the route.

'Looks lovely,' remarked Felix's mum. 'We should think about Belgium for our holidays next year.'

The programme cut back to the road for last few kilometres of racing. The breakaways had been hoovered up by the main pack, the pace had increased and the commentary was heading into overdrive. It looked like chaos out there as the tightly-packed peloton belted, hell-for-leather around the impossibly narrow, crowd-lined streets of the busy Belgian city.

Thundering onto the finishing straight, half a dozen barrel-chested sprinters had somehow elbowed their way to the front, lurching crazily from side to side as they powered for the line. And then, from somewhere deep within their midst, the faintest of wobbles, a touch of wheels, and a bike catapulted high up over their heads as if someone had put a bomb under it. The carbon frame twisted in mid-air, spewing its rider across the road, arms and legs flailing. Felix could barely watch as those behind and on either side, toppled like skittles.

Felix's mum stared, open-mouthed, as the walking wounded dragged themselves across the line, shredded Lycra revealing red-raw wounds. Bikes costing roughly the same amount as an unimproved terraced house in Burnley, lay bent and broken on the tarmac behind them.

'Freddie! My baby!' she shrieked. 'Brian, you've got to stop him – it's not safe!'

'Don't worry yourself, love – it's nowt a massage and a plaster or two won't put right.'

Her husband's words did little to calm the situation as the TV images showed a team of paramedics scraping one of the riders up off the tarmac and onto a stretcher.

'Actually, there's no chance of our Fred getting caught up in something like that,' said Felix. 'He'll be twenty miles back down the road when the bunch sprint gets going.'

His dad turned on him, angrily. 'That's typical of you, Felix. Our Freddie's trying to make something of himself and all you can do is sit there and snipe!'

'Shhh.' Felix's mum called them back to order and attention switched, once again, to the welcoming face of veteran Tour commentator, Greg Sprocket.

'And there you have it, folks – just another incredible day of drama, here in Belgium. And searing through the chaos of the last two hundred metres, one man and one man alone, emerged victorious. National Champion of Australia and sprint specialist for Team CodPiece Credentials – Brad Mullet has bagged the first stage of this year's Tour.'

The footage showed the blond-haired Aussie, climbing up on the podium, in his skin-tone body-suit, complete with its lime-green mankini motif. As he was presented with the leader's yellow jersey, he made a grab for one of the pretty race promo-girls who was standing by his side. In a flash she'd swooned, into his arms.

'So, it's business as usual for the man from down under,' announced Sprocket. 'Watch out, you podium lovelies, there's plenty more juice in Mullet the Bullet's tank! But before we wrap up, there's just time for an update on another matter which looks set to darken every stage of this year's race – the ongoing *Domestique du Jour* fiasco. Over to you Darren.'

'Thanks, Greg.' Darren Ackhurst grinned into the camera. 'Team SpamFritter Deluxe pulled today's short-straw, hosting Stage One's *"DDJ"*, Clement Ferrand, a pig farmer from Belgium's Juprelle region. To be fair, no one could possibly accuse Clement of causing the finish line shunt, this afternoon – he'd only made it half way around the course when the sprint action got going. Despite this, the row has kicked off again, with team managers claiming that this daily farce is a danger to their riders as, well as disrespecting the tradition and history of the race.'

Back in Scundale Chase, the awkward silence was shattered by the ring of the landline. Felix's dad reached across to pick up the call. 'It'll be Freddie,' he said quietly, clamping a hand over the mouthpiece. 'Not a word on this, OK…? Oh, it's you, Dr Brown…' His voice immediately switched to a more formal tone. 'Sorry about that, I was expecting a call from France… Yes, a most regrettable turn of events for Mr Llewellyn-Evans – it could have happened to anyone.'

Felix's blood ran cold as he heard his sentence being handed down through one side of the conversation.

'I understand completely, Dr Brown,' his dad continued. 'Serious breach of school rules… Immediate exclusion… And that's permanent is it…? Yes, I see. Well, not the conversation I wanted to have with you, obviously, but thanks for letting us know so quickly. We'll start looking for an alternative, immediately.'

They say time flies when you're having fun – perhaps not so much when you're completely and utterly miserable. Looking out of the lounge window that drab Tuesday morning, just forty-eight hours before the big race, Felix was only too well aware of the effect his dark mood was having on the clock on the wall, which seemed to have stopped dead.

Cracking his knuckles, he sat down in front of Flo's laptop, only to discover close on one hundred unread emails received since the last log-on. He scanned the messages, quickly: 'Moondancer', 'Marshman', 'WombWalker' – *what the heck?* Their antivirus software must have broken down again. At least that was one thing his dad couldn't blame him for. He clicked on Nicole's email address and started typing:

Hi Keira, So sorry to hear you got the chop as well. I've really messed up, haven't I? The whole thing's a total disaster and I wish there was a way I could put it right.

No sign of Titch or the bike yet. No one knows they're missing, apart from Flo. It'll kill Doreen when she finds out and then my dad will kill me. Things are not looking good.

I still can't believe Wiseley could stoop so low. I just hope he keeps his word and we get Titch back in one piece when this is over.

Team ChocolatBanane are staying over at the Majestic in Slaidforth tomorrow, so Fred is coming with us to visit Doreen at the hospital. He's still feeling sorry for himself, but not half as sorry as he'll be after he's made a complete arse of himself in the big race!

Hope you're OK. Looking forward to getting together again.

Felix XX

He sat back, reading and re-reading his words. Signing it off like that was alright, wasn't it? He used to put kisses on his Christmas and birthday 'Thank You' messages... but this was a bit different. He pressed 'Send' before he could agonise over it any longer.

Strolling into town, that lunchtime, Felix had to keep reminding himself that he was still in Frecklesall-on-Sea – still in the same one-horse dump at the end of the road to nowhere. Now, as he looked out across a sparkling vista, magically transformed by two weeks of hard labour and a limitless budget, he saw a place where things were most definitely 'Happening'. Frecklesall had been buffed and polished to perfection, and was buzzing with an exotic array of visitors, all looking forward to the big day. To top it all, a huge white yacht had appeared out in the bay, lending the place an unlikely air of Mediterranean sophistication.

Heading down Marine Drive, he had an excellent view of the usually desolate town moor, which was now a hive of activity. An army of workers was beavering away, erecting a city of marquees, awnings and pop-ups, in anticipation of the thousands of riders, support staff, media types and hangers-on, who would be rolling into town in thirty-six hours or so. Their temporary home, the 'Tour Village', had to be ready in time.

Down on the Prom, a small gathering had clustered around the top of the slipway, peering out towards a pristine motor launch that had set off from the yacht. It was rumoured that Madonna might be paying a visit, so Felix decided to hang around, just in case. Tucked away behind a conveniently placed phone box, he tried to make sense of what was going on. There were about twenty people in the group, all told. White, male and middle-aged, they looked unshaven and scruffy, their clothes crumpled. Most were toting cameras with huge telephoto lenses.

It didn't take Felix too long to work out that the grumbling rabble were actually the cream of the nation's *paparazzi.*

Half-smoked cigarettes were flicked aside as the motor launch moored up. Felix felt an involuntary shudder run down his spine as the massive frame of Randy Pike lumbered onto deck, the whole boat tilting as he jumped ashore. A few seconds later, a tall, slim figure, concealed in a white, three-quarter length coat, matching headscarf and designer shades, was helped across onto the quayside.

The place went wild.

''Erbina, them stories about you and 'Ollywood superstar, Dwayne Valderrama – are they true?'

'How did 'e pop the question? Was it when you was together in the hot-tub on *Celebrity Love Lagoon*?'

Their estuary accents grated across the Prom, questions fizzing in like guided missiles.

'Flash us a bit of leg willyer, babe? Camera loves you, darlin'!'

'This way love – into the lens for me!'

Randy held his arms up in a plea for silence. No one was about to argue.

'It's such an honour for me to be here in Ferck-Les-Hall, an' I thank y'all most kindly.' Herbina began, in her Texan twang. 'It's true – Dwayne and I are so very much in lurrve.' She fluttered her left hand, which was weighed down with a dazzling diamond engagement ring. 'I was gonna keep it a secret, but I'm so excited – an' you folks are like family to me now.'

'When's the 'appy day then, babe?' someone shouted.

'I'd love to tell y'all about my man,' she replied, coyly, 'but shoot! I have an important message to share with all my fans over here in Ing-er-laynd!' In the next instant she'd dropped her coat and headscarf to the floor, revealing a pair of skimpy pink shorts with matching bikini top, her long blond hair now flowing free. And then she was striking poses, pouting away beside a copy of her new DVD – *Get Legs Like Herbina Smilerski (or your money back!)*.

The 'paps' were in heaven.

Felix headed home in a state of barely contained fury. The whole thing was pathetic! Frecklesall was going down the pan, he'd uncovered the biggest scandal to hit his home town – ever – and all the media cared about were Herbina's legs. It was only as he was trudging along Winthrop Avenue that the significance of her words finally clicked. She was engaged to Hollywood heart-throb, Dwayne Valderrama.

It was, as Freddie would have said, 'game over'.

'Stage three, and on a scorching-hot day when most of the GC contenders were content to sit back and let their *domestiques* do the hard yards, we're really no nearer to knowing how the general classification is going to shape up,' announced Greg Sprocket. 'Modesto Scaglioni, Bert Camembert, Manley Torso, Heinz Krankel – just take your pick from the Tour's elite. And let's not forget Britain's Derek Trundle – a dark horse, but one more than capable of challenging for honours in the mountains, next week.

'But of course, the day belongs to that man, Mullet. Following the drama of yet another bunch sprint, the Aussie now has *three* consecutive stage victories and a third yellow jersey to add to his collection. What a rider!'

The picture cut to the bestubbled, heavy-jawed Australian as a handful of microphones were thrust into his face for the post-race interview. 'Totally stoked!' he drawled. 'Aaabsolute ripsnorter! An' I just wanna say to all you pommie bastards over there in the UK – hook up your hosepipes boys, 'cos Brad Mullet is so hot, he's literally settin' the road on fire!'

Greg Sprocket appeared back on screen. 'Three down and if he wins again tomorrow, he'll equal the legendary "Super Mario" Cippolini's '99 Tour best, of four stage wins on the bounce! Darren?'

'Indeed, Greg. Mullet isn't everyone's cup of tea, but you can't argue with his record. And talking of the nation's favourite beverage, Greg, spare a thought for poor old Pierre Choufleur – today's *Domestique du Jour* – who stirred up further controversy as a guest of the Storm Teabags boys, finishing a full two hours behind the main field on this one-hundred-and-seventy-kilometre stage. As he crossed the line, he said, and I quote: "I don't care – they're all on drugs, anyway". Greg?'

'Bit of a storm in a tea cup, there, Darren?'

'I tell you what, Greg – Pierre has brewed up some real trouble for race director, Patrice Perpignan. The team managers have scheduled an emergency summit meeting for tomorrow evening, where they'll be calling for the whole *Domestique du Jour* category to be scrapped, with immediate effect.'

18

'*He doesn't know about Herbina, does he*?' Felix whispered to his sister as they sat together in the waiting area outside the hospital ward.

'I don't think so,' she replied earnestly. 'We should leave it until after the race before we tell him. Let's face it, he's not going to win, is he? He's never going to actually meet her.'

The return of the prodigal son had been a low-key affair. Arriving late and without apology, he looked ridiculous in his yellow and brown ChocolatBanane tracksuit and matching baseball cap. After tears from his mum and a manly pat on the back from his dad, Freddie and the rest of the family were ushered through into the cardiac ward.

Felix recognised a familiar face heading towards them. 'Miss Catlow, what are you doing here?' he asked.

The aged school secretary looked startled. 'Visiting Doreen actually – we're old friends. Now, if you'll excuse me…' She scurried past, leaving the Haythornthwaites to cluster around Doreen's bed.

It sounded like the old lady was on the mend. 'Oh, it's you, Freddie,' she said, sharply. 'Take that stupid hat off, lad – you're not impressing anyone looking like that, y'know. Now, tell me what you've been up to.'

'Err, I dunno really – this and that,' Freddie grunted, swiping the branded cap from his head. 'Riding a bike up the Pyrenees, for the most part. They're these mountains. Kinda big... somewhere over Italy way, I reckon.'

The conversation struggled on as torturously as a first category Alpine climb and it didn't take long for the patient to lose her patience.

'Right, you two.' Doreen gestured towards the parents. 'I need to spend a bit of time with your kids. Go and get yourselves a coffee from the shop. I'll send them down to you, later.'

'But Doreen,' said Felix's dad, 'you must be tired, and Freddie needs to get back to the Majestic soon so he can be with the team.'

'Be told, Brian!' she snapped, before reverting to a frailer voice. 'I... I'm really not sure how much more time I have left. There are some things I need to say to the youngsters before I... I pass.'

'But—'

His wife frowned. 'For goodness sake, Brian – can't you see how important this is?' She turned to her kids. 'I want you all to listen really carefully to what your Aunty Doreen's got to say. She's a very wise woman.'

The two of them walked away, arguing, leaving the siblings to gather around their great-aunt, who offered Felix a sly wink.

'Right, you lot,' she announced, brightly. 'What's the plan?'

Felix couldn't believe what he was hearing. 'What plan? What d'you mean?'

'The Tour de France is coming to town tomorrow. If you think I'm hanging around in here while all that's going on, you want your bumps feeling. One way or another, I'll be out there, cheering on our Freddie. And when that's done and dusted, I'm sorting out that bastard Wiseley, good and proper.'

Felix felt the knot tighten in his stomach. He was going to have to tell her what had happened or he'd be waking up in the middle of the night next to Titch's severed head. 'Actually, I'm not sure that's such a good idea, Doreen,' he ventured, nervously.

'Never had you down as a backslider, lad. What's up?'

'It's just that… well, you've had a heart attack, haven't you? You need to rest.'

'Let me worry about that,' she replied, defiantly. 'I feel fine – never better.'

'But, Aunty Doreen, you need to stay here where they'll look after you,' pleaded Flo.

'There's nowt to fret about, Florence, love,' she said, reaching out to hold her great-niece's hand. 'I've been through worse. Anyway, Freddie, as it's your special day, I've brought you a present.' She reached under the bed and passed him a crumpled plastic carrier bag.

Freddie's face lit up. 'Nice one. What is it?'

'Just a special T-shirt I had made up for you. I thought you could wear it under your uniform, in the race tomorrow. Why not try it on?'

Seconds later, his tracksuit top was in a heap on the floor and he was pulling the bright orange T-shirt over his head. Puffing out his chest, he struck a pose.

'Lovely!' said Doreen. 'Just two things you need to do for me – do you think you can remember?'

He nodded uncertainly.

'Number one: when you get into the lead in the big race – whenever that is – I want you to get that horrible

236

chocolate banana top off your back, so that everyone can see your new T-shirt.'

Freddie pulled a face.

'And number two.' She drew him in close. 'As soon as you've done that, I want you to press the button – the one tucked away on the inside.'

He wriggled around, grappling with himself for a few seconds. 'Like this, Doh?'

The whole ward erupted into cheers as a flashing message lit up across Freddie's chest:

SAVE
FRECKLESALL LIDO!

'Turn around lad,' she said. 'Show us the back.'

SAVE FRECKLESALL'S
FAMOUS DONKEYS!

Doreen was beside herself. 'Perfect! Bob Bulgy gave me the idea in that Grand Prix race. Never misses a trick, our Bob – he's been doing a roaring trade ever since. When I looked at those cycling mags you brought in for me, Florence, I realised they're all at it. Most of the riders only bust a gut on the breakaways to get their sponsor's name on the telly. And whoever wins, well...' She reached down and fished out an old copy of *Pro Cycling*. 'Look at the state of this lot – shameless.'

She was right. Every victorious rider was pictured crossing the line, arms aloft, proudly displaying his sponsor's corporate logo.

'They're nowt more than mobile advertising hoardings,' she continued. 'And we've got prime space for free, thanks to our Freddie! What d'you say, lad?'

Felix could feel the panic welling up inside. It was a brilliant idea but he couldn't allow it to happen – not if they were ever going to see Titch alive again. It took him a moment to find his voice. 'The thing is, Doreen—'

'Sorry Doh, no can do.' His brother jumped in. 'I signed this really heavy contract. I've gotta keep the Chocolate Banana gear on all the time or they'll sue my ass.'

Doreen fixed him with her hard stare. 'You might want to rethink that answer, Freddie.'

'No way, José, as they say in Fra—'

She cut across him, sharp as a knife. 'It were way back in 1917 when your great-great-granddad eventually made it home from the First World War. The silly bugger left one of his legs behind at the Somme, so no one was about to offer him a job. In the end he scraped all his brass together and borrowed a load more, so he could take on the donkeys. They've been in our family ever since. And now *you* want to chuck it all away.'

'It's legal stuff!' spluttered Freddie. 'I can't.'

'That don't wash with me, lad. The council have got their fancy lawyers lined up to kick me out of my home. They say it's legal and maybe it is, for all I know, but it's not *right*. And think on this – you're only in that race tomorrow because of me... well, me and Billy. The Hill Special was his bike, after all. He always wanted a crack at the big one – the Tour. He'd have got his chance too, if only...'

One of the nurses came over to check that everything was alright.

'I'm fine, nurse – really.' The frailty switched seamlessly back into Doreen's voice as she pointed to the bedside curtains, tied back against the wall. 'Would you mind, dear? I'd really appreciate a bit of privacy while I talk to these youngsters.'

The nurse drew the curtains around the bed and the old lady beckoned her visitors closer.

Felix gave it one last go. 'You must be tired, Doreen. We should let you get some rest.

'No one's going anywhere!' she snapped. 'Not until I've told you about my Billy – Billy Rankin.' She coughed loudly, her chest heaving with the effort. 'It was down at the lido, back in the summer of '63. I remember that first time we met, like it were yesterday. He had such a lovely smile – so handsome. I was queuing up to get an ice cream and managed to drop mine on the floor. Billy did the chivalrous thing and bought me another.'

Freddie was impressed. 'Wow! Lucky break, or what?'

She rolled her eyes. 'I did it on purpose, you idiot. Anyway, we got to talking, and soon after, we started seeing each other, proper-like. I was quite a looker back then.'

Freddie was unable to hide his surprise.

'It's true – she was a stunner,' said Felix, remembering the old photo albums.

'What do you mean "was"?' Doreen corrected him.

'Absolutely!' he laughed. 'Still is!'

'Everyone knew Billy,' she continued. 'People liked their cycling back then and he was at the top of his game. He'd just won his first North of England title and we knew it was only a matter of time before he got snapped up by one of the European teams.

'We got on so well, it was like we were meant for each other. One thing led to another and not long after, we got engaged. He proposed to me while he was sat on the Hill Special, y'know.'

Felix shifted uncomfortably at the mention of the missing bike.

'We were due to be wed the weekend after the Nationals. They were being held in Preston that year.' She paused to blow her nose. 'But then everything went wrong.'

'Why? What happened?' asked Flo.

Doreen closed her eyes as the memories came flooding back. 'It was just an ordinary training ride, a few days before the race. The weather was closing in so I told him he shouldn't go out. He was having none of it, as usual. I can hear him now – said he loved me and he'd be back soon… And that were that. He never stood a chance, poor love. Can't blame the lorry driver – the fog was down, something terrible.'

They all heard the sniffling sounds coming from the other side of the curtains. Flo pulled them back to reveal a trio of nurses in floods of tears.

'I went off the rails a bit after that, if I'm being honest,' the old lady continued. 'I couldn't come to terms with what had happened. Eventually it was my brother, Ron – that's your granddad – who sorted me out. He and Edith let me stay on at the Paddock and I helped them with the donkeys. I've been there ever since.'

'I'm so sorry,' said Felix. 'That's awful.'

She waved away his sympathy. 'The point is, Freddie, that's why I need you to do this for me. The lido, the donkeys, the Hill Special – they're all I've got.

I can't just sit back and let some giant American supermarket chain steamroller the lot!'

Freddie got to his feet, his face a picture of angst. 'I… I can't do it, Doh. I'm really sorry.' Head down, he dashed out of the ward.

There was an uneasiness about the drive home that afternoon which was about much more than the chaos on the roads.

'I don't know what was up with him, do I?' said Felix. 'Nerves, probably – it's his big day tomorrow.'

'I've never seen him so upset,' said his mum. 'He ran past us without even saying goodbye. Are you sure you don't know what's mithering him?'

Felix sat there in glum silence. He'd been too afraid to tell his great-aunt that her beloved Billy's Hill Special had been stolen, let alone that one of her precious donkeys had been kidnapped. And now it was eating him up.

'Felix!' shouted his mum. 'I'm talking to you.'

'Sorry, Mum. I've no idea what it's about.'

'Bloody hippies,' muttered his dad, as they inched past an old VW camper van, stranded at the side of the road. 'What the hell are they doing here anyway?'

'They've as much right as we have, Brian,' his wife replied.

'Hmmph… maybe – when they start paying their taxes like the rest of us.' He leaned out of the window to shout at the two grungy men, who were poking around in the engine at the back of the van. 'Get your hair cut – you look like a couple of girls!'

'Brian!'

'No, I'm sorry, Christine, it's not on. Look at that heap of junk – "Save the Whales", "Troops Out of Afghanistan", "Meat is Murder"? It's ridiculous! A couple of years in the army is what they need.'

Felix peered through the Fiesta's rear window as they crawled past. The rusted bodywork on the battered old van had been daubed with slogans supporting every right-on cause from the past twenty-five years. But what was it doing in Frecklesall?

As they accelerated away, he did a double-take. There it was, emblazoned across one of the front panels:

Say 'No' to Globalisation!
Save Frecklesall's Donkeys!

'Bloody hell!'

His mum tutted. 'Language, Felix! What is it now?'

'Nothing Mum. I was… err… just looking at the state of that van.'

They drove on in silence until they were flagged-down by a young constable at the side of the road.

'Sorry about this, folks,' he said, leaning in through the open window. 'Everyone's heading into town for the race tomorrow, but we've got wind of some bother. It's this anti-globalisation mob. We're not sure why they're here or what they're up to, but we're turning them back as best we can.' Satisfied there were no protestors hiding in the car, he stood aside and waved them on their way.

Felix's dad put his foot down and five white-knuckle minutes later, they landed on the settee in the lounge, the remote control firing the TV into life, just as the title music was running on the Tour highlights show.

And then the doorbell rang.

Flo cracked first, grumbling as she made her way out to the hall to see who could be calling at such an inconsiderate time.

Felix heard the front door open and the beginnings of a conversation. Assuming it was friends of hers, he settled in to watch the race action. But by the first advert break, his sister was still out there. Eventually, her irate father dragged himself up from the settee to check what was going on. Moments later he was bellowing from the doorstep, 'I don't care who called you or what bloody planet you're from – she's nine, and she's *not* coming out to your meeting!'

Felix dived over to the bay window to see what was going on.

Three new-age travellers, dressed from head to toe in black, facial piercings and matted hair to the fore, had made a tactical withdrawal to the end of the driveway.

'That's bad Karma, man – Flo is our leader!' one of them shouted from a safe distance. 'We come to seek her aura, her wisdom!'

'I'll give you some wisdom,' Felix's dad yelled back. 'Clear off home to your wigwams before I call the police!'

The new-age trio turned and shuffled away.

'And get yourselves jobs while you're about it!'

The front door slammed shut and a shout went up from the hallway. 'Florence Haythornthwaite, what the hell have you been up to on that bloody computer?'

'Mullet Mania has quite literally taken this Tour by storm!' gushed Darren Ackhurst. 'Today's victory puts him level with 'Super Mario' Cippolini's legendary best, but it was way back in 1909 that Luxembourg's Francois

Faber set one of the longest-standing Tour records, bagging five stage wins on the bounce. With a flat circuit in store at Frecklesall-on-Sea up in Lancashire, tomorrow, and a sprint finish a near-certainty, Brad Mullet will really fancy his chances! Greg?'

'Without a shadow of a doubt, Darren,' chimed Sprocket. 'But there's one young man who must be quaking in his boots tonight. Frecklesall Cyclonics' Freddie Haythornthwaite is tomorrow's *DDJ*, hosted by the Team ChocolatBanane boys. Following yet another fiasco on today's stage, there's talk of a rider protest. Let's just hope it doesn't spoil the spectacle for UK race fans, and that the seventeen-year-old poolside attendant doesn't make too much of a fool of himself! Darren?'

'Couldn't agree more, Greg. I've got some sound advice for young Freddie, if he's watching, and it's simply this. Mate – stay at home tomorrow, put your feet up and enjoy the race with us, right here on ITV3.'

19

As Felix shuffled into the kitchen for his breakfast the following morning, it was clear that someone else had taken his place in the family doghouse. It was his little sister who'd 'overstepped the mark' and 'brought shame on the family name'.

What a refreshing change!

As an unexpected bonus he'd been reunited with his mobile, his mum overriding his dad's objections on the basis that they needed to stay in touch, on this of all days.

The evening before had seen a steady stream of unwelcome callers to 21 Scundale Chase, a grungy array of new age protest groupies rolling up to pledge allegiance to their spiritual mentor – nine-year-old Florence Haythornthwaite. Sadly, they were all given short-shrift by her increasingly irate father, who, by the end of the evening, looked like he might explode.

Flo cracked quickly under interrogation. Frustrated by her brother's floundering campaign and outraged by the injustice of it all, she'd launched SOLD! (Save Our Lido and Donkeys!) a hard-hitting web-blog set up to highlight what was going on in Frecklesall. Suffice to say, things had got a little bit out of hand.

'Cyber-crime!' her dad yelled. 'The FBI, the CIA – they monitor this kind of stuff, y'know. And if they trace it back here, I'm the one who'll end up in Guantanamo Bay wearing one of them orange boiler suits.'

Chance would be a fine thing, Felix thought as he made his excuses and headed off to do his early morning chores at the Paddock – at least, that's what he'd told his parents.

Even at half-past-eight in the morning, the pavements were awash with race fans of every shape, size and nationality. Many had been out all night and they'd certainly been busy, the jet-black tarmac of the newly resurfaced roads now scarred with graffiti in support of their favourites: 'Forza Scaglioni!'; 'Allez Camembert!'; 'Go! Torso'. Away from the crowds, clusters of anti-globalisation protestors, who'd somehow managed to dodge the police road blocks, were gathered in subversive huddles. And all because of Flo and her SOLD! blog.

The roads were even busier than a normal Thursday morning – clogged with a crazy cavalcade of promotional vehicles. ChocolatBanane cars vied for position alongside low-loaders converted into Storm Tea Bags pirate ships. Super U-bend had transformed their vans into giant mobile toilets, while SpamFritter Deluxe's giant frankfurters on wheels and a fleet of Quelle Fromage? motorised cheeses, maintained the surreal theme. Europop blared from speakers accompanying dancing chocolate bananas, hardy Scandinavian types wearing multi-coloured mankinis, and Frenchmen in overalls, juggling plastic plumbing accessories.

The race fans were sporting an array of fancy dress outfits, many of them wearing Mullet wigs. Shouts of 'G'day cobber!' and 'Rripper!' followed Felix up the street. It would have been brilliant to find a decent spot and enjoy the spectacle, but he had bigger fish to fry. After checking his rucksack one more time, he hurried on his way.

The gathering at the Paddock was their first get-together since the fire. Shuffling into the lounge, the mood was distinctly downbeat – anticipation of the following morning's appointment with Sergeant Pluck casting a shadow over the excitement of the day. But Felix was grappling with a more immediate concern.

'Calm down, willyer?' pleaded Bernie. 'There's no way your aunt's turning up. She'll be lying in her hospital bed with a nice cup of tea and a biscuit, watching it on telly.'

'You don't know what she's like,' muttered Felix. 'She had this look about her, like nothing's going to stop her. And if she does make it here, I'm dead meat.'

Spuggie gave him a playful thump on the shoulder. 'Yeah, and if she kicks off on the lido thing again, it's Titch who's gonna be dead meat!'

Keira pulled them back to order. 'Can we get on with it, please? The race starts in less than two hours. If you want us to do something, Felix, now would be a pretty good time to tell us what it is.'

'Oh… Right,' he began uncertainly. 'Everyone's in town today, and I mean *everyone*, so I've had these flyers printed. I need you to mix in with the crowd and hand out as many as you can.'

There were groans as he pulled a thick wad of leaflets from his rucksack.

Keira studied the black and white picture of Titch, scanned from the ransom note. 'Are you sure about this?

I mean, this reward you're offering – have you even got two hundred quid?'

'Don't worry about that,' he replied, realising for the first time he hadn't a clue where the money was coming from. 'I'll be stuck in the VIP area with my mum and dad – we've got these special tickets because of Fred. If I try doling these out in there, I won't last long, so I'm going straight to the organ-grinder.'

Naz looked bemused. 'You what?'

'Wiseley. I'm going to put him straight – tell him we've dropped the lido story and that there aren't any photos. Then I'll ask him where Titch is, and the bike, for that matter. And if he's not playing ball, I'm taking it straight to Herb.'

Keira shook her head in disbelief. 'You've lost your marbles, mate. Randy's half-killed you already, and Roy will be out for revenge after what you did to him at the Pig the other night. Don't even think about it.'

It was a hot, humid day, the early sunshine giving way to ominous-looking clouds that billowed upwards, towering over the horizon like heavenly sky-scrapers. Frecklesall town centre was heaving, but the scrum of the Tour Village was even worse. Thousands of fans were cruising the array of merchandise and food stalls, spending money hand over fist – some already showing signs of a few too many beers.

Felix joined the crush, navigating his way past the tantalising smells of French patisserie and the roar of overworked espresso machines. Five minutes later, he landed at what he thought was the right entrance, and waited. Eventually, his mum and dad appeared, dragging their unhappy-looking daughter along behind them.

Brandishing lanyard passes, they were waved through the security checks into the rarefied surrounds reserved for Very Important People.

The Haythornthwaites instantly found themselves in another world – an altogether more agreeable place, where uniformed catering staff waited hand and foot on an army of suits, all intent on guzzling their brunches and downing as many Aperols as possible, before the inconvenience of the race.

Being in a prime spot, they were able to watch the riders warm up on the rows of static turbo machines, while race officials scurried about barking unintelligible French into two-way radios. Down at the start line, Lancashire Constabulary's entire fleet of motorbikes and a handful of powerful, exotic-looking French police machines, were polished, primed and ready for action.

Felix spotted the Smiler Corporation enclosure and his heart raced at the thought of heading in there to put Wiseley straight.

'Get a move on, will you?' grumbled his dad. 'Mum wants to catch up with our Freddie and when we've done that, we'll grab a coffee.'

They strolled over to the barrier by the technical area, just as the sleek, yellow and brown Team ChocolatBanane cruiser-line coach purred to a halt. As the riders disembarked, one shrill voice rose above the cheers of the crowd.

'Cooeee, Modesto! Over here!' It was Felix's mum.

Felix cringed in embarrassment.

'Christine!' her husband snapped. 'You're old enough to be his mother. And in case you'd forgotten, you're already wed to me!'

'More's the pity,' she muttered.

Last off the bus, Freddie looked forlorn and fed-up. He offered them a half-hearted wave.

'What's up with him, then?' asked Felix's dad, but before anyone could respond, they were joined by Frecklesall's Tour Ambassador, Giselle Lacroix.

'Ahh, Felice! It is so nice to see you. *Sacre bleu* – I am loving this new *coiffure*! I can actually see your face for once. You really are quite 'andsome, underneath.'

Felix blushed.

'Ferdie has done well, *non*?' she continued. 'You must be very proud. And remember, I am still so grateful for your *assistance* the other day. If there is anything I can do for you, you must say, *oui*?'

Now that really was an offer he couldn't refuse!

The giant, on-stage screen burst into life and suddenly, the image of Greg Sprocket was beaming down at them. 'Welcome to Frecklesall-on-Sea, here in sunny Lancashire!' he began. 'We've had word from the Met Office that thunder storms are heading our way, but you won't have to wait long to see lightning in the sky, because there's always electricity in the air when my next guest is on the scene! Ladies and gentlemen, please welcome our current race leader and yellow jersey holder – the man who is, today, looking to equal Francois Faber's 1909 record of five successive stage wins – Team CodPiece Credentials' Brad MULLET!'

The crowd erupted, even the suits standing up to applaud.

'G'day Grig! Howz the dangle on yer dingo, mate?' Mullet greeted the race pundit.

Sprocket's earnest expression cracked, for just an instant, but he quickly regained his composure. 'So, today's the day, Brad – a record no one ever thought could be equalled. How are you feeling?'

'Ah, look mate – I'll give it a fair go. The way I'm seein' it, if it comes down to a head-to-head in the last keelo, there's only one guy gunna hit the mark, and that's yours truly – the Mullet Man!' He grinned and winked into the camera.

Giselle turned to Felix. 'That Brad Murllet is a sprinter *par excellence*, but 'e is not such a nice man. I would like to see 'im, 'ow you say, knocked down a peg or two.'

'I'll have a word with Freddie,' Felix said, laughing. 'See if he can sort that for you.'

The riders began drifting towards the start line about forty-five minutes later. The crowd was buzzing with excitement, but for the men in Lycra it looked like just another day in the office.

Straining their eyes to see through the forest of frail, whippet-like torsos and ridiculously muscled legs, the Haythornthwaites searched for Freddie, who, apart from the initial wave, had kept a low profile. Suddenly a temporary parting of bodies and bicycles gave them a clear view of Frecklesall's *Domestique du Jour*.

Amidst all the slick designer outfits and high-tech carbon framesets, Freddie stood out like a sore thumb. As if the yellow and brown bumblebee stripes of his jersey weren't bad enough, the large red 'L' emblazoned across its back must have rubbed salt into his already wounded vanity. His helmet was also different, and not in a good way. Designed to replicate the top half of a partly-peeled chocolate banana, it looked like it had been stolen from a Smurf. There was a battery pack and a bulb in there somewhere and the whole thing was flashing away.

His bike continued the same low-tech theme. A monster heavyweight, it featured a solid-looking frame and big, chunky tyres. A multi-tiered racking arrangement, stuffed with drinks bottles, had been bolted over the back wheel. The whole package must have weighed a ton.

Freddie was being set up to fail and Felix could tell from the look on his brother's face, that he knew it all too well.

Street lamps began flickering into life as the first rumbles of thunder signalled the despatch of the police motorbikes. A yellow Peugeot estate led the procession along the Prom, and a mighty cheer went up as Patrice Perpignan emerged through its sun-roof to wave the red starters' flag. The peloton followed on behind, rolling across the start line pursued by a monster traffic jam of horn-tooting support vehicles.

As the riders set off up the sea front, the 'corporates' in the VIP area shuffled back to their cocktails and canapés, wondering how best to fill the fifty minutes or so until the race returned for its second circuit. The Haythornthwaites stayed put, watching the spectacle on the big screen.

It looked like the riders were tootling along at little more than walking pace, the action a million miles away from the thrills and spills everyone had been following on TV. Past the Big Lamp roundabout and the front row was like a Hall of Fame of international pro cycling, but in slow-motion. Brad Mullet was blowing kisses to his many admirers and beside him, Bert Camembert was engaged in an animated conversation with Manley Torso. Pedro Zapatista, Bent Smorgasbord and Sven Klanger were sitting up in their saddles, finishing off a shared bag of croissants, while other riders were admiring the scenery, or checking messages on their phones. And twenty metres back, bobbing along in the midst of a sea of aerodynamically profiled cycling helmets, Freddie's chocolate banana hat was flashing away like a Belisha beacon.

Felix pointed to the bottom of the screen, where a link to one of the motorbikes, showed the riders' average speed. 'Blimey,' he remarked, 'they're only doing twenty K an hour. What's going on?'

'That's more than fast enough,' said his mum. 'We don't want our Freddie caught up in one of those awful crashes, do we?'

A support car eased up beside the leaders and a cardboard tube, about a metre in length, was handed to Heinz Krankel. The German tore it open and a banner was slowly unfurled across the front row of the peloton, its message spelt out in bold lettering:

ABANDONNER le DOMESTIQUE DU JOUR – MAINTENANT!

'What does that even mean?' asked Felix's dad.

'It means,' his daughter replied in an instant, 'Abandon the *Domestique du Jour* – Now!''

'Bad news, ladies and gentlemen. We've just received an emergency communiqué from Race Control, which confirms our worst fears.' Greg Sprocket sounded decidedly downbeat. 'It's now official – we have a rider protest on our hands. The teams are demanding an immediate end to the *Domestique du Jour* rider category, and to make their point, they've declared a 'go slow' until the final circuit – Darren?'

'Thanks, Greg.' The picture on the big screen cut to the former pro rider, who was crammed into the back of one of the support cars, his knees up round his chin. 'A huge disappointment for all the fans here today, but feelings are running high and the guys are totally united on this issue – which means everyone can relax until lap four.'

'Outrageous!' Felix's dad yelled, at no one in particular. 'Bloody foreigners! They come over here, close our roads, and what do they do then? They go on strike, don't they? Typical of the French! Our Freddie should show 'em what's what. COME ON, LAD. GET STUCK IN!'

The embarrassing rant was curtailed by his mobile's ringtone. 'What d'you mean "missing"?' he barked into the hand-set, after listening for a few seconds. 'You're supposed to be looking after her, aren't you? She can't just have disappeared!'

Ashen-faced, he closed the call and told them the news. 'Doreen's missing. She walked out of the ward this morning. No one knows where she's gone.'

Felix and Flo told their parents what their great-aunt had said at the hospital. There was no point in holding anything back, not when her life was at stake. They split up to look for her – Flo tagging along with her mum, their dad stomping away on his own, grumbling under his breath.

Felix set off in the opposite direction, beside himself with worry. Searching for his great-aunt might have been an easier task if the race had actually got going, but with the go-slow providing entertainment on a par with watching paint dry, the Tour Village was rammed with punters, more interested in buying tacky souvenirs and knocking back the beers, than watching the sedate, multi-coloured parade wending its way along the country lanes of north Lancashire.

His mood sank ever lower as each minute passed. Trudging on through the crowd, he all but missed the arrival of the peloton at the end of the first circuit, only catching the briefest of glimpses on the screen as the riders rolled by.

And then his mobile rang. It was Spuggie's number, but Keira was on the line.

'Felix? Guess who we just bumped into?'

His heart raced – it was too much to hope for, surely? 'I… I don't know. Just tell me, will you?'

'Alright – keep your hair on! It was your old mate, Fudgeley-Smythe – at least I *think* it was him. Looked like he'd lost an argument with a brick wall. He had this metal frame taped over his nose and the two blackest eyes I've ever seen.'

'That's a pity,' said Felix, drily.

'You're telling me! I've got something else that might cheer you up. We may have a lead on Titch.'

'Oh...' He should have been jumping for joy, but Titch's wellbeing didn't seem that important now.

'Hey, don't get too excited about it, will you?' snapped Keira, clearly put out. 'If you don't want us to bother, just say the word.'

'Sorry – I've a lot on my mind at the moment. What have you got?'

'Well, I just had a chat with these hippies who spent the night in their van, down by the lock-ups on the Fishfoot Lane estate. They heard something kicking off, late on. They thought it was kids messing around at first, but when we showed them the picture of Titch and explained what had happened, they weren't so sure. It'll take us ages to get down there, but I'll let you know how it goes. How about you?'

Felix sighed. 'Couldn't get much worse. Doreen's done a runner from hospital. She'll end up killing herself unless we can find her.'

'Oh… I'm sorry, Felix – you must be worried sick. Listen, she's a tough lady, I'm sure she'll be OK. We'll keep an eye out for her, as well. One more thing, though – there's no way you can go and talk to Wiseley, now.'

'I've got other things to worry about, to be honest. But why – what's up?'

'Look at the road, you numpty.'

He turned to focus on the distant screen. There wasn't that much to see from the motorbike cameras, but as soon as the picture switched to the aerial view from the helicopter, it all became clear. The road painting graffiti artists had been out in force the night before, but apart from the usual slogans in support of their heroes, there were another couple of unmissable messages screaming out every few hundred metres:

SAVE FRECKLESALL LIDO!

WE ♥ FRECKLESALL'S DONKEYS!

'Who did that?' he croaked, his throat suddenly feeling incredibly dry.

'It must be the anti-globalisation mob,' Keira replied. 'There are loads of them hanging around. I guess no one told them the campaign was off.'

Felix felt like crying. Just about everything that could have gone wrong, had done – and then some. Doreen was on the run, Titch had been kidnapped, the Hill Special was missing… and any chance he might have had of convincing Wiseley that the lido campaign was over, had disappeared beneath a few tins of white emulsion. It was a disaster!

The rain was falling now, and as the first crackles of lightning ripped across the leaden sky, the crowd's carnival mood shifted towards a more pressing search for shelter. Head down, Felix began the long walk back towards the VIP compound, only to be stopped, dead in his tracks, by the iron grip that locked onto his shoulder.

It was Randy Pike.

'Hey Romeo! Nice to see you again, buddy! Kinda convenient as well – you got an appointment with the Mayor, I believe?'

Felix's groan of dismay was drowned out by the ominous boom of thunder, rumbling away in the distance.

Randy laughed, in his weird, high-pitched snicker. 'Mayor Troy is exercised somewhat by the stoopid games you kids bin playin'. First the shots and now these dumb-ass protests.' He shook his head, sadly. 'I gotta tell you, this whole scenario reminds me of that schmuck, Fudgeley-Smythe. Guy had this terrible accident. You hear 'bout that?'

Felix grimaced.

'And what I find upsettin', from a personal perspective,' continued the American, 'is how the same thing could so easily happen to someone else. Maybe someone who broke a deal they signed with Mayor Troy, for instance.' He offered up a sickly smile. 'You understand what I'm sayin'?'

'I… I can explain everything, Randy—'

KAABBOOOOOM!!

The lightning bolt struck the far end of the town moor, the earth-shaking roar sending the crowd into a frenzy. Suddenly, clog-wearing Dutchmen, onion-toting Frenchmen, and Bavarians sporting tight-fitting leather *lederhosen*, were running for their lives, slipping and sliding on the rain-soaked grass. Unperturbed, Randy strode on, pushing his reluctant charge in front of him.

KAABBOOOOOM!!

A second nuclear blast was followed by a cloudburst of near biblical proportion – an instantaneous curtain of bone-soaking precipitation that hissed and fizzed as it hit the saturated turf.

Felix never knew whether it was the spectacular pyrotechnic show, now crackling overhead, or the heady waft of sizzling beef from a nearby Chicago Rib franchise, but something distracted the Smiler Corp enforcer and his pace began to slow.

Gripping his wriggling captive by the arm, Randy stopped, peering through the deluge as if he'd suddenly lost his bearings. A blur of humanity hurried past on all sides, but it was the thunderous reverberation of much weightier traffic that caused Felix to twist around, just in time to spot the two heavyweight Vikings, who were hurtling towards them through the chaos.

The crashing momentum of the first Dane would have flattened most people, but Randy simply stood his ground, twisting around to swat the inebriated Scandi-warrior aside.

The follow-up strike was something else, however.

Travelling at speed, while clutching a two-litre bottle of lager in one hand and an open jar of pickled herring in the other, the second Norseman skidded on the treacherous surface, somersaulted over his friend's prone body, and slammed, head-first, into the substantial mass of Randy's rear-end.

The two cow horns fixed to either side of the Viking's helmet, buried themselves deep into the twin slabs of the American's buttocks.

'Owwooo!'

Squealing like a stuck pig, and with the Nordic headgear still wedged firmly in-situ, Randy shot high into the air. The earth shook as he hit the ground, backside-first, the shuddering impact pile-driving the twin prongs still further into his glutes.

Felix hesitated. Instinct told him to stop and check that everyone was OK, but he quickly came to his senses. Deftly sidestepping Randy's flailing arm, he took off, running for his life.

Ten lung-bursting seconds later, he risked the briefest of glances over a shoulder. Somehow, the American was back on his feet and giving chase. Stiff-legged and limping along like a toddler carrying a fully-loaded nappy, his face was contorted in pain.

All but blinded by the rain, Felix skidded around the next corner, and seeing his way clear, splashed full-pelt along the deserted avenue.

'Ooff!'

It felt as if he'd run into a brick wall. Gasping for breath, he was hauled into the downmarket souvenir stall, the flaps of the marquee mysteriously opening from inside, before he even knew what had hit him.

'Turned out nice again, ain't it?' Sergeant Pluck greeted him.

PC MacCruiskeen handed him a souvenir Tour de France tea-towel from a nearby display. 'There you go, lad. Dry yourself off with that.'

'Nice interception, Steve!' said the sergeant. 'Almost makes up for the one you missed at school t'other week.' He turned to their guest, who was still trying to wipe the rain and snot from his eyes. 'Bit of a rush on, there, Haythornthwaite? D'you think now might be a good time to tell me and the constable, here, what the hell this is all about?'

The rain was hammering down onto the shelter in a noisy thrum, but another altogether more disturbing sound had grabbed Felix's attention – heavy, irregular footsteps approaching at speed... then slowing to a stop.

'Ay up, sounds like we've got company!' Pluck announced brightly, before slipping through the marquee's front flaps to greet the new arrival. Felix and PC MacCruiskeen were left trying to catch the sergeant's side of the exchange over the noise of the rain.

'Can I help you, sir?' He sounded as cool as a cucumber. '...Sorry, no. I've not seen anyone of that description round these parts. D'you want me to put out a missing person's call...? Blimey, that must smart a bit, sir. You'll not be sitting down with them stuck up there like that, will you...? I'd get it seen to, if I were you. You'll end up with a nasty infection if you're not careful... Not a problem – always happy to help our American cousins.'

They heard the squelch of footsteps limping away into the distance as Pluck ducked back into the stall. 'Bloody hell, he were a big bugger. I'd like to see you try to stop him, Steve!' He turned back to Felix, a stern look on his face. 'Reet then lad – no more of your flannel. Out wi' it, now.'

*

Half an hour later, Felix was delivered into the waiting arms of his mum, who'd been sheltering from the rain, under an awning in the VIP compound.

'Where've you been?' she asked. 'We've been calling you for ages.'

'Sorry, Mum. I got caught in the rain and—' He began frantically patting his jacket pockets. 'Oh no, I think I've lost my phone.'

'Never mind about that now, Felix,' she said brightly. 'They've found Doreen! She's with a friend of hers – that Miss Catlow from school. The two of them were trying to drive into town but were stopped at a police road block. They can't get her back to hospital until the race is over, so they're bringing her in to one of the first aid centres, until the roads have cleared.'

Doreen was OK – it was the best news, ever! And then it hit him – Titch was still missing, the Hill Special was gone, and now his great-aunt was in town. Unless Keira came up with a miracle, there was going to be some fairly awful music to face, and he didn't mean *Barry Manilow's Greatest Hits*.

'And who is this handsome young man?' his mum asked, smiling coyly at PC MacCruiskeen.

'Oh… this is Steve,' muttered Felix. 'He's, err… he's going to stick with us for a while – just to make sure we're all OK.'

'Ooh, aren't policemen getting younger these days?' she said, fluttering her eyelids.

20

'Ladies and gentlemen, our apologies for the loss of mobile picture transmission,' Greg Sprocket announced, over the groans of the crowd. 'The chopper will be back in the sky as soon as this storm passes but in the meantime, we'll keep you right up to date with the action from the roadside cameras, backed by the live audio feed from our very own, Darren Ackhurst. Darren, can you hear me?'

'Loud and clear, Greg!' Darren's voice boomed out through the speakers. 'Atrocious conditions out here on the road, but as far as we know, all the riders are still in one piece, which means the local youngster, Freddie Haythornthwaite, is still somewhere in the mix. I can tell you from personal experience that all these guys want to do now is get through the next few kilometres and pray that things brighten up for the last lap.'

'Thanks, Darren. And what about the protesters – are they causing much trouble out there?'

'Tell you what, Greg, these anti-globalisation guys are absolutely everywhere. They reckon today's sponsors, the Smiler Corporation, are planning to bulldoze Frecklesall-on-Sea to make way for a Garganto MonsterMart. I don't know where they've got that from but if it's true, it would be a scandal. I used to come here on my holidays when I was a kid.'

'Bloody hell!' shouted Felix's dad, from his spot beneath a café umbrella. 'You heard what Darren just said – our Freddie's still in with a chance. He could actually win this thing!'

Felix begged to differ. 'Dad, the race hasn't even started yet. Wait until the last lap – you'll see.'

His dad shot him a black look, before yelling at the top of his voice, 'COME ON, FREDDIE LAD! SHOW THEM FOREIGNERS WHAT YOU'RE MADE OF!'

The crackles of lightning flickering across the skyline, drew 'Oohs' and 'Aahs' from the spectators, as the roadside cameras showed the bedraggled pack rolling along the Prom.

Greg Sprocket was doing his best to get the crowd going. 'The peloton is still together but trust me, the attacks will start the moment they cross the line for the final circuit. Come on everyone, let's give the guys a big cheer as they go past!'

Felix tried to focus on the action, but with the riders shrouded in their wet weather gear, he couldn't tell who was who. 'I can't see Freddie,' he said. 'There's no sign of that stupid banana hat.'

'No worries there, Felix,' said Steve MacCruiskeen. 'He chucked it into the crowd at the start of the second lap. Cracked someone on the head, apparently.'

Wet and miserable, the peloton looked like a collection of drowned rats, but the moment they crossed the line the acceleration was instantaneous. Team members clustered around their leaders, while some of the less-fancied riders sprinted forward for a shot at glory. Felix chuckled to himself – Freddie keeping up with this lot? Not a chance!

Sprocket suddenly sounded a lot perkier. 'Lap four and it's game on! And to cheer you all up, we're getting reports of a break in the weather. Boy, do we need it. Over to you, Darren?'

'I'm with you there, Greg. The attacks are coming thick and fast, now. Quelle Fromage? are pushing the pace as we leave Frecklesall town centre for the final time, heading up the category four climb of *Col du* Top o' the Moor. Turbo Ring's Gerhart Gherkin is trying to create a gap, but Sven Klanger has jumped straight onto his wheel. And isn't that our very own Derek Trundle, hitching a ride at the back of this high-powered breakaway?'

Felix watched on in awe as the riders sprinted up one of the biggest hills in the borough, like it wasn't there. The crowd was waking up now, the boredom of the previous four hours swept away on a wave of pent-up, alcohol-fuelled enthusiasm.

Felix's mum had Steve MacCruiskeen in a corner and the policeman looked mightily relieved when a call came through on his radio.

'Mr Haythornthwaite!' he shouted across, moments later. 'Doreen's just arrived at the medical centre. They'd like you to pop over and see her, please.'

'Bloody NHS,' grumbled Felix's dad. 'Isn't that what we pay them for?'

It took a while for Felix and his dad to work their way across to the first aid centre. When they eventually got there, they found Miss Catlow talking with the paramedics and Doreen hunched up in a wheelchair, a tinfoil blanket tucked over her knees. She looked less than impressed when she spotted them.

'About bloody time, Brian!' she barked.

'What the hell are you playing at?' he snapped back. 'You can't just go walking out of hospital like that, Doreen – you could've died.'

'I am going to die, and sooner rather than later if you keep using that tone with me! Listen, if you think I'm going to stay parked up in that hospital ward with all them sick people, while *this* is going on, you're dafter than you look. All I want is to see our Freddie in the Tour de France. If I drop dead the minute he crosses the line, it'll be fine by me.'

After a stern look from one of the paramedics, Felix's dad started backpedalling. 'Oh… alright then. No need to get upset. It's just that… well, we've all been so worried about you. Promise me you'll head back to hospital as soon as this is over.'

'Straight back,' added Felix. 'No need to go to the Paddock. Everything's under control down there.'

'Really?' she said. 'Are the donkeys OK? I'd hate for anything to happen to them.'

After stopping off to pick up a brew, they wheeled Doreen back through the mud and blagged her into the VIP enclosure. Finding a sheltered spot, they settled in to watch the on-screen action.

Greg Sprocket's commentary was building nicely as the riders readied themselves for the 'business end' of the race. 'Under the five-kilometre marker and how many times have we seen this? Slowly but surely, the breakaway is being reeled in. The gap has come down to just three hundred metres and the question is this: Gherkin, Klanger, Trundle – do these guys have the legs and the organisation to keep clear? Closing in on the finish line, will their collaboration go out of the window as they start dreaming of that elusive stage win? Darren?'

'Only time will tell Greg!' Darren chipped in from the back of the team car. 'As you'd expect, the mankini-men are organising the chase-down. They're under orders to get Brad Mullet into position so their awesome lead-out train can sling-shot him into the history books. But take a look at 'Deadly Derek' Trundle, up there in the leading group. They'll be dancing in the streets of Cleethorpes if he pulls this one off!'

Felix was standing next to Doreen as they watched the action unfold.

His great-aunt pointed up at the screen. 'Ha! See that "Save the Donkeys!" banner? Good work, lad! But where's our Freddie? I haven't seen owt of him yet.'

'He's in there somewhere, but don't get your hopes up,' replied Felix. 'He's never going to get to the front and even if he does, he won't be flashing your T-shirt. He's under contract.'

Doreen looked up at him, the determination shining through in her eyes. 'You underestimate your big brother. He may not be the brightest candle in the box, but he's got a lot more about him than you realise.'

Their exchange was cut short by Greg Sprocket's gleeful announcement. 'Fantastic news, ladies and gentlemen - the chopper has got the "all clear". We'll be bringing you the aerial shots and the action from the motorbike cameras in no time at all. Darren – how are things looking out there?'

'Totally awesome, Greg!' the pundit replied. 'Things are brightening up out here on the road, as well!'

The big screen showed the leading trio slowing to peel off their rain gear. Stuffing it away in back pockets, they glanced nervously over their shoulders, checking out their dwindling lead.

'Under the three-kilometre marker and the gap is closing,' said Sprocket. 'It's been an incredibly brave effort from these guys but it looks like their race is done. Once they've been caught, this will be another day for the sprinters and *that* is right up Brad Mullet's street! I never thought it would happen in my lifetime, but Francois Faber's 1909 record could well be equalled today – and just how much would that mean to the man from down under?'

A cheer went up as the on-screen picture fizzed with static. Suddenly, viewers were gazing down on the race from the helicopter camera, high above, watching the peloton as it snaked its way through the countryside towards the southern edge of town. The image cut to a motorbike shot of the three leaders, two of them now sitting up in their saddles, surrendering to the inevitable. But Deadly Derek was having none of it. Sprinting away in one last, heroic effort, he was giving it everything he had.

'Look at Trundle, firing up the after-burners!' shrieked Sprocket. 'Gherkin and Klanger are toast, but the plucky Brit is leaving it all out on the road. The CodPiece boys thought they'd timed their chase to perfection – that this was to be Brad Mullet's day – but they didn't reckon on Deadly Derek. Just listen to the crowd roaring him on as he speeds past the two-kilometre marker… The gap has closed to one hundred and fifty metres… Can he hold it? It's a massive ask but–
– Oh my word, he's down! His front wheel just slid away on the greasy surface. He's trying to get to his feet but it's too late. Here comes the catch!'

There were howls of dismay as the tearful figure of Derek Trundle was left in a crumpled heap at the side of the road.

As if to mark the end of Britain's hopes in the race, the sun finally found a gap in the clouds and began streaming through, with eye-scrunching brilliance. Steam started to rise from the saturated road surface and in no time, the Tour Village was transformed, spectators abandoning their shelters to flock back outside, some of the luckier ones scrambling for places in the stand overlooking the finish line.

'The T-shirt – come on lad, you can do it,' muttered Doreen, as the peloton wound itself up for the grand finale.

Greg Sprocket's commentary had moved up a couple of gears. 'The riders are back together now and they're cranking the wattage into the red! Look at the teams trying to drag their sprint specialists up for a shot at glory. Mullet may be just off the pace at the moment, but we all know how this is going to play out. The CodPiece boys have formed a ring of steel around the Australian and are literally bulldozing him into contention. This is road racing at its absolute best!

'That's Pedro Zapatista out in front, tracked closely by Super U-bend's Hans Flugelhorn. It's looking a little too tasty for the SpamFritters, who are dropping back, but the ChocolatBanane boys are on the move! Look at Scaglioni bossing his team! They're riding just inches apart, now, at speeds touching sixty kilometres an hour. Phenomenal bike-handling skills from these guys!'

The close-up shots from the motorbike cameras showed the concentration on the faces of the riders, as the tightly packed group steamed down the hill towards the Fishfoot Lane cutting.

'Approaching the one-kilometre red kite and it's all about nerve,' Sprocket continued. 'There's nothing between them as they head into this small area of woodland which leads directly onto the seafront, where we're expecting the mother and father of all sprint finishes. It's a highly technical part of the course – no margin for error, here – but these guys really are the best in the business. I can't see any of them making a mistake this late in the game.'

After skirting the edge of the council estate, Fishfoot Lane burrows into a steep-sided cutting that slices through the surrounding woods. From the helicopter, high above, the peloton looked like multi-coloured grains of sand running through an hourglass, the teams, now liberated from their wet weather gear, funnelling through into the single-track lane.

It happened just as the leading riders were half way along the narrowest section.

'My goodness, there's something on the road! It's some kind of… Is it a horse?' For once, Sprocket was struggling to find the words. 'I'm no expert but I'd say it looks more like a donkey. And there's a boy – two boys... They're chasing it up the hill. This is unbelievable…! It's completely out of control and it's on a collision course with the peloton!'

Everyone gasped in horror as the donkey, kicking out its hind legs and braying furiously, charged up Fishfoot Lane towards the main pack. There was an eardrum-piercing squeal of brakes and moments later, the leading riders were skidding across the greasy road surface, grappling with their handlebars in a desperate bid to stay upright.

It was an impossible task.

Elite pro cyclists fell like dominoes, crunching to the tarmac as the entire field came to a wheel-buckling, clavicle-snapping, frame-shattering halt. The pursuing motorcade screeched to an emergency stop, rear-ending each other in a second monster pile-up.

Having created the chaos, the wayward donkey executed a sharp U-turn and galloped back down the narrow lane, after the two lads who'd been trying to catch it.

Back at the Tour Village, Doreen stared, wide-eyed, at her great-nephew. 'Bloody hell! That donkey – it couldn't be, could it?'

But Felix knew, all too well, that it was.

The on-screen shot switched to the back of one of the now stationary motorbikes, further along the lane. The live-feed showed the petrified faces of Bernie and Spuggie as they ran, flat-out, towards the camera. The crowd held its breath as the pair swerved either side of the motorbike and disappeared out of view.

Tour Villagers were left with the nightmare vision of a rampaging donkey heading straight for them. The flared nostrils, bared tombstone teeth and looping strings of slobber, were enough to send everyone scattering for cover, convinced the thing was going to burst out through the screen. At the last moment, an almighty THUNK! marked the demise of the camera as it was smashed from the back of the motorbike.

The picture fizzled away into static.

As the crowd tried to take in the enormity of what they'd just witnessed, the screen flickered back into life, the helicopter shot revealing the full extent of the devastation.

'A disaster, ladies and gentlemen! Unprecedented!' yelled Sprocket. 'The entire field has been wiped out by a rogue donkey! Some of the riders are trying to pick themselves up, but the road's completely jammed, the cutting too steep. There's no way they can get through…' The veteran commentator paused to take breath. 'Hang on a minute, I can see a rider on the tarmac, now… I don't quite know how he's done it, but he appears to have worked his way around the carnage! Who is this…? I can't make out the team... My goodness, it's… it's unbelievable!' Greg Sprocket could hardly get the words out. 'It's the local lad – the youngster! With just over one kilometre left to ride, seventeen-year-old Freddie Haythornthwaite is climbing back onto his bike and once he gets moving, he'll have a clear run!'

Felix and Doreen watched on, dumbstruck, as two frazzled figures appeared through the foliage at the edge of the shot. Tumbling and sliding down the steep banking, Keira and Naz landed on the lane, immediately in front of Freddie, who was back in the saddle but barely moving as he grappled with the bike's ancient gear change mechanism. Fortunately, there were no microphones around to catch the heated exchange that followed, although everyone could see Freddie's frantic gesticulations as he screamed out for help from the new arrivals. The hiatus lasted just a few seconds, and then the hapless pair were running along behind the bike, pushing for all they were worth.

Propelled on his way, Frecklesall Cyclonics' finest, sprinted off along the bottom section of the cutting and emerged onto the south end of the Prom, with the finishing line in his sights.

Doreen was first to find her voice. 'That donkey – I'd recognise her anywhere… It was Titch. What the hell's going on, Felix?'

'I… I'll tell you later, Doreen,' spluttered Felix. 'But look… it's our Fred, and he's going to win the Tour de France!'

'I'm not blind, you idiot, but what's that bike he's riding?'

It was impossible to tell from the aerial shots – all you could make out was a tiny figure, hammering along, highlighted hair streaming out behind. But when the view switched to one of the motorbike cameras…

He's swapped!' yelled Felix. 'That's not the bike they gave him – it's the Hill Special!'

'I can't quite believe what I'm seeing!' Sprocket exclaimed, breathlessly. 'Seventeen-year-old lifeguard, Freddie Haythornthwaite, riding what appears to be some kind of vintage museum piece, is clear of the pack. Less than seven hundred metres now stand between the youngest ever Tour rider and the ultimate prize in pro cycling! Never in the history of the—' Something stopped the commentator in mid-sentence. 'Hang on, everybody… Hold your horses… or should that be donkeys? I'm hearing from race control that another rider is trying to muscle his way back into contention.'

The screen flashed over to the scene of the crash, where a grazed and bedraggled Brad Mullet was screaming at his team leader, Frank Schnitzel, who just happened to be in possession of one of the few serviceable bikes left in the race. Landing a devastating uppercut on Schnitzel's jaw, the Australian snatched up his bike, clambered over the wreckage, and launched himself down Fishfoot Lane, like a man possessed.

'Look at this! Brad Mullet is back in business. He's totally emptying the tank – but it's too late, surely?' Greg Sprocket was right – it *was* too late. Freddie had about three hundred metres on the Australian, with less than five hundred to go.

'GO ON, FREDDIE! GIVE IT SOME WELLY, LAD!' Felix's dad roared his son on to victory, but somehow his words seemed to be having exactly the opposite effect.

'My word! What on earth is Haythornthwaite up to now?' screamed Sprocket. 'He's taken his hands off the handlebars! Mullet is gaining ground with each turn of the pedals. He's literally eating up that gap!'

Wobbling all over the place, Freddie was fumbling with the zipper of his bumblebee top. He managed to pull it down just a few centimetres before it jammed, and then he was clawing at the stretchy material, pulling and ripping, furiously.

Sprocket was aghast. 'What the heck is he doing? Never in all my years on the pro circuit…'

The crowd let out a collective gasp at the sight of the Hill Special, slaloming from one side of the Prom to the other, while Freddie set about tearing his ChocolatBanane top to shreds. And there, revealed for all to see, was the brilliant orange of Doreen's T-shirt. In one swift movement, he'd reached around and clicked the switch, sending the message flashing out across his chest.

SAVE FRECKLESALL LIDO!

'I knew he'd do it!' shrieked Doreen. 'Come on, Freddie, lad! Win it now – win it for Frecklesall!'

Cheering for all he was worth, Felix was momentarily distracted by a fracas high above them, up on the stage. Randy Pike had Wiseley by the lapels, pinning him against one of the speaker stacks, while a clearly furious Herb T Smilerski was yelling into his face.

But no one cared about that. All eyes were focussed on the Prom as the two riders sprinted, hell-for-leather, along the home straight.

With a couple of hundred to go, Freddie still had a good fifty metre advantage and had picked up the pace again. To any other rider, it would have been a lost cause, but Mullet was a man on a mission. Nose pressed to the handlebars, legs spinning in a blur, his super-lightweight, aero-profiled bike lunged crazily from side to side with each heave of his gigantic thighs.

This was the moment Greg Sprocket had been waiting for, and he rose to the occasion. 'Look at the Aussie – he wants that record! Surely there's no way he can catch the local lad... My word – what's going on now...? It's the pedals on the youngster's bike! The cranks... they're... they're...'

Something terrible had happened to the Hill Special. Freddie was still belting along, the messages on his T-shirt flashing away, but the fluidity of his pedal strokes had disappeared. Legs jerking uselessly, his speed began to dwindle.

'It's the cotter pins!' yelled Felix. 'Dad told me they were a bit dodgy. The pedals – they're going to fall off!'

An expression of disbelief was etched across his brother's face. The finishing line was almost within touching distance but the pedals were useless, the left crank wobbling crazily on the bottom bracket, incapable of transferring the power from his legs, through the chain and on to the back wheel.

'The youngster's had a mechanical of cataclysmic proportions!' screamed Sprocket. 'What a cruel twist. Look at Mullet go – he has him now, surely!'

The Australian steamed up on the outside, timing his effort to perfection. Sitting up in the saddle, jaw set in a beaming grin, he cruised by his stricken rival, raising both arms aloft to punch the air in extravagant celebration.

'COME ON, SON – YOU CAN DO IT! DON'T GIVE UP NOW!'

Spurred on by his dad, Freddie offered up one last, despairing lunge… and in that moment, the history of the Tour de France was turned on its head.

It was all too much for the badly-worn cotter-pin that had secured the Hill Special's left-sided crank to its bottom bracket for the best part of sixty years. It snapped, sheared off, gave up the ghost – sending the crank, with pedal still attached, slamming down onto the tarmac, to ricochet away with the deadly accuracy of a laser-guided missile.

Freddie's final thrust met with no resistance, whatsoever, and he slipped from his saddle, crunching groin-first onto the crossbar.

Brad Mullet never saw the blur of rusted Sheffield steel now fizzing towards his bike. Moments later his front wheel had exploded into a twisted tangle of buckled spokes, its profiled carbon rim snapping clean in two. The laws of physics being what they are, the sprinter was propelled over the handlebars, at speed. Flying through the air like a mankini-clad human cannonball, he face-planted to the ground, centimetres short of the finish line. What remained of thirty grands'-worth of top-end kit, lay shattered and broken in his wake.

Face creased in pain and with a hand groping down the front of his shorts, Freddie dribbled across the line, before toppling to the tarmac.

There was a moment of stunned silence, and then Greg Sprocket, voice cracking with emotion, remembered he had a job to do. 'Ladies and gentlemen, *mesdames et messieurs*, I can hardly believe I'm saying this, but give it up, please, for the youngest ever stage winner in the Tour de France's one-hundred-and-twenty-year history! Representing the United Kingdom and Team ChocolatBanane – or should that be Team Save Frecklesall Lido and Frecklesall's Famous Donkeys? I give you today's *Domestique du Jour*, the quite remarkable, FREDDIE HAYTHORNTHWAITE!'

A huge roar went up as a wave of ecstatic fans swept forward, shunting aside the crowd control barriers and the race marshals to embrace their new-found hero, who was down on all fours, depositing what was left of his breakfast into the gutter.

21

'*Mesdames et messieurs*, I 'ave an important announcement to make on be'arf of the race director!' The whistles and jeers faded as everyone strained to hear Giselle Lacroix's update. 'We 'ave received a formal protest from *le* Team CodPiece Credentials, alleging illegal interference with their rider, Brad Murllet. The *commissaires* will need to carefully review the video evidence before a result can be confirmed. *Merci beaucoup* for your patience.'

Felix could have stood there listening to Giselle's voice all afternoon, but around him, the thousands of people crammed into the Tour Village were becoming restless. The cacophony of boos and whistles began to grow. And then it started – quietly at first.

'Freddie! Freddie! We want Freddie!'

'Freddie! Freddie! We want Freddie!'

Felix was standing between Steve MacCruiskeen and Miss Catlow, just behind his great-aunt, praying she wouldn't ask him any difficult questions.

Like that was ever going to happen.

'Where's Titch, then?' snapped Doreen. 'And what the bloody hell was she doing in the middle of the road, scared out of her wits like that?'

'I… err—'

Steve came to Felix's rescue. 'Nothing to worry about, there, Miss Haythornthwaite. The animal welfare are taking her back to the Paddock, and we've nicked the perpetrators. It was some local kids, apparently. They're for the high jump, I can tell you!'

'Actually, Steve, this is all Wiseley's doing,' Felix began, earnestly. 'He's been behind this right from the start and I've got the evidence to prove it! I still have the ransom note he sent me.'

The constable looked at him like he was mad, but before he could respond, Miss Catlow jumped in.

'Look, there's Freddie!'

They all craned their necks to get a better view of the man of the moment, who was doubled over, hands on knees, at the side of the stage.

The crowd had been infiltrated by an army of anti-globalisation protestors bearing banners in support of the donkeys and the lido. There was even a samba band in the midst of it all, thumping out a deafening drumbeat. *Something for everyone*, Felix thought, brightly, his problems of just half an hour earlier already a fading memory.

But the good-natured atmosphere was on the turn. There were shouts and screams as a barrage of missiles flew through the air. Worried-looking officials scurried about while Giselle Lacroix crouched down at the side of the stage to remonstrate with Frecklesall's *Domestique du Jour*. A few minutes later, she dragged him down to where the Haythornthwaites were standing.

'Felice, we have a problem, *oui*?' she began, breathlessly. 'The police are worried about these protestors. They think maybe they are not so interested in *le cyclisme* and all they want is, 'ow is it you say, a

278

punch-urp. So now, we are asking young Ferdie to go on stage to calm the *ambiance* a little, but he is saying *non*!'

Freddie clutched at his groin. 'I'm injured, man! No way can I get up there. Hey, why don't you give it a go, Dad?'

His dad winced. 'You're not the only one with a problem down below, Son. My hernia's been giving me proper gyp these past few days.'

Doreen rolled her eyes. 'Felix'll do it, won't you, lad?'

Felix laughed, expecting everyone else to share in what was quite obviously a joke. It was only when he saw the look of anticipation on their faces that he realised quite how much trouble he was in.

'Very good on his feet, this one – very calming,' his great-aunt continued. 'Like just now, when I was fretting over Titch.'

His dad clapped him on the back. 'Good on you, Son. Get up there and knock 'em dead. The honour of the Haythornthwaites is at stake!'

It was a stitch-up like no other, but after everything that had happened, there was no way out. All but paralysed with nerves, Felix stood there as they pulled Freddie's sweaty T-shirt over his head. And then Giselle was half-leading, half-dragging him up the steps.

'The whole world's watching!' Miss Catlow shouted after him. 'Don't let Doreen down!'

Marching confidently onto the stage, Giselle unclipped the microphone from its hefty, chrome-plated stand, while behind her, Felix closed his eyes, hoping the whole thing was just a bad dream.

'*Mesdames et messieurs*,' she announced, 'still we await the outcome of *les commissaires'* deliberations. But as you 'ave requested it, I would like to present to you now, your most fabulous *Domestique du Jour*, Ferdie 'Aythornthwaite!'

There was a pause in proceedings while Felix gawped at her in disbelief.

'I would very much *like* to do that,' she continued, above the cheers of the crowd, 'but regrettably, young Ferdie 'as sustained a most unfortunate injury to 'is groin region and therefore cannot join us at this particular moment in time. So instead, I am introducing you to the next best thing – 'is lovely brother, Felice!' She clipped the microphone back into its stand and stood aside, leaving Felix centre stage.

Stumbling forward, he realised he hadn't a clue what he was going to say. 'Oh… err…' His hesitation boomed out over the PA system.

'Felice, you must say something, *vite*. I am begging of you!' hissed Giselle.

And then he caught Keira's voice, shouting above the rumblings of discontent.

'Turn it on, you idiot!'

He'd completely forgotten about the T-shirt. He wriggled around a bit and after a reassuring click, the flashing light show burst into life. The hostility of the crowd immediately gave way to cheers, while the samba band launched back into their groove. Felix waved, and two thousand people waved back.

How cool was that?

An agitated group, gathered at the side of the stage, caught his eye. It was like a 'Who's Who' of people he didn't want to meet in a dark alley on a Saturday night. An irate Troy Wiseley was flanked by the squat, no-necked figure of his brother, Roy. Beside them, Isiah Wolfe was involved in an intense discussion with the Stetson-wearing Herb T Smilerski. And just behind, towering above all of them, Randy Pike smiled chillingly at Felix, before drawing his forefinger slowly across his throat.

'*S'il vous plait*! *Maintenant,* Felice!' urged Giselle.

He took a deep breath. He had to do this – for Doreen, for Frecklesall.

'I… I can't begin to tell you how proud I am of my brother,' he began, hesitantly. 'I always thought our Fred was a loser, but I was wrong – he's a hero, whatever the result today.'

His words were greeted with loud cheers. Looking down at the VIP area, immediately in front of the stage, he saw his mum and dad smiling approvingly.

'But for me and Fred, and my little sister Flo, it isn't just about winning this great race,' he continued. 'It's also about Frecklesall-on-Sea – the place we were born and have always lived. As I speak to you now, our home town is fighting for its life and we need your help.'

He was bathed in warm applause.

'And someone else who needs your help is my Aunt Doreen. She's recovering in hospital after a heart attack, having just been told by the council that they're kicking her out of the home she's lived in these past fifty-five years. Why would our mayor want to do something like that? Well, I reckon most of you already have a pretty good idea—'

'Hold it right there, boy!' Wiseley boomed as he stomped onto the stage, clutching a cordless microphone. 'Ladies and gentlemen, for those of you who don't know me, my name is Mayor Troy Wiseley MBA, and like it says on the tin, I'm the democratically elected mayor of this wonderful town.'

The anti-globalisation mob were trying to shout him down, but most people seemed keen to hear what he had to say.

'Give him a chance! Let him say his piece!'

'Thank you so much,' said Wiseley, in his familiarly oily tones. 'Freedom of speech is a basic human right – one we must defend at all costs.'

Felix could hear his dad bellowing, 'Hear, hear!' at the top of his voice.

'Now, it pains me to say this,' the mayor continued, his elbow resting, casually, on the mic stand, 'but the feckless juvenile on stage before you now, is the ringleader of a criminal cell of feral yobbos, based right here in Frecklesall-on-Sea. A gang that will stop at nothing to disrupt our decent, law-abiding way of life!'

Felix glanced down at his parents, who were looking horrified. 'That's rubbish,' he spluttered. 'I'm no criminal.'

Wiseley laughed. 'So how do you explain the destruction of our beloved lido, last Saturday night? Look yonder, ladies and gentlemen.' He pointed across to the burnt-out shell of the outdoor swimming pool. 'There lies Frecklesall's heritage, vandalised beyond repair by this *über* yob and his cohort of criminality!'

Felix was rocked back onto the ropes, but the smug expression on Wiseley's face was enough to bring him out fighting. 'I didn't do it – it was a set-up!' he shrieked. 'It's the Smiler Corporation who wrecked the lido and I've got the evidence to prove it. They framed me and my mates so they could steal *our* land to build a Garganto MonsterMart. Smilerski's going to sign the contracts with the council, today, and if we allow that to happen, Frecklesall will be ruined forever!'

There were cheers from the anti-globalisation gang, but a split had developed in the crowd and things were beginning to turn nasty. Police snatch teams piled into action as tempers started to fray.

Wiseley wiped the sweat from his brow with a grubby handkerchief. 'Fine words, Haythornthwaite, but someone's got to sort out the mess you've left behind. Yes - a Smiler Corp Garganto MonsterMart is but one of the many blue-sky scenarios my team are road-mapping for option appraisal. It's a total no-brainer – jobs, growth and access to quality, affordable produce from around the world!'

'But it's not going to be like that,' Felix countered. 'Anyway, there's only one criminal around here, and that's you. You're the one who kidnapped Titch.'

The mayor looked at him, blankly.

'Don't give me that. You know all about Titch – one of Frecklesall's Famous Donkeys, kidnapped and being held at knifepoint. It's all here, in black and white.' Felix waved the ransom note in the mayor's face. '"An offer you can't refuse"? "Drop the lido story or the donkey gets it"? Your mafia tactics won't work with me, *Mr* Mayor!'

Suddenly the air was alive with plastic plumbing accessories, hurtling towards the villain of the peace.

Frecklesall's first citizen seemed unfazed. 'For the record, ladies and gentlemen, these allegations are completely and utterly baseless. The truth is, it was this boy's flea-ridden donkey and his hoodlum gang who caused the chaos we've all witnessed here today.' He flourished his own piece of paper, holding it up for the crowd to see. 'I have in my hand a bulletin from the Chief Constable of Lancashire, no less, which proves my complete innocence in this matter.' He put on his glasses and began reading out loud. '"Following disruption to stage four of the Tour de France, in Frecklesall-on-Sea, earlier today, two local juveniles, Bernard Devaney and Sean Spugley, have been detained and charged with public order offences. A third juvenile, Richard Sowerbutts, has been taken to hospital with multiple leg fractures. The injuries were sustained whilst a donkey, understood to be one of Frecklesall's Famous Donkeys, was being held captive in a lockup garage on the Fishfoot Lane estate. Preliminary enquiries suggest the incident was a schoolboy prank that went horribly wrong. Police investigations are continuing".'

The mayor's words echoed around inside Felix's head, the mention of Ricky Sowerbutts' name, suddenly making him feel very, very sick. He turned to Wiseley. 'But it was you,' he mumbled. 'It had to be you.'

Frecklesall's first citizen smirked back at him. 'These louts, Devaney and Spugley – accomplices of yours, I believe?'

Felix nodded – there was nothing else he could do.

'The same accomplices who helped you burn down our magnificent lido?'

Wiseley guffawed as Felix suffered a direct hit from a family-sized Storm tea bag, cold brown tea dribbling down the side of his face. A mini-cheese fizzed past his left ear. The fickle tide of public opinion was on the turn and the mayor was only just getting into his stride.

'Over recent weeks, the hard-working, law-abiding folk of Frecklesall-on-Sea have been terrorised by a lout going by the name of ASBO Boy!' Wiseley began. 'Rest assured, as part of my YobWatch! initiative, my enforcement team have been working tirelessly to track down this low-life scum.' He jabbed a finger towards Felix. 'We captured images of *this* particular delinquent, our prime suspect, on CCTV some weeks ago, but were unable to make a positive ID because of poor picture quality. Now, however, thanks to the generosity of our friends at the Smiler Corporation, footage of the infamous Bus-Surfing incident has been enhanced, using a revolutionary digital technique pioneered by the FBI, over in the States. I'm delighted to confirm that the recording was received by my team earlier this afternoon and has just this minute been downloaded onto a secure council laptop. I'd anticipated some kind of disruption from these hooligans, today, so I took the liberty of setting up a viewing platform. Ladies and gentlemen, don't take my word for it – I respectfully ask that you watch this footage and decide for yourselves.' He gestured to the side of the stage with a flourish. 'Run the tape, Enrique!'

Felix's heart sank. He'd relived those moments so many times in his nightmares, and now the whole thing was being played out once more, in front of an audience of thousands.

The CCTV footage had been shot from a distance, the images, grainy and low quality. Felix could just about make out the shadowy shape, launching itself from the third-floor window of the town hall. The screams of the crowd turned into a collective gasp as the gangling figure slammed into the arm of the lamppost, writhing frantically for a few seconds before abandoning the struggle and hanging there, motionless.

'Zoom in and engage software – now, Enrique!' barked the mayor.

There were more gasps as the clarity of the picture snapped into focus and the pale, ghost-like face with the oil-slick hair and wonky cardboard bow tie, filled the screen.

'OK, Enrique, I think we can all see through that pathetic disguise. You can take it back out now.'

Pulling back to the opaque fuzziness of the original shot, the mayor ordered a further cut and zoom. The samba band stopped drumming as everyone watched the double-decker pulling away from the town hall, its illicit, bus-surfing passenger lying spread-eagled across its roof.

Wiseley broke the stunned silence. 'And *that*, ladies and gentlemen, is what this young offender has been up to. Breaking and entering! Fare evasion! And of course, setting fire to our beloved lido! And as if all of that were not enough, he now has the brass neck to accuse me of kidnapping his aunt's mangey old donkey, when all along it was part of a plot to help his brother cheat his way to a spurious victory.' He turned to the grizzled old policeman who'd joined them up on stage. 'Sergeant Pluck, no more of this namby-pamby dither and delay. I hereby command you – arrest this boy!'

The crowd cheered as Pluck marched up and placed a hand on Felix's shoulder. 'Sorry about this, lad,' he said quietly, before announcing into the mic he was holding, 'Felix Haythornthwaite, I am arresting you on suspicion of—'

But then a familiar voice piped up from the wings. 'Wait yer 'urry, sarge – hang fire a minute, willyer!'

Felix twisted from the sergeant's grip to see Spuggie springing onto the stage, two riot policemen in hot pursuit.

'Oreet, Thwaitey lad!' he shouted cheerily.

'Stop that youth!' screamed Wiseley. 'He's one of the gang!'

Pluck cursed under his breath as the policemen chased Spuggie around the stage, Keystone Cops style, before eventually clattering him to the deck.

'Gerroff me, willyer!' he yelled, from beneath a pile of body armour. 'You gotta run that tape again, sarge. I were there – I saw what went on and it weren't that!'

The mayor bristled. 'Enough is enough. Pluck - take these two down to the cells and charge them both.' He turned back to his audience. 'And there you have it, ladies and gentlemen – a tragic microcosm of the broken society in which we now live. But there is another way – the Troy Wiseley Way! YobWatch! Zero tolerance for criminals here in Frecklesall, and in time, across the nation as a whole! As my dear friend, Nelson Mandela, once said to me – "I have a dream…".'

Felix and Spuggie were being dragged from the stage when Giselle Lacroix stepped forward to block their exit.

'Sergeant Plurck! I beg of you,' she pleaded. 'Felice is a good boy, *oui*? You must allow 'im this final chance to clear 'is name. 'Is friend, 'e is knowing something *important*, of that I am most certain. I respectfully ask that you run the tape again. *S'il vous plait.*'

Pluck paused. He didn't really know why, it just seemed like the right thing to do. Giselle smiled at him, sweetly. Memories of a hugely enjoyable holiday romance, in Calais, back in '74 – prior to the current Mrs Pluck, of course – washed gently through his mind.

'*S'il vous plait*, sergeant,' urged Giselle. '*C'est tres important*!'

Just at that moment, Steve MacCruiskeen dashed up the steps onto the stage, having temporarily abandoned his posting with the Haythornthwaites. 'You need should this, sir,' he said, thrusting a crumpled piece of paper into his sergeant's hand.

Pluck scanned it briefly. Eyebrow arched, he folded it up and tucked it away in a breast pocket. 'Excuse me, Your Worshipfulness!' he shouted across, interrupting Wiseley's lengthy monologue on the fabulousness of the Smiler Corporation and his world-beating plans for upper-quartile excellence. '*Mademoiselle* Lacroix has requested another airing of your ASBO Boy footage. The way I'm seeing it, we should be doing everything we can to promote Anglo/French *bonhomie*, today of all days. Wouldn't you agree?'

The mayor was incensed. 'Outrageous! An appalling disregard for my authority! I play a monthly four-ball with your Chief Constable, y'know!'

After a nod to the riot police, Spuggie and Felix were released and allowed back onto the stage. 'Ladies and gents,' announced Pluck, 'we've had a special request to run that tape again. Could you do the honours for me, please, err… Enrique?'

A mic was passed to Spuggie, who responded by grinning idiotically and striking a rock star pose.

'Gerron wi' it, lad!' growled the sergeant.

And then the images were running once more – the town hall looking strangely serene in the glow of the street lighting, given the drama that everyone knew was about to unfold. A few seconds in and the now-familiar figure was standing on the third-floor window sill, readying himself for his death-defying leap.

There were cries of 'Boring!' from the crowd, one wag shouting, 'Can we change channels, mate? I've seen this episode before!'

Felix had been hoping for some kind of last-minute reprieve, but all he seemed to be getting was a re-run of his most traumatic greatest hits.

'Stop it right there, En… err… Reeky, lad!' Spuggie shouted to the unseen technician. 'Now, that window at the top, where he's standing. Can you just, kind of, make it a bit bigger and get it into focus for us?'

The screen jumped back a few frames and a computer target symbol locked onto the window to focus the picture definition software. Moments later, everyone could see a bizarrely disguised and obviously petrified Felix Haythornthwaite, teetering on the brink.

Wiseley was furious. 'Switch it off, Enrique. That's an order!'

'Just ignore 'im,' Spuggie said, coolly. 'Could you run it on from there, please, mate? Slow-mo if you can manage it… It should be coming up… about… now!'

'Flippin' 'Erry! What were that?' exclaimed Pluck as the window behind Felix's head, shattered from the inside, forcing him to hurl himself from the sill. Moments later, the on-screen image froze, showing him suspended in freefall, amidst a cloud of glass fragments.

The place was in uproar.

'It's no wonder he jumped!'

'Poor bugger – must have been scared out of his wits!'

'Well?' Pluck turned to the mayor, who was flapping like a landed mackerel.

It took Wiseley a few seconds to regain his composure. 'I, err… I can explain everything, sergeant! It's this thing the experts call, err… spontaneous fragmentation! Interesting phenomenon. It's the old Victorian glass, see? It just explodes – no one knows why. Bad luck for the boy, although he deserved it if you ask me.'

There were howls of protest from the crowd, but Spuggie had not quite finished. 'Just pull it back a gnat's todger for us willyer, Reeky, mate. We need to see the lamppost and the window in the same frame.'

The image definition sharpened again and Felix felt his throat go dry as the remainder of the scene was played out once more. The first time around, on Wiseley's instruction, Enrique had zoomed in and clicked on the picture definition software for just a few seconds when Felix was hanging from the lamppost, and again, when he'd landed on top of the bus. The more comprehensive sequel, with Spuggie in the director's chair, told a completely different story.

Felix was clinging on for dear life when a previously unseen face appeared at the window. It was a woman – distraught, hair ruffled, makeup smeared across her face.

A ripple of recognition swept through the crowd. What was celebrity roving reporter Marje Spangles doing up there?

But there was more. Everyone saw Marje being grappled away from the window and in the next instant, Troy Wiseley's pudgy face poked out through the broken pane. Incandescent with rage, he was screaming abuse at the unfortunate boy. After ducking back inside, he reappeared, wielding a couple of big, weighty volumes. The first book narrowly missed its target but the second scored a direct hit, causing Felix to scream out and twist violently.

And then gravity took hold again.

'Nice one, Reeky. Thanks, mate!' Spuggie offered the technician a thumbs-up. 'So that's how it went down, sarge!' He pointed at Wiseley. 'That fella there, were trying to murder my mate Thwaitey. He's the one you should be nickin'!' Job done, he bowed to the audience and was escorted from the stage by a police officer.

Tears welling in her eyes, Giselle walked across the stage, arms outstretched, to give Felix a hug.

Suddenly, a larger-than-life, middle-aged woman, wearing a shocking-pink trouser suit, burst onto the scene. She was wielding a huge handbag.

'Gladys! Munchkin! Please – I can explain!' pleaded Wiseley, his arms failing to deflect the blows now raining down onto his head.

'You filthy lying toe-rag!' she screamed. 'I knew something was going on up there. I just knew it!'

Randy started forward from the wings but a terse command from Herb T stopped him in his tracks. Felix knew what that meant – Smilerski was distancing himself from the mayor, hanging him out to dry. If that's how it was, maybe, just maybe, the American multi-billionaire would fly out from Manchester airport later that evening, without signing the land deal.

A police officer stepped in to restrain the soon-to-be-ex Mrs Wiseley, but there was no stemming the torrent of abuse aimed at her husband.

'Liar! Cheat! I'll take you to the cleaners when this gets to court!'

Sweating profusely, the mayor's face had turned ashen-grey. 'A perfectly rational explanation, for those with an open mind,' he mumbled into the mic. 'Miss Spangles did, indeed, pay a brief visit to my office that particular evening, but it was a completely innocent encounter. We'd already done an interview but she wanted something a bit more in-depth.'

'I bet she did, the slag!' his wife shouted back as she was being hauled away.

'And the books?' asked Pluck. 'Why were you throwing them books at the lad when he was hanging from that lamppost? It looked to me like you were trying to knock him off!'

'Not at all sergeant, I was merely having a tidy-up – creating a little shelf space, as it were.'

'Rubbish!' yelled someone in the crowd. 'You were trying to do 'im in!'

'Hmm…' The sergeant seemed to be weighing up the case for the defence, although Felix couldn't possibly think what there was to consider, the whole story being about as believable as, 'But sir, the dog ate my homework'.

'With all due respect, Mayor Wiseley, there is one other matter you might be able to help me with,' Pluck began, almost casually. 'A letter has recently come into my possession – well, it's more of an email, actually.' He reached into his top pocket and pulled out the piece of paper Steve MacCruiskeen had given him, a few minutes earlier. 'It's addressed to you, Mr Mayor, and it's marked "private and confidential", but I'm going to read it out, anyway.'

Peering over the sergeant's shoulder, Wiseley had turned as white as a sheet. 'No! Absolutely not!' he shrieked. 'Through the power vested in me as the democratically elected mayor of Frecklesall-on-Sea, I hereby command you to desist, forthwith, from this outrageous witch-hunt!'

Pluck produced a pair of reading glasses and balanced them on the end of his bulbous nose. 'It's dated the thirtieth of May this year, and it's from an American law firm – Crannage, Saighton and Wolfe.'

Felix's ears pricked up. He knew those names! It had to be the email Keira had sent from Wiseley's office – the one with the attachment Naz had handed over to Sid. But how on earth had the police got hold of it?

'I met Mr Wolfe earlier today as it happens, Mr Mayor,' the sergeant continued. 'He's the Smiler Corporation's legal adviser, and this email is all about your *remuneration*.' He turned to the crowd. 'Anyone out there know what that means?' He cupped a hand to his ear, like a character in a pantomime. 'What's that you say...? Pay...? Reward...? Did I hear, *bribe*?'

Wiseley went to grab the paper from him, but thought better of it. 'Nonsense! Absolute rubbish—'

'Forgive me, sir, but it's important we all have an understanding of what's gone on here.' Pluck began reading the email attachment out loud. '"On completion of the Frecklesall lido and town moor transfer (proposed site of Europe's first Garganto MonsterMart), on a date no later than the tenth of July, a free option on Smiler Corporation (UK) shares valued at one million dollars (US) will be transferred into your personal account".' He turned to the mayor. 'Now, I'm no expert, but as *remunerations* go, that seems like a pretty big one!'

Wiseley looked like he was about to have a heart attack.

And then something snapped.

He twisted away from the sergeant, with surprising agility for such a hefty man. Grabbing hold of the microphone stand, complete with its heavily weighted base, he began whirling it around his head, like a demented highland hammer-thrower

'I'm not taking the rap for this, Pluck!' he screamed, as the mic stand transformed into a lethal silver blur. 'It's yobbos like ASBO Boy, here, you should be arresting, not honest, hard-working public servants like me!'

The mayor stomped off across the stage, leaving the sergeant to handle the formalities.

'Troy Wiseley,' he announced, calmly, 'I am arresting you on suspicion of attempted murder, and various offences relating to Section 4 of the Fraud Act 2006. You do not have to say anything but it may harm your defence if—'

There was a rumpus from behind and suddenly, Roy the Bulldog was running across the stage towards his brother. 'Troy, it's over! Put it down before someone gets–'

THUNK!

Troy's backswing caught him on the side of the head, dropping him to the deck like a sack of potatoes.

'Right!' snarled Wiseley, his eyes bulging madly. 'Anyone else want a piece of me? YOU!' He pointed at Felix, who was still standing next to Giselle, wondering what the hell was going to happen next. 'You think you've won, but you've lost, boy. That land already belongs to the Smiler Corporation and there's nothing you can do about it.'

Felix tried to push Giselle out of harm's way, but the mayor was on them in just a few strides. Face contorted with rage, he heaved the mic stand over his shoulder, ready to strike. There was no time to think – Felix launched himself head-first at their assailant, the element of surprise giving the Frenchwoman just enough time to scramble clear.

But Wiseley was a man of substance. Bouncing off his hefty midriff, the young reporter landed flat on his back, gasping for breath. He looked up, and for a moment, time seemed to stand still. Frecklesall's first citizen towered above him, the crazed expression on his face, transporting him back to the terror of that fateful night at the town hall. He heard the screams of the crowd as the mic stand's solid, weighted base, arced towards his head.

And then, in mid-swing, Wiseley froze – the expression of shocked surprise that flashed across his face, instantly dissolving into slack-jawed vacancy. Knees crumpling, the mic stand clunked down on top of him as his whole body convulsed in a series of near-comical twitches. Moments later, he was lying face-down on the stage, a thick string of saliva drooling across the stage from his half-open mouth.

'Handy piece of kit, these Tasers,' Sergeant Pluck announced cheerily, blowing imaginary smoke from the barrel of the device, like a Wild West gun-slinger. 'More of a truncheon man myself, but we all need to move with the times, don't we?'

Freddie struggled up onto the stage, alone, the other riders boycotting the ceremony in protest at the *commissaires*' decision to uphold the original result – a judgement based purely on police advice that there'd be a riot if they did anything else. Riding without a helmet; failure to wear official team colours; failure to use an authorised team bike – even interfering with another rider during a sprint? All minor deviations from the Tour's rules and regulations, as it turned out!

Flashguns popped as the startled, still-bent-double stage-winner, made his way up onto the podium. The paramedics had kitted him out with a pair of inflatable, knee-length bloomers, designed to ease the pressure on his sore bits, and he'd reclaimed Doreen's lido T-shirt, Team ChocolatBanane gracefully standing aside to allow him, and Frecklesall, their moment of glory. Podium girls fluttered about, lavishing him with bouquets and gigantic cuddly toys while the crowd chanted his name.

Felix cheered, alongside his friends. Keira was standing next to him and beside her, Spuggie was revelling in a sea of backslapping and high-fives. Bernie was there too – recently released from police custody, although not before he'd fleeced the arresting officers in a one-sided poker game. And then there was Naz – wandering around in a daze, still traumatised by his role in the afternoon's proceedings.

'That's my boy!' bellowed Felix's dad, gazing up proudly at his eldest son, who was blowing kisses into the crowd as he milked the applause.

Doreen was sitting quietly in her wheelchair, and Felix crouched down to talk to her.

'I'm so sorry,' he began. 'I wanted to tell you what was going on but I was worried about your heart attack. And then I thought, maybe I could sort it myself. I was certain it was Wiseley who'd kidnapped Titch. I had no idea it was that plonker, Sowerbutts.'

She smiled at him. 'You did well up there, lad – Freddie too. He only went and won the bloody thing!'

Felix laughed, and then he remembered Wiseley's final words. They may have won the battle, but if the now-disgraced mayor was to be believed, the war had already been lost. The Smiler Corporation owned the land and things were about to change in Frecklesall, for ever.

Greg Sprocket had pulled the short straw and was presiding over the award ceremony. 'And now ladies and gentlemen, *mesdames et messieurs*,' he announced, 'the lovely Miss Herbina Smilerski will present the trophy to the youngest ever stage winner in Tour de France history.'

Felix glanced up at the beautiful billionaire heiress, only belatedly clocking his nervous-looking brother, who was rummaging around, down the front of his inflatable pants. Pulling out a pocket-sized breath-freshener, he squirted what looked like its entire contents into his mouth.

Confused, Felix turned to his sister. 'But Herbina's engaged to someone else, isn't she? That movie star – whatsisname?'

'Dwayne Valderrama,' she replied, without taking her eyes off the stage. 'Although I'm pretty sure Freddie doesn't actually know that yet.'

'You what? Surely someone should have told him. I mean—'

'Eeugghh!'

A nearby security gorilla dived in to separate the pair who were now locked in a one-sided embrace, Herbina struggling for air and waving an arm furiously as Freddie lunged in for the full-on snog.

'Security code red!' the heavy yelled into his sleeve. 'Backup required! We have a situation!'

22

Most of the guests had arrived early and were out in the back garden, where the burgers were charring to an indigestible crisp on the barbecue. Felix's dad had been despatched to the Paddock to pick up the star of the show, on what was only her second day out of hospital. Doreen would normally have been down on the beach with the donkeys on such a balmy Sunday afternoon, but that was a non-starter, and anyway, everyone agreed it was about time Freddie did something useful for a change. Pressganged into service he was now the guardian of Frecklesall's last remaining visitor attraction – for the rest of the season, at least.

Felix gazed out from the lounge window, across the unremarkable suburban normality of Scundale Chase. The TV crews had disappeared a few days earlier and while the hard-core freelancers had hung around a bit longer, they'd eventually thrown in the towel. The *Journal's* Dave Heptonstall had made a surprise appearance at the house, just the day before – hammering on the back door to beg for an exclusive. Felix's dad took great pleasure in telling him where he could stick his notepad.

The role of dishonour of Tour de France cheats is too long and depressing to list here. Suffice to say, Freddie had become the latest addition to its ranks.

Everyone assumed that the genteel pace of the rider protest had allowed him to keep up – that his local knowledge of some mysterious, hidden footpath had helped him sneak around the ruins of the peloton for that final, dramatic kilometre.

Alas, this was a long, long way from the truth.

After the call to Felix, just before the thunderstorm, Keira had dragged Naz, Spuggie and Bernie down to the Fishfoot Lane estate to follow up on the tip-off they'd received. They spent the best part of half an hour, dodging cloudbursts while searching the decrepit garage colony for signs of a kidnapped donkey. Just as they were about to give it up as a bad job, Keira heard a whimpering sound coming from one of the lock-ups they'd already checked. Spuggie eventually booted his way in, and there, lying amidst the straw and piles of donkey dung, was Ricky Sowerbutts, his leg shattered in three places courtesy of a flailing hoof from his disgruntled captive.

With light flooding into the garage, Titch seized her moment and bolted off, like a frisky pit pony on its summer holidays. Spuggie and Bernie gave chase, in the direction of the nearby woods… and the Fishfoot Lane cutting.

Staying behind with Ricky, Keira and Naz soon discovered the Hill Special, which had been buried under some hay in the gloom at the back of the lock-up.

They were hanging around outside, waiting for the medics to arrive, when Keira spotted the Tour de France's youngest ever rider, shuffling past in his ChocolatBanane kit. Grateful to see some friendly faces at last, Frecklesall's *Domestique du Jour* slumped down by the garage wall and the whole, sorry tale came out.

The weather had been awful, even by Lancashire standards, while the heavyweight bike and humiliating outfit were amongst any number of final straws. But it wasn't just that. Even at the snail's pace of the rider protest, Freddie couldn't keep up. Drenched and down-hearted, he'd abandoned the race, and his dream of living happily ever after in Bug's Tussle, at the start of the third lap. With the usually forensic TV coverage disrupted by the thunderstorm, which had also taken out the transponder system used to track the bikes, no one had even noticed.

Freddie said that deep down, he'd always known the Herbina thing was a bit of a long-shot. Having had plenty of time to reflect, during his first two, miserable laps, he'd come to the conclusion that an afternoon in the welcoming arms of Tracy Scoggins, an 'ex' who lived just off the race route, was a far more enticing option.

And with the benefit of hindsight, that would have been a good place to call a halt. No one would have blamed him for dropping out of the race – in fact, it would probably have been Team ChocolatBanane who'd have got it in the neck for treating him so shoddily.

Hindsight is a wonderful thing, of course…

The moment Freddie set eyes on the Hill Special and heard that the peloton was due any minute on its final lap, some kind of unstoppable force took control. Brushing aside Naz's protests, he heaved the ancient bike onto a shoulder and sprinted off towards the nearby woods, shouting something about, 'Doing it for Doreen… and Billy!'.

Abandoning Ricky to his fate, Naz and Keira set off in pursuit, and just a few frantic minutes later, found themselves sliding down the steep banking onto Fishfoot

Lane, just in time to push-start Freddie's final sprint for the line.

In the end, it was the *Sunday Scorcher's* headline-grabbing exclusive – 'My Afternoon of Passion with Frecklesall Tour Cheat' – courtesy of 'Curvaceous Stunner' Miss Tracy Scoggins (cheque received with thanks), that blew Freddie out of the water.

Whatever! Freddie reckoned that a lifetime ban from competitive cycling and the Tour de France in particular, was something he could live with. But none of the Haythornthwaites could have imagined the awfulness of life under the media spotlight, following the calamitous 'misunderstanding' that took place up on the podium. According to the gossip mags, Wayne Valderrama was threatening to pay Frecklesall a visit to sort Freddie out. It was all PR froth, of course, but the tabloids lapped it up.

Keira peered around the door into the lounge. 'Why don't you come out the back, Felix? The karaoke's started.'

'I'm fine here, thanks,' he replied. 'I thought I'd keep an eye out for Doreen.'

'She does know, doesn't she? I mean, a surprise party for someone just out of hospital after a heart attack, isn't the smartest idea you ever had.'

She came in and sat down next to him. It was pretty cool having a girlfriend, he thought – at least that's what he assumed was going on. Having never had one before, he wasn't entirely sure. Every time he'd raised the subject with her, she'd either blanked him or accused him of being a 'big soft lad'.

To say things had been a bit sticky for the newly dubbed 'ASBO Gang', in the days following the race, was something of an understatement. Troy Wiseley may have been carted off in the back of a police van to face any number of criminal charges, but the lido had been torched and Sergeant Pluck was not about to let bygones be bygones.

Eventually, it was the fire service's discovery of the cause of the blaze – the unusual American cigarette butt – that turned the tide. Of course, Randy – who'd swiftly done a runner back to the US – was the only person in Frecklesall who smoked those Lucky Gaspers, so it had to be him, didn't it? And even though that wasn't quite the whole truth, the CCTV footage of Roy filling a brace of twenty-litre petrol cans at Halfbarrel Motors, the afternoon before the blaze, dragged the Wiseley boys firmly into the frame. Combine that with the recovery of Felix's lost mobile, from the mud of the Tour Village – complete with Rupert Fudgeley-Smythe's incriminating message – and to quote Sergeant Pluck, it was nothing less than 'an open and shut' case.

But that wasn't the end of it. Somehow, the TV pictures of Freddie wobbling over the line in Doreen's flashing T-shirt, with a hand stuffed down the front of his shorts, had inspired the nation. The lido had become, as Giselle Lacroix put it, a *cause célèbre*, with cash donations pouring in from all corners. A fighting fund had been set up, with lawyers hired to block the Smiler Corporation's planning application at every turn. Old Herb may have bought the land, but getting permission to develop it out was another thing, altogether. The case looked set to run and run and although no one knew how it would turn out, there was a glimmer of hope – a chance.

And that was good enough for Felix.

The doorbell rang as the tortured strains of his mum's rendition of *I Will Survive* filtered through from the back garden. A few seconds later the school secretaries – the Misses Pomfrett and Catlow – almost unrecognisable in their bright summery frocks, breezed into the lounge.

'It's so kind of you to invite us,' said Miss Pomfrett as they all sat down. 'We've been friends of Doreen since we were girls. It's lovely to be able to celebrate her homecoming with you.'

'I'm really glad you could make it,' replied Felix. 'Apart from anything else, we haven't had the chance to thank you. If you hadn't stuck your necks out and passed on that email from those American lawyers, we'd have been kicked out of school for good.'

'Yeah,' added Keira. 'Thanks for that, ladies. We owe you one.'

'I hope you don't mind me asking,' said Felix, 'but why did you do it? You could have both lost your jobs.'

Miss Catlow smiled. 'To be honest, Felix, we're both of an age now where we're not that worried about our future career prospects.'

'We were horrified when Doreen told us what was going on,' added Miss Pomfrett. 'Kicking her and the donkeys out of the Paddock? Knocking down our lido? Outrageous behaviour! So, when Miss Sidhu brought us that email attachment for Arse… I mean, Dr Brown, we just kind of… mislaid it.' She shrugged, innocently. 'Of course, we really should have taken it straight to the police, but Doreen wanted us to wait for the right moment. She said it was all about timing.'

Typical of his great-aunt, thought Felix. It wasn't enough just to destroy Wiseley's career – she wanted to do it in front of thousands of onlookers and a global TV audience.

'Even so,' said Keira, 'I'm surprised Arsey changed his mind. He's not usually one for U-turns, is he?'

Miss Catlow smiled. 'Actually, you've got yourselves to thank for that. You see, you really hit the nail on the head with that Bradley Halfbarrel story from a few months back – the one Mr Brush wouldn't let you run in the *Pen*.'

'We've seen a lot of head boy and girl appointments over the years, but this one was something of a surprise to us both,' said Miss Pomfrett. 'Bradley's a nice enough lad, but hardly head boy material. So, the whole thing seemed rather *odd*. Naturally, we'd processed the original receipt for the new school minibus – the one bought from his father's garage. Dr Brown assured us that the discount was a generous gesture by Mr Halfbarrel, made for the benefit of the school, but soon afterwards he took delivery of his own, brand-new BMW from Halfbarrel Motors. Our friend, Brenda, does the books there, and she let slip that the sale had gone through at something of a knock-down price. And then, of course, Bradley went on to become head boy. We decided it was time to remind Dr Brown of a few of those *coincidences*. Funnily enough, he was keen to reinstate you both, straight away.'

Felix and Keira were left speechless.

'It's a pity Freddie can't be with us this afternoon, though,' said Miss Catlow. 'I really wanted to have a chat with him. You see, I had that special T-shirt made up for Doreen, but she told me he couldn't wear it. There was some kind of legal problem, apparently. We asked her why he changed his mind, but she wouldn't say.'

Felix laughed. 'That would be down to Billy.'

'Billy?' the ladies repeated the name in unison, unable to hide the surprise in their voices.

'Billy Rankin,' Felix added brightly, before remembering the tragedy of his great-aunt's lost love. 'Doreen told us all about him when we visited her in hospital – how they fell in love and were due to be wed. And then he was killed, out on his bike, the day before the Nationals. It's such a sad story. Freddie's an insensitive moron, but I guess it must have sunk in, eventually.'

The secretaries exchanged glances, but before they could say anything the doorbell rang again and Felix dived out into the hallway.

He swung the door open, ready to greet his great-aunt, only to be confronted by a dishevelled old man in his late seventies. Wearing a grubby, open-necked shirt and a pair of stained brown trousers held up by a length of frayed rope, the smell of stale booze wafted from his breath.

'Can I help you?' Felix asked, uncertainly.

'Haythornthwaite is it?' slurred the man, revealing an absence of front teeth as he spoke.

Felix nodded.

'Reet then – you can give it back to us. I don't want no trouble. Hand it over an' I'll be on me way. Worth a bob or two now, I reckon.'

'I'm sorry, what is it you're after?' asked Felix. Glancing over the old man's shoulder, he saw the Fiesta swinging into the drive with Doreen in the front passenger seat.

The man shuffled forward, poking him in the chest with a bony, nicotine-stained finger. 'Give over, willyer! Tha'll not get away wi' it, tha' knows. I've come all t'way from Blackpool to pick it up and it's mine by rights, so you can fetch it for us now. Spotted it on t'box a few weeks back, in that big race.'

Felix looked at him, blankly.

The Fiesta had parked up now, and his dad was helping Doreen out of the car, just a few metres away.

The visitor doubled up, his whole body convulsed in a chest-wracking coughing fit. 'The bike!' He spat the words out, eventually. 'The Hill Special – it belongs to me!'

'But who are you?'

The old man hawked noisily, before gobbing a quivering blob of phlegm onto the carefully tended front lawn. 'Name's Rankin, lad – Billy Rankin.'

Acknowledgement

With special thanks to:

Scott Cockerham, for a great cover design.
Clive Barker, for top-notch proof reading and relentless encouragement.
Sharon Pimbley, for timely technical and moral support.
Chorley & District Writers' Circle, for continuing inspiration and pedantic (but crucial!) grammatical and layout tips. Special thanks to Dr Greg Hall, who really does know his onions.
My dear friend and *super domestique*, Nigel Fisher, for his support, comradeship and wise counsel, over too many years to mention.
The awesome Peter Carey, for services to cotter-pins, big hammers, and well-turned calves.
My old mate, Nick Bryning, who has witnessed the true horror of unfeasibly short bathrobes.
All those involved in the brilliant Channel 4/ITV Tour de France coverage, from the Phil Liggett and Paul Sherwen era, to this present day.
And all the fantastic pro riders who have provided, and continue to provide, such a compelling sporting spectacle each year.
Franz Kafka, for the evolving chaos of my editing strategy.
Bill Nickson Cycles (Leyland), for keeping me in cotter pins (metaphorically and practically) for the past thirty years.

Richard Branson and the Virgin Trains West Coast Main Line team, for a fast-moving writing environment with the occasional tilt.

The intrepid journalists who worked for the Chorley Guardian and Lancashire Evening Post in the 80s, 90s and noughties. Those were the days!

Flann O'Brien and Freya North, whose brilliant cycling/bicycle-themed novels have always been an inspiration.

My sister, Kathryn, for enduring way too many drafts of this book (32 and counting!) and regularly reminding me that the first one remains her favourite.

And most importantly, my lovely Louise, for her love, friendship and support, which includes hauling me up countless double-arrow climbs on her e-bike, ensuring everything (including my dignity) is always left out on the road.

About the Author

Al Ramsay

When not hiding in an undisclosed location, somewhere on the West Pennine Moors, Al lives with his wife, Louise, in the beautiful Lancashire market town of Chorley. Until the recent call of the pipe and slippers, he worked for a national housing association, helping build affordable homes across the north of England. His career objective was to solve the UK housing crisis, and in this, he failed. Some say he may even have made things worse – although that never stopped him from trying. Travelling all too frequently by train, between Wigan and 'That London' as part of his job, *The Felix Haythornthwaite Files* series was conceived during down-time on board the Virgin Trains' Pendolino fleet (quiet carriage 'A'), the creative process fuelled by way too many bacon rolls.

Al now spends his time riding his bike, writing and getting mildly disheartened (and sometimes overly excited) by the travails of his three favourite football teams: Everton, Leyton Orient and, of course, Chorley. He's a member of the Chorley Writers group and a regular contributor to the town's literary festival, 'What's Your Story, Chorley?' His lifetime ambition is to appear in *Lancashire Life*.

alramsay2@gmail.com

January 2023

Books by this Author

The Felix Haythornthwaite Files

The Decoy

When sixteen-year-old trainee reporter, Felix Haythornthwaite, has a chance encounter with a beautiful young woman at Preston station, he thinks his luck is in. But following her surprise arrest on the platform and the discovery that he's taken her bag home by mistake, Felix and his feckless brother, Freddie, are dragged kicking and screaming into a murky world of kidnapping, murder and deception. Nothing like this has ever happened before in the dead-end Lancashire resort of Frecklesall-on-Sea, a town surprisingly shortlisted for the prestigious UK Capital of Culture award. Felix should be reporting on Frecklesall's culture bid – filing copy on the Edelweiss Nursing Home's armchair aerobics team and the antics of the local Wild West Society. Instead, he finds himself caught up in a life-or-death struggle involving a ruthless international crime cartel, a kick-ass tribal princess, and an overdose of industrial-strength laxatives. The story could be a global exclusive, a dream start for a young reporter – even one as petrified and incompetent as Felix Haythornthwaite – the question is, will he live long enough to break it?

Currently available on Kindle and in paperback format

Underground

When Felix Haythornthwaite's on-line news blog, the *Frecklesall Exposer*, is picked up by billionaire energy mogul, Donald Kincaid, it seems the sky's the limit. But after Felix is cajoled into welcoming Donald's wayward son, Cameron, onto his team, and crosses swords with visiting delegates from the Russian GulaGaz energy giant, things quickly get out of hand.

And then legendary ladies' man and mainstay of Felix's dad's ManShed male support group, Archie Crowfoot, dies. The police say it's from natural causes but after teaming up with a bunch of feminist eco-warriors, Felix stumbles across unexplained goings-on at Archie's remote Pennine farmhouse, and suddenly he's the one at risk of ending six feet under. But who would want to kill Archie, and why? And could there be a connection between his death and some of the weird things that have been happening in the area?

Mislaid novelty underpants, low-flying offal and a publicity-hungry celebrity undertaker on a mission to put the 'FUN' back into FUNerals are woven into a fast-moving plot of dodgy dealings, international duplicity and environmental calamity, where nothing is quite what it seems.

Publication delayed due to global events. Watch this space!

Printed in Great Britain
by Amazon

18764056R10183